P O C I

FUNGI

POCKET NATURE
FUNGI

SHELLEY EVANS
GEOFFREY KIBBY

DK

DORLING KINDERSLEY

LONDON, NEW YORK, MUNICH,
MELBOURNE, AND DELHI

DK LONDON
Senior Art Editor Ina Stradins
Project Art Editor Vanessa Thompson
Senior Editor Angeles Gavira
Editor Georgina Garner
DTP Designer Adam Shepherd
Picture Editor Neil Fletcher
Production Controllers
Elizabeth Cherry, Melanie Dowland
Managing Art Editor Phil Ormerod
Managing Editor Liz Wheeler
Art Director Bryn Walls
Category Publisher Jonathan Metcalf

DK DELHI
Designers Romi Chakraborty,
Mugdha Sethi, Kavita Dutta,
Shefali Upadhyay
Editors Sheema Mookherjee,
Ritu Malhotra, Dipali Singh,
Glenda Fernandes
Editorial Consultant Anita Roy
Editorial Support Chumki Sen,
Sunrita Sen, Bhavna Seth
DTP Designers Sunil Sharma,
Balwant Singh, Jessica Subramanian
DTP Co-ordinator Pankaj Sharma
Managing Art Editor Aparna Sharma

First published in Great Britain in 2004 by
Dorling Kindersley Limited
80 Strand, London WC2R 0RL

A Penguin Company

Copyright © 2004
Dorling Kindersley Limited

ISBN 0-7513-3696-3

Reproduced by Colourscan, Singapore
Printed and bound by South China
Printing Co. Ltd, China

Disclaimer Many fungi are poisonous, with
effects ranging from stomach upset to organ failure
and death. Collection for consumption is entirely
at the reader's own risk.

see our complete catalogue at
www.dk.com

CONTENTS

How this book works

This guide covers over 440 species of fungi from northwest Europe.
These are divided into three groups. Within each, the fungi are arranged
by type and then by colour so that similar species appear together. So,
the Cap and Stem chapter has fungi with gills, then spines, then pores;
Bracket and Shelf has fungi with teeth, then pores, and finally gills or
folds. Ball, Club, and other Fungi has ball- and pestle-shaped fungi,
followed by cup- or golf-tee shaped, club-shaped, and finally crusts.

CHAPTER HEADING

▽ GROUP
INTRODUCTIONS
Each of the three groups opens
with an introductory page
describing the group's shared
characteristics. Photographs of
representative species show
the diversity in the group.

COMMON NAME
*Some species do not have a
common name, in which case
the scientific name is given as
the entry heading.*

SCIENTIFIC NAME

DESCRIPTION
*Conveys the main features
and distinguishing characteristics
of the species.*

DETAIL PICTURES
*These tinted boxes show
individual parts of the fungus in
greater detail, and may include
sections, gill undersides, spore
surfaces, or different stages of
development.*

SCALE DRAWING
*To give an indication of the
height of the species, a drawing
of the fungus is set next to an
artwork that represents this guide.
See panel top right.*

COLOUR BANDS
*Bands are colour-coded, with a
different colour for each chapter.*

Grisette

Amanita vaginata (Amani

This *Amanita* should only be
certain it is not one of the d
damp, the cap has a distinct
veil patches. It is oval when
flat, often retaining its centra
a frosted edge; the stem has m
with pale grey, zig-zag markin
baggy grey volva.

emerging
fruitbody

thick, cup-
volva

SPORES *White.*
FRUITING *Summer to autumn.*
DISTRIBUTION *Common and wid*
EDIBILITY *Edible when cooked.*
SIMILAR SPECIES *The edible A. b*
and the inedible and rare A. maire
which are also grey and have no ri
on the stem.

Wood Pink

Entoloma rhodopolium (En

This poisonous species chang
progresses from creamy yello
It has a broad central umbo a
grooves. Grey at first, the gills
the slender stem is silvery gr
be odourless or smell nitrous

cap up to
12cm wide

lined, wavy
margin

Ball, Club, & other Fungi

These fungi include a huge range of fruitbody shapes, but
nearly all lack gills, pores, or spines. Very much a simplified
grouping, it includes an enormous variety of unrelated fungi,
accounting for around 6,900 species in temperate northern
Europe. Their sizes, colours, and methods for survival and spore
dispersal are correspondingly varied. Among the huge variety
of shapes are cups such as Bay Cup, pictured, fingers, cages,
and clubs, as well as the more bizarre brain-shaped fungi.

▷ SINGLE-PAGE
ENTRIES
Species that exhibit
greater or more
complex features, or
are of special interest,
are given a full page.

NOTES
*Describe striking or unique
physical features that will
help you identify the species,
or provide other interesting
background information.*

Orange Birch Bolete
Leccinum versipelle (Boletaceae)

A popular edible species, the Orange Birch Bolete often
grows in a very large size. Bright yellow-orange to orange,
its cap is rounded and firm when young, but later expands
broadly. A ragged, overhanging margin is visible on the
"bottom" of young fruitbodies. The tubes of the fungus are
up to 3cm long and pale buff to colour. Very young pores
are almost black, but then soon become pale ochre-buff
and bruise to a darker brown. The stout, often quite tall
stem is off-white and densely covered in small black scales.
When cut, the thick white flesh rapidly turns lavender-
grey, and later becomes
grey-black.

SPORES *Brown.*
FRUITING *Summer to autumn.*
DISTRIBUTION *Common throughout northern & Europe.*
EDIBILITY *Edible and tasty.*
SIMILAR SPECIES *Poplar Bolete (L. quercinum) which is reddish-orange and grows with Populus species. Sabr Bolete (L. duriusculum) which is a darker, more coffee-brown, and grows with Populus species.*

▽ SPECIES ENTRIES

The typical page describes two fungi species. Each entry follows the same easy-to-access structure. All have one main photograph of the species, which is taken in the species' natural setting in the wild. This is supported by one or more detail pictures that show individual parts in close-up. Annotations, scale artworks, and a data box add key information and complete the entry.

SCALE MEASUREMENTS

Two small scale drawings are placed next to each other in every entry as an indication of the typical height of the fungus (cap or fruitbody diameter is provided in the annotation). The drawing of the book represents this guide. The silhouette is a stylized representation of the species.

Fungi Height
15cm

Book Height
19cm

FAMILY NAME

D STEM FUNGI **169**

)

cooked; make absolutely
pecies. Sticky when
margin and hardly any
gradually becoming
. The gills are white with
but is tinged
l has a

OCCURS *singly or in small numbers on the ground in woods, especially with broadleaf trees.*

lined
margin

central
umbo

cap
up to
15cm
wide

faint
markings
on stem

POISONOUS FUNGI

The toxic effect of fungi can range from stomach upset through to organ failure and death. Even some fungi classed as edible can cause stomach upsets. If in any doubt about the identification of the species, do not eat it. It is a good idea to keep a sample of the species. If poisoning is suspected, seek medical advice and take the sample of the fungus for identification. Two symbols are used in this guide for species that are poisonous or potentially so.

Poisonous 🕱   Poisonous but edible after cooking ⚵

ANNOTATION
Characteristic features of the species are picked out in the annotation.

PHOTOGRAPHS
Illustrate the plant in its natural setting.

ataceae)

ur on drying. The cap
ey to greyish brown.
avy margin with
become pink, while
Wood Pinkgill can

SEEN *singly, or in small numbers, in broadleaf woods, in rich litter; often with beech.*

creamy to
greyish brown
cap

notched
gills

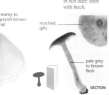

pale grey
to brown
flesh

SECTION

SPORES *Pink.*
FRUITING *Autumn.*
DISTRIBUTION *Common and widespread.*
EDIBILITY *Poisonous.*
SIMILAR SPECIES *Various large autumn-fruiting Entoloma species including Livid Pinkgill (E. sinuatum), which is more robust, paler, with yellow gills, and smells of meal.*

DISTRIBUTION
While many fungi in this book will be found across most of Europe, the area covered by this guide and referred to in the entries is indicated here in blue.

HABITAT PICTURE
Shows the type of habitat in which the species may be found growing.

HABITAT CAPTION
Describes the habitat or range of habitats in which you are likely to find the fungus.

OTHER KEY INFORMATION
These coloured panels provide consistent information on the following points:
SPORES: *the spore colour.*
FRUITING: *the seasons during which the fruitbody can most commonly be found.*
DISTRIBUTION: *the status of the fungus, be it very common, common or frequent, locally common, occasional, rare, very rare, or rare and endangered; followed by an indication of where in the region covered (see map above) it may be found. Fungi distribution is not well documented so cannot be given precisely.*
EDIBILITY: *whether the species is edible, inedible, or poisonous.*
SIMILAR SPECIES: *lists some fungi that look similar to the featured species, often describing a distinguishing feature to help tell them apart. Species not covered in this book may be listed, in which case a distinguishing feature is always given.*

Anatomy

From familiar toadstools with cap and stem to stranger fungal forms with spines, tubes, or wrinkles, the structure and the anatomical details of all fungi reflect the main function of dispersing their single-celled reproductive spores. The different fruitbodies – the visible, fertile part of the fungus – represent varying methods of overcoming the common problem of releasing spores into an often-harsh environment. All fruitbodies have an area of spore-producing tissue, known as the hymenium, which may be spread over thin gills, spines, tubes, wrinkles, the entire fungus, or even enclosed inside the fruitbody. These varied structures help us to initially divide and classify the fungi. The finer details will help you to identify the fungus species.

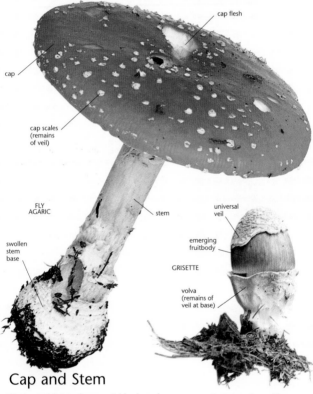

cap flesh

cap

cap scales
(remains
of veil)

FLY
AGARIC

stem

swollen
stem
base

universal
veil

emerging
fruitbody

GRISETTE

volva
(remains of
veil at base)

Cap and Stem

The typical fungus has a variably shaped cap lifted up on a central stem. On the underside of the cap are thin gills, spines, tubes, or fleshy wrinkles, where spores are produced and discharged. The cap and stem shape, any surface structures, and the colour are all diagnostic features.

Universal veil

Many fungi are covered by a cobweb-like or fleshy protective tissue. As the fungus grows, this "veil" ruptures, leaving patches on the cap, stem, or base.

Section

Cutting a fungus in half reveals many identifying features. For example, the way in which the gills, tubes, or other spore-producing structures attach to the stem, the shape of the stem, and whether the stem is solid or hollow. Also, the remains of a partial veil – in the form of a ring on the upper stem – may be revealed more readily in section.

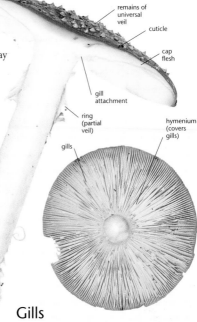

remains of universal veil

cuticle

cap flesh

gill attachment

ring (partial veil)

hymenium (covers gills)

gills

cobweb veil

WEBCAP

Gills

Observing the shape of the gills, their thickness and spacing, and how they attach to the stem will help in identification. Shorter, intermediate gills may also be present. Gill colour is often – but not always – a guide to spore colour.

OTHER SPORE BEARING SURFACES

spines

veins

tubes with pores

EARPICK FUNGUS

TRUMPET CHANTERELLE

SUEDE BOLETE

Spores

The colour, size, and shape of spores can assist in the correct identification of a species. To assess the spore colour, collect a thick spore deposit (see page 12). You need a good-quality microscope to measure and assess the spores accurately: most are less than 0.02mm long or wide.

SPORES OF GLISTENING INKCAP

Identification

To accurately identify fungi, you need to take detailed notes in the field, while the specimens are still fresh and untouched. Take great care when handling, so as not to damage the often delicate surface, or any other diagnostic character. Use a hand lens to study fungi in detail and, if possible, always examine a range of specimens.

Fruitbody shapes

Identifying the shape of the fruitbody is often the first step in identifying the species. The broad classification of fungal groups in this book is based in part on the extraordinary shapes and structures of the fruitbody. Every possible variation may be encountered, many of which are pictured here, from the typical cap, stem, and gills, to fungi with animal-like arms or tentacles.

cap and stem
LILAC BONNET

multiple brackets
LUMPY BRACKET

ear-shaped
JELLY EAR

coral-like
GOLDEN CORAL

sponge-like
MOREL

skin-like crust
COBALT CRUST

phallus-like
STINKHORN

cup-shaped
BLISTERED CUP

club-shaped
trumpet-shaped
HORN OF PLENTY

SMOKY SPINDLES

star-shaped
cage-like
COLLARED EARTHSTAR

RED CAGE

ball-shaped
COMMON EARTHBALL

brain-like
FALSE MOREL

antler-shaped
YELLOW STAGSHORN

Cap shape

It is very important to make a record of the shape of the cap. In many species, cap shape is consistent and diagnostic; in others, it is more variable, changing as it matures.

convex
SPECTACULAR RUSTGILL

conical
BLACKENING WAXCAP

funnel-shaped
TAWNY FUNNEL

umbonate
FRUITY FIBRECAP

saddle-shaped
WHITE SADDLE

honeycombed
MORCHELLA ELATA

depressed
BROWN ROLLRIM

folded
FALSE MOREL

lined
LILAC BONNET

pleated
PLEATED INKCAP

inrolled margin
BROWN ROLLRIM

grooved
TAWNY GRISETTE

Texture

Cap textures include many variations, ranging from smooth and sticky to dry, fibrous to scaly. Some species will have an external veil of tissue, which may be thick and skin-like, fine and cobweb-like, or even sticky.

fixed scales

loose scales

fibrous

shaggy-woolly

sticky

PANTHERCAP

SHAGGY SCALYCAP

SPLIT FIBRECAP

SHAGGY INKCAP

VERDIGRIS ROUNDHEAD

Colour

The colours of the different parts of the fungus are some of the most important characters to record, but are also some of the most variable and difficult to define. Try to examine a range of specimens and look at every part of the fungus – the underside of the cap, for example, is often very different to the upper surface. Colour may change with age or if you bruise the fungus.

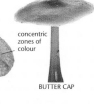

darker cap centre

concentric zones of colour

WOOLLY MILKCAP

BUTTER CAP

Stem

In fungi that have a stem, the proportion of stem length compared to cap width, and the shape, girth, and flesh of the stem are diagnostic features. Viewing the base of the stem is often crucial since there may be special shapes or structures here; the presence or absence of a stem ring can also be diagnostic.

swollen

slender

GIANT KNIGHT

PLEATED INKCAP

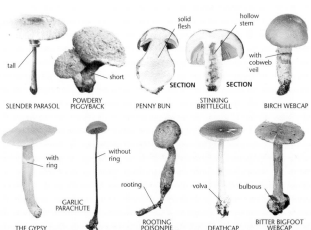

tall

short

solid flesh

hollow stem

with cobweb veil

SLENDER PARASOL

POWDERY PIGGYBACK

PENNY BUN
SECTION

STINKING BRITTLEGILL
SECTION

BIRCH WEBCAP

with ring

without ring

rooting

volva

bulbous

THE GYPSY

GARLIC PARACHUTE

ROOTING POISONPIE

DEATHCAP

BITTER BIGFOOT WEBCAP

Flesh

Cutting through a specimen with a sharp knife will provide useful information. The texture and solidity of the flesh varies from species to species; some being very solid and fleshy, others fragile and crumbly. When cut or bruised, the flesh may also change colour or exude a "milk", or latex.

latex

flesh stains when cut

OAKBUG MIILKCAP

CORNFLOWER BOLETE

Gills

With gilled mushrooms, you should make a note of their colour, their general spacing (crowded or widely spaced), and whether the gills are flexible or brittle. Examine how the gills are attached to the stem; they may be attached narrowly, broadly, or with an indent or notch, or the gills may run down the stem slightly or markedly. Also check whether the gills exude a latex when broken. Gill characteristics are usually constant within a species.

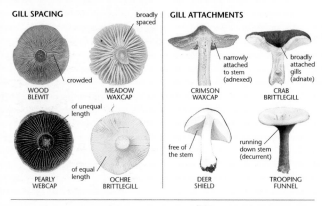

GILL SPACING

broadly spaced

crowded

WOOD BLEWIT

MEADOW WAXCAP

of unequal length

of equal length

PEARLY WEBCAP

OCHRE BRITTLEGILL

GILL ATTACHMENTS

narrowly attached to stem (adnexed)

broadly attached gills (adnate)

CRIMSON WAXCAP

CRAB BRITTLEGILL

free of the stem

running down stem (decurrent)

DEER SHIELD

TROOPING FUNNEL

Spore Colour

The colour of fungal spores is easily determined. Remove the cap, lay it gills downward on white paper, cover, and leave it, for several hours, to deposit its spores. When the spores are dry, scrape together to assess the colour. You need a high-magnification microscope to see the structure.

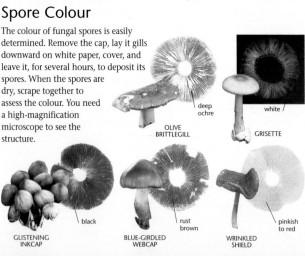

deep ochre

OLIVE BRITTLEGILL

white

GRISETTE

black

GLISTENING INKCAP

rust brown

BLUE-GIRDLED WEBCAP

pinkish to red

WRINKLED SHIELD

Odour

The smell of fungi can be quite peculiar, but it is often subtle and difficult to define: different people may have different opinions on an odour. With gilled fungi, try smelling the gills and the cut flesh. Enclosing the specimen in a box can help to concentrate the odour.

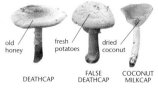

old honey

fresh potatoes

dried coconut

DEATHCAP

FALSE DEATHCAP

COCONUT MILKCAP

Variations

Individual fungi can be vary extraordinarily, particularly young and old specimens. You need to see as many examples within a species as possible to become experienced with all of their forms and variety.

stains strongly when young

older fungi

young fungus

SECTION

INKSTAIN BOLETE

SNOWY WAXCAP

Occurrence

The occurence of a species may distinguish it from similar-looking species. The manner in which it grows – singly, in clusters, in rings etc – can be diagnostic. Also, not all species are common or widespread; some are very rare and exciting to find, and some are also restricted to certain times of the year.

clusters

troops

singly

CLUSTERED BONNET

FAIRY RING CHAMPIGNON

ROOTING POISONPIE

FALSE PARASOLS IN A FAIRY RING

common

CHICKEN OF THE WOODS

OAK POLYPORE

rare

late summer to autumn

LIVID PINKGILL

spring to early summer

ST GEORGE'S MUSHROOM

Habitats

Fungi are often very specific about where they grow. Many grow with particular tree species, in an association called a mycorrhiza; others grow on decaying leaves and debris or even other fungi.

DECIDUOUS WOODLAND Bitter Poisonpie

CONIFEROUS WOODLAND Larch Bolete

BROADLEAF LEAF LITTER Blackedge Bonnet

SAND DUNES Winter Stalkball

DEAD WOOD Smoky Bracket

Cap & Stem Fungi

There are an estimated 3,000 identified cap and stem species in northern temperate Europe, and still more to be discovered. Often referred to as "mushrooms" or "toadstools", these fungi have soft, fleshy caps and more or less central stems, with most of the edible and poisonous species occurring in this group. Their fruitbodies only appear for short periods of time; the main part of the fungus lives permanently underground. All produce spores on the underside of the cap, which fall by gravity. The spore-bearing structures may be gills, spines, or pores.

SHEATHED WOODTUFT

MAGIC MUSHROOM

SHAGGY INKCAP

EGGHEAD MOTTLEGILL

Destroying Angel ☠

Amanita virosa (Amanitaceae)

Fatally poisonous, as the common name suggests, this species is pure white all over. The often sticky cap is pointed and egg-shaped when immature and later flattens out. The slender, shaggy stem has a floppy ring at the top, which is often torn, and an egg-like volva enclosing the base. This fungus develops a sickly sweet odour with age.

FOUND *in damp woodland on acidic soils, especially with birch or conifers.*

egg-shaped cap

cap 5–10cm wide

volva encloses base

white gills

white flesh

SECTION

SPORES *White.*
FRUITING *Summer to late autumn.*
DISTRIBUTION *Rare to occasional, N. temperate regions.*
EDIBILITY *Highly poisonous.*
SIMILAR SPECIES *White* Agaricus *species, which can look very similar but lack a volva and develop pink then brown gills and spores.*

White Dapperling

Leucoagaricus leucothites (Agaricaceae)

All parts of this inedible species are white to pale cream. The cap has a dull, almost matt surface and may turn greyish with age. The crowded gills start white but are often pink-tinged when old. A narrow, collar-like ring is situated high up on the slender, smooth stem. Spore prints for this species may vary from white to dull pink.

APPEARS *in grassy meadows, lawns, and gardens where there is rich soil.*

cap 5–15cm wide

dry, suede-like surface

crowded gills

rounded cap

narrow ring on stem

smooth stem

SECTION

SPORES *White to pinkish.*
FRUITING *Summer to late autumn.*
DISTRIBUTION *Occasional to common, widespread in temperate regions.*
EDIBILITY *Inedible.*
SIMILAR SPECIES *Var. carneifolius, with pink gills that later turn brown, could be mistaken for Field Mushroom (p. 21).*

Warted Amanita

Amanita strobiliformis (Amanitaceae)

A robust, sometimes massive species, the Warted Amanita has a creamish white cap that is covered in thick, flattened chunks of soft veil fragments. The gills are crowded and pale cream, while the stout stem has a thick ring at the top with the texture of cream cheese. Bulbous at the base, the stem is usually rooting and has rings or ridges of veil on the upper part. This fungus has a faint odour of old ham.

APPEARS *in grassy meadows and on woodland edges, sometimes at a distance from trees, on warm, chalky soils.*

cap 5–20cm wide

rounded cap with warts

thick, soft ring

ragged veil remnants

stout stem

SPORES *White.*
FRUITING *Summer to late autumn.*
DISTRIBUTION *Rare to occasional, widespread in warm, southern regions.*
EDIBILITY *Not known; possibly poisonous.*
SIMILAR SPECIES *Solitary Amanita (A. echinocephala), which has sharp, spine-like warts.*

Blue Spot Knight

Tricholoma columbetta (Tricholomataceae)

The white cap of the Blue Spot Knight is smooth and silky in texture, sometimes slightly sticky, with a prominent central umbo. The white gills are notched where they meet the white stem, which may be smooth to fibrous. There are often tiny blue or pink spots on the cap or on the tapering stem base.

FOUND *in leaf litter or moss of broadleaf woods and moorland, on acidic soils.*

silky white cap

cap 5–10cm wide

SPORES *White.*
FRUITING *Summer to late autumn.*
DISTRIBUTION *Rare to occasional, widespread in temperate regions.*
EDIBILITY *Inedible.*
SIMILAR SPECIES *Aromatic Knight (T. lascivum), which has a pale ivory to buff cap and a strong aromatic, gassy smell.*

white gills

SECTION

Conifer Sawgill

Lentinus lepideus (Polyporaceae)

The tough cap of this species is buff with darker, flattened scales. Rounded at first, it later flattens out, retaining its inrolled margin. The crowded, pale cream gills have a finely serrated edge, while the tough, rooting stem has a prominent ring above and is ringed with bands of veil. It is often offset to one side of the cap. The tough flesh has an aromatic odour when cut.

FOUND *on stumps and logs of coniferous trees; sometimes also on woked timber.*

pale buff cap

cap 5–15cm wide

dark, flattened scales on cap

bands of scales on stem

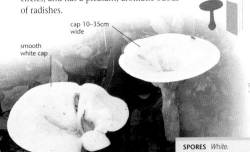

SPORES White.
FRUITING *Summer to late autumn.*
DISTRIBUTION *Rare to occasional, mainly in mountainous regions.*
EDIBILITY *Inedible.*
SIMILAR SPECIES L. conchatus, *which has a purplish lilac flushed cap with narrow gills running down its short, stout stem.*

Giant Funnel

Leucopaxillus giganteus (Tricholomataceae)

This often very large, inedible species is white to cream with a suede-like surface. The cap is depressed and funnel-shaped, with a strongly inrolled margin when young. The cream gills are crowded and run partially down the short, tough white stem. Giant Funnel frequently grows in large circles, and has a pleasant, aromatic odour of radishes.

SEEN *in short grass in woodland margins, parks, and gardens, often in circles, where it may kill the grass in broad zones.*

cap 10–35cm wide

smooth white cap

cap diameter bigger than stem length

SPORES White.
FRUITING *Summer to late autumn.*
DISTRIBUTION *Locally common, widespread in temperate Europe.*
EDIBILITY *Inedible.*
SIMILAR SPECIES Lactarius vellereus *which, unlike Giant Funnel, exudes a white milk or latex when cut.*

Peppery Milkcap

Lactarius piperatus (Russulaceae)

This white to cream-coloured species has a firm, funnel-shaped cap with extraordinarily crowded gills that run a little way down the stem. The texture of the cap is dry to slightly velvety, while the stem has crumbly, brittle flesh. The stem is usually as tall as the cap is wide. All parts of this fungus, but especially the gills, bleed white latex or milk, which tastes very peppery and dries to a dull olive-green colour. The whole fungus frequently becomes spotted with olive-brown stains when old. It is tasty if well cooked but can cause gastric irritation.

ABUNDANT *in small troops in broadleaf woods, occasionally under conifers, in leaf litter, often pushing up through soil.*

extremely crowded gills

latex dries to olive-green

depressed, funnel-shaped cap

tall stem

gills run slightly down stem

SECTION

cap 5–15cm wide

creamy white cap

brown spots appear with age

NOTE

No other white Milkcap has this combination of extremely crowded gills with white latex. To best observe the latex, try running a fingernail across the gills. It will ooze out and dry to small olive-green spots.

SPORES *White.*
FRUITING *Summer to late autumn.*
DISTRIBUTION *Occasional to common, widespread in temperate N. Europe.*
EDIBILITY *Edible, but may cause stomach upset or gastric irritation.*
SIMILAR SPECIES *Willow Milkcap* (L. controversus), *which has a buff-coloured cap, more widely-spaced, pinkish gills, and grows under poplar and willow.*

Snowy Waxcap

Hygrocybe virginea (Hygrophoraceae)

The slippery cap of this small to medium-sized fungus is domed at first, but later expands and flattens with a small central umbo or occasionally a central dip. It is cream to ivory with translucent bands at the cap edge. The waxy white gills are arched when young and run down the tapering stem.

SEEN *in grassland including lawns, dunes, and cemeteries; occasionally in woods and mossy scrub.*

cap up to 5cm wide

well-spaced gills

waxy gills

cream to ivory cap

dry, solid stem

SECTION

SPORES *White.*
FRUITING *Autumn to winter.*
DISTRIBUTION *Common and widespread throughout.*
EDIBILITY *Edible.*
SIMILAR SPECIES *Ivory Funnel (p.20) is poisonous with a blotchy cap; Cedarwood Waxcap (H. russocoriacea) smells of cedar.*

The Miller

Clitopilus prunulus (Entolomataceae)

Very variable in shape, the white to greyish cap of The Miller can be domed to quite flat, or even funnel-shaped. The gills are crowded and run down the stem, white at first, but turning pink when mature. Similarly coloured, the stem may be shorter than the cap diameter. This fungus has a floury smell and tastes of fresh meal.

FOUND *along woodland paths, in gardens, and parks; in groups in both broadleaf and coniferous woods.*

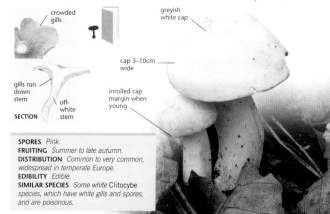

crowded gills

greyish white cap

cap 3–10cm wide

gills run down stem

off-white stem

SECTION

inrolled cap margin when young

SPORES *Pink.*
FRUITING *Summer to late autumn.*
DISTRIBUTION *Common to very common, widespread in temperate Europe.*
EDIBILITY *Edible.*
SIMILAR SPECIES *Some white Clitocybe species, which have white gills and spores, and are poisonous.*

Ivory Funnel ☠

Clitocybe dealbata (Tricholomataceae)

GROWS *in a wide range of grassy places including lawns, parks, gardens, cemeteries, fields, meadows, wood edges, and coastal dunes.*

This small to medium fungus, commonly found in grassy places, is extremely poisonous. Symptoms caused by eating it are serious, and include a lowered heart rate, sweating, tears, and gastric upset. However, these are all reversible if treated with atropine. The cap is funnel-shaped or flat, and cream to pinkish beige with a white bloom that makes it look frosted. It can be zoned or blotched and sometimes cracks when old. White to greyish cream gills run slightly down the creamy beige stem. Ivory Funnel can smell mealy when young and can easily be mistaken for several edible species. It is not uncommon to find Ivory Funnel growing in fairy rings along with the common, edible Fairy Ring Champignon (p.47). Great care must be taken to distinguish between this poisonous species and its edible counterparts.

cream gills

frosted white bloom on cap

cap 2–6cm wide

cap cracks in older fungi

gills run slightly down stem

SPORES *White.*
FRUITING *Early summer to late autumn.*
DISTRIBUTION *Very common and widespread throughout.*
EDIBILITY *Poisonous.*
SIMILAR SPECIES *Other species that grow in grass, but which are edible, such as Fairy Ring Champignon (p.47), which is brownish with a bump in its cap, and The Miller (p.19), which has a mealy smell but pink gills and spores.*

Field Mushroom

Agaricus campestris (Agaricaceae)

The edible Field Mushroom has a flattened white cap with bright pink gills when young. Later the cap may turn pinkish grey, while the gills become chocolate brown. It has a short, tapering or cylindrical stem with a very fragile ring that is often visible as just a faint zone at the top of the stem.

FOUND, *often in large numbers, forming fairy rings in grassy meadows and field and grass verges.*

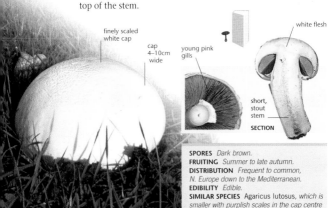

finely scaled white cap

cap 4–10cm wide

young pink gills

white flesh

short, stout stem

SECTION

SPORES *Dark brown.*
FRUITING *Summer to late autumn.*
DISTRIBUTION *Frequent to common, N. Europe down to the Mediterranean.*
EDIBILITY *Edible.*
SIMILAR SPECIES *Agaricus lutosus, which is smaller with purplish scales in the cap centre and stains dull yellow.*

Blue Band Brittlegill

Russula chloroides (Russulaceae)

The white to yellowish cap of the Blue Band Brittlegill is depressed at the centre and inrolled at the margin. It has a dry, slightly roughened surface. The crowded white gills have a faint blue-green tinge and the short white stem has a narrow blue-green zone at the top. Inedible and hard, the white flesh later turns dull yellow. It is crumbly and smells strongly fruity.

GROWS, *often in small groups, in broadleaf woodland, especially with beech, usually on neutral to acid soils.*

cap 5–15cm wide

roughened cap surface

crowded white gills

SPORES *Pale ochre.*
FRUITING *Summer to late autumn.*
DISTRIBUTION *Occasional to frequent, widespread in N. Europe down to the Mediterranean.*
EDIBILITY *Inedible.*
SIMILAR SPECIES *R. delica, which lacks the bluish tones in the gills and stem top.*

Livid Pinkgill ☠

Entoloma sinuatum (Entolomataceae)

Responsible for a number of accidental poisionings, this species generally has a large cap which is pale silvery grey to greyish ochre, often with a domed centre. The medium to widely spaced gills start pale grey but rapidly mature to deep salmon-pink. They are notched or curved where they join the stem. White to pale greyish cream in colour, the stem is tough and cylindrical to pointed. The fungus has a strong mealy, sometimes unpleasant smell. Because of its similarity to some edible fungi, it is often eaten by mistake; it causes severe stomach upsets and may even be fatal.

silvery grey to greyish ochre cap

dry, smooth cap

cap 15–20cm wide

domed cap

gills turn deep pink

notched gills

tough, fleshy stem

SECTION

stout, tapering stem

NOTE

To distinguish from similar edible species check for habitat near trees, pink gills, leaden grey cap, and an unpleasant mealy smell. St. George's Mushroom (right) can be confused but is a spring to late summer species with cream spores.

SPORES *Pink.*
FRUITING *Summer to late autumn.*
DISTRIBUTION *Occasional to frequent, widespread in temperate S. Europe.*
EDIBILITY *Highly poisonous.*
SIMILAR SPECIES *Flowery Blewit (p.54), which has a fibrous stem; Clouded Funnel (p.171), which has grey-white gills that never turn pink, and white spores. Neither has a mealy odour.*

St. George's Mushroom

Calocybe gambosa (Tricholomataceae)

A well-known edible mushroom, this species fruits around St. George's Day, April 23, hence the common name. The fleshy cap is rounded, smooth, and slightly inrolled at the margin and may have a lumpy or irregular surface in some forms. It is a pale cream-buff to dull yellowish colour when old or wet. The white gills are crowded, and join the rather stout, fleshy stem, which is also white and fibrous. When cut, St. George's Mushroom has a strong smell and tastes of freshly ground meal; the flavour is robust, but becomes milder on being cooked.

FOUND *often in groups in open grasslands, broadleaf woodland clearings, and parks; also on pathsides, preferring rich, alkaline soils.*

NOTE

Its occurrence in the spring and early summer, rather than autumn, the strong smell of fresh meal, and the white to cream spores are all features that help distinguish this highly regarded edible species from any other.

---

crowded, pale cream gills

gills join stem

tough, fleshy stem

SECTION

cap 5–12cm wide

domed cap

slightly inrolled cap margin

stout fibrous stem

SPORES *White to cream.*
FRUITING *Spring to early summer.*
DISTRIBUTION *Occasional to common, widespread in temperate Europe.*
EDIBILITY *Edible.*
SIMILAR SPECIES *Some other* Entoloma *species, which grow in the spring and have pale caps, but they differ in their pink gills and spores. Particulary check features of Livid Pinkgill (left).*

Dewdrop Dapperling

Chamaemyces fracidus (Agaricaceae)

FOUND *singly or in small groups, usually in broadleaf woodland margins or wooded pastures; prefers alkaline soils.*

The rounded, pale buff to cream cap of the Dewdrop Dapperling is dry to slightly sticky when wet, and often wrinkled. The crowded white gills are free of the stem, which is also white with numerous tiny brown dots or glands spread over its surface up to the narrow ring-zone. In wet weather the stem oozes drops of brown fluid.

slightly domed cap

free white gills

pale ring zone

cap 3–6cm wide

tiny brown dots on stem

SPORES *Cream.*
FRUITING *Summer to late autumn.*
DISTRIBUTION *Rare to occasional, widespread in N. Europe.*
EDIBILITY *Inedible.*
SIMILAR SPECIES *Several Lepiota species that look similar but lack the brown droplets on the stem.*

Weeping Slimecap

Limacella guttata (Amanitaceae)

GROWS *singly or in small groups, in both broadleaf and coniferous woods, in leaf litter on rich, alkaline soils.*

This species has a domed, pale beige cap, which is slightly sticky when wet. The white gills are very crowded and free of the stem. Tall and club-shaped, the white stem has a large floppy ring at the top, and is smooth and dry to the touch below the ring. Clear drops of liquid are exuded from the ring, which dry olive-brown. The flesh of this fungus has a strong smell of meal or cucumber.

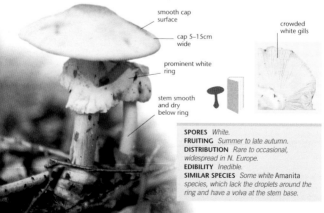

smooth cap surface

cap 5–15cm wide

crowded white gills

prominent white ring

stem smooth and dry below ring

SPORES *White.*
FRUITING *Summer to late autumn.*
DISTRIBUTION *Rare to occasional, widespread in N. Europe.*
EDIBILITY *Inedible.*
SIMILAR SPECIES *Some white Amanita species, which lack the droplets around the ring and have a volva at the stem base.*

Porcelain Fungus

Oudemansiella mucida (Tricholomataceae)

Striking and edible, the Porcelain Fungus has a pure white to pale grey cap that is often wrinkled at the centre. The slimy cap resembles glistening porcelain and is difficult to grip. The stem, which is very tough, thin, and roots on the wood in which it grows, has a narrow ring that is white above and grey on the underside. The base of the stem is often dark brown and the broad, widely spaced gills are white and attached to the stem.

OCCURS *in large numbers on fallen dead wood or on the trunks of standing beech trees, usually deeply rooted into the wood.*

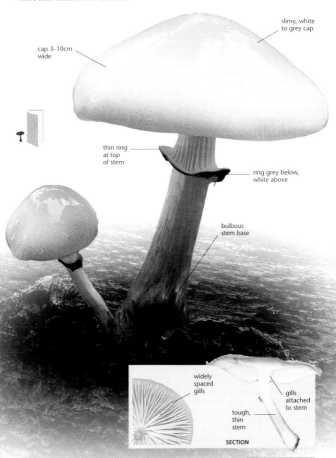

slimy, white to grey cap

cap 3–10cm wide

thin ring at top of stem

ring grey below, white above

bulbous stem base

widely spaced gills

gills attached to stem

tough, thin stem

SECTION

SPORES *White.*
FRUITING *Late autumn to early winter.*
DISTRIBUTION *Common and widespread in temperate N. Europe.*
EDIBILITY *Edible.*
SIMILAR SPECIES *White or grey species of* Mycena, *which also grow on wood but are not slimy and do not have a ring on the stem. Most other fungi that grow directly on wood and have a stem ring, have coloured spores.*

NOTE

No other species growing on wood has this particular combination of a slimy white cap and a clear ring on the stem.

Piggyback Rosegill

Volvariella surrecta (Pluteaceae)

FOUND *only on old or rotted fruitbodies of the Clouded Funnel, which grows in a range of woodland habitats.*

The Piggyback Rosegill emerges from the rotted remains of another fungus, the Clouded Funnel (p.171). Its small, rounded or domed caps are silky-white to greyish, with extremely fine radiating fibres, while the free gills are whitish, later becoming salmon-pink. The slender white stem emerges from a fragile white volva at the base.

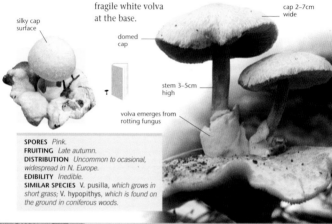

silky cap surface

domed cap

cap 2–7cm wide

stem 3–5cm high

volva emerges from rotting fungus

SPORES *Pink.*
FRUITING *Late autumn.*
DISTRIBUTION *Uncommon to ocasional, widespread in N. Europe.*
EDIBILITY *Inedible.*
SIMILAR SPECIES V. pusilla, *which grows in short grass;* V. hypopithys, *which is found on the ground in coniferous woods.*

Powdery Piggyback

Asterophora lycoperdoides (Tricholomataceae)

GROWS *only on old or decaying fruitbodies of* Russula *and* Lactarius *species.*

Resembling a small puffball, the Powdery Piggyback emerges from other species of rotting fungi. Its rounded white cap is soon covered with brown powder that is made up of spores. The very blunt gills are reduced to shallow veins, while the very short white stem also becomes powdery and later turns black.

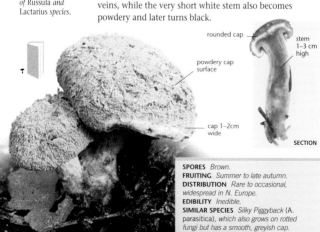

rounded cap

stem 1–3 cm high

powdery cap surface

cap 1–2cm wide

SECTION

SPORES *Brown.*
FRUITING *Summer to late autumn.*
DISTRIBUTION *Rare to occasional, widespread in N. Europe.*
EDIBILITY *Inedible.*
SIMILAR SPECIES *Silky Piggyback (A. parasitica), which also grows on rotted fungi but has a smooth, greyish cap.*

Stinking Dapperling ☠️

Lepiota cristata (Agaricaceae)

The small, domed cap of the Stinking Dapperling is white with red-brown scales concentrated at the centre and radiating out to the margin, growing paler as they spread out. The free gills are white to pale cream and crowded. Slender and cylindrical, the white stem becomes dull brown lower down and has a silky surface. At the top of the stem is a thin, easily detached white ring. The gills and white flesh strongly smell of fresh rubber or chemicals; the flesh is poisonous, but not fatal.

SEEN *in small groups, usually in grass along woodland paths, field edges, on lawns, and meadows, or sometimes near nettle beds; prefers rich soils.*

NOTE

The white cap of this fungus always has the dark central spot of scales, and its flesh has a strong, chemical smell. The tiny ring on the stem is another identifying feature, although it may slip off from older specimens.

free cream gills

dark spot at centre of cap

cap 2–4cm wide

scales radiate outwards from centre

paler scales near outer margin

tough, thin stem

SPORES *White.*
FRUITING *Summer to late autumn.*
DISTRIBUTION *Common and widespread throughout.*
EDIBILITY *Poisonous.*
SIMILAR SPECIES *Other small species of* Lepiota, *which differ in colour of scales or lack the strong smell; several are fatally poisonous including Star Dapperling* (L. josserandii), *which has pinkish brown scales and is occasionally found in gardens and parks.*

Skullcap Dapperling

Leucocoprinus brebissonii (Agaricaceae)

A very delicate, fragile, inedible species, the Skullcap Dapperling has a snow-white cap with a dark, blackish central spot of fine scales. The white gills are free and only moderately crowded. Slender, with a club-shaped base, the stem is white and smooth with a fragile white or slightly grey ring on the upper half.

SPRINGS *up in flower-pots, greenhouses, terraria, occasionally outside in warm areas or on compost heaps.*

central dark spot

cap 2–4cm wide

fragile ring

free, white gills

smooth, white stem

slender, club-shaped stem

SPORES *White.*
FRUITING *Late summer to autumn.*
DISTRIBUTION *Rare to occasional, widespread in N. Europe.*
EDIBILITY *Inedible.*
SIMILAR SPECIES *L. ianthinus, which has paler grey-lilac central scales; L. luteus is entirely bright sulphur-yellow.*

Shield Dapperling ☠

Lepiota clypeolaria (Agaricaceae)

The cap of this medium-sized, poisonous species has fine, ochre-brown scales concentrated at the centre, with the cottony remnants of a veil hanging from the cap margin. The free gills are white to cream and crowded. Tall and slender, the stem is pale brown with dense, shaggy belts of veil and a ring-zone. The faintly scented flesh is white or pale brown.

FOUND *in both broadleaf and coniferous woods, in leaf or needle litter, on rich soils.*

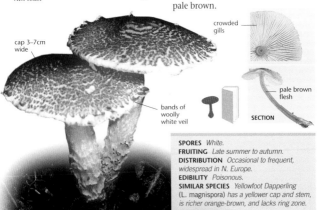

cap 3–7cm wide

crowded gills

bands of woolly white veil

pale brown flesh

SECTION

SPORES *White.*
FRUITING *Late summer to autumn.*
DISTRIBUTION *Occasional to frequent, widespread in N. Europe.*
EDIBILITY *Poisonous.*
SIMILAR SPECIES *Yellowfoot Dapperling (L. magnispora) has a yellower cap and stem, is richer orange-brown, and lacks ring zone.*

Yellow Stainer ☠

Agaricus xanthodermus (Agaricaceae)

A toxic species easily confused at first glance with other field mushrooms, it is bright white throughout when young, becoming a dirty orange-brown in patches when older. The smooth stem has a large, floppy ring with a cogwheel pattern on the underside, and the base is swollen, often with a distinct bulb. When young, the whole mushroom very easily bruises a bright chrome yellow especially in the stem base; this is less obvious when it is older. The gills change from grey to pink to brown as it ages and it has a strong, unpleasant, chemical smell, like that of ink.

SEEN *in grassland or woodland edges, in bare soil, grass, or bark mulch, especially in man-made habitats like parks and cemeteries.*

cap flattened in centre

cap 5–13cm wide

silky white cap

crowded gills

hanging, double ring

bulbous stem base

SECTION

NOTE

For identification, always test by rubbing the stem base which quickly turns yellow. The strong, unpleasant chemical smell (phenol) is characteristic of the Yellow Stainer and other toxic species in this group.

SPORES *Chocolate-brown.*
FRUITING *Summer to autumn.*
DISTRIBUTION *Common and widespread throughout northern temperate regions.*
EDIBILITY *Poisonous.*
SIMILAR SPECIES *Horse Mushroom* (A. arvensis), *The Prince* (A. augustus), *and Wood Mushroom* (A. silvicola) *are all edible, stain more slowly, and smell of almonds.*

Horse Mushroom

Agaricus arvensis (Agaricaceae)

OCCURS *in grass meadows, parks, or near broadleaf woods. Also in gardens on manured soil.*

This is a well-known edible species formerly cultivated in rural districts. Often quite large, the fungus has a mainly smooth, rounded white cap, becoming dull bronze-yellow with age. The cap may crack into fibres when exposed to hot sun. Its similarly coloured stem is cylindrical to slightly club-shaped, thickening towards the base. It is smooth below a large, soft floppy ring that hangs down from the top. The underside of the ring has thick flakes of veil arranged rather like a cogwheel. The crowded gills are pinkish to brown in colour and free from the stem. The thick white flesh slowly bruises to a dull yellow and smells of aniseed.

gills age from pale pink to brown

ring with "cogwheel" on underside

SECTION

cap 6–10cm wide

white cap ageing to dull yellow

cylindrical to club-shaped stem

flattened, thimble-shaped young caps

NOTE

The pleasant anise smell of the cut flesh distinguishes this popular edible species. You can also identify this fungus by its pink gills which turn brown.

SPORES *Dark brown.*
FRUITING *Summer to late autumn.*
DISTRIBUTION *Occasional to frequent, widespread in Europe to the Mediterranean.*
EDIBILITY *Edible and tasty.*
SIMILAR SPECIES A. macrocarpus *is more robust, with a woolly stem below the ring, and prefers woodlands;* A. nivescens *is whiter, woolier on the stem, and prefers chalky soils.*

Lilac Mushroom

Agaricus porphyrizon (Agaricaceae)

A medium to large edible species, the Lilac Mushroom's rounded cap has fine purple to purple-brown flattened scales on a buff background. The slender white stem has a small, floppy ring which yellows when touched. The gills are pale pinkish grey at first, then dark brown. When scratched or cut the flesh turns a dull brassy yellow to orange-yellow.

GROWS *singly or in small groups in broadleaf woodland, especially on sandy soils, also around coastal sand dunes.*

cap 5–10cm wide

purple scales on buff background

small, floppy ring

gills free from stem

SECTION

SPORES *Dark brown.*
FRUITING *Summer to late autumn.*
DISTRIBUTION *Rare to occasional in temperate Europe down to the Mediterranean.*
EDIBILITY *Edible.*
SIMILAR SPECIES A. impudicus *is darker brown and smells of rubber when cut.*

Bitter Knight

Tricholoma acerbum (Tricholomataceae)

This large, inedible species has a rounded cap, noticeably grooved or crimped on the margin, like a pie crust. It is pale cream to yellow-brown in colour, darker at the centre and more yellow at the margin. The cream-coloured gills are crowded, with rust-red spots. Coloured like the cap, the firm stem has a granular surface at the apex. The white flesh is hard and bitter to taste.

SEEN *in groups in leaf litter of broadleaf trees; along woodland margins and pathsides, on chalky soil.*

grooved cap margin

cap 6–15cm wide

tawny cap darker at centre

firm white flesh

SECTION

SPORES *White.*
FRUITING *Summer to late autumn.*
DISTRIBUTION *Rare to occasional; widespread in temperate Europe.*
EDIBILITY *Inedible.*
SIMILAR SPECIES Birch Knight (p.100) *is much darker red-brown, has yellow gills and flesh, and grows with birch.*

Cultivated Mushroom

Agaricus bisporus (Agaricaceae)

ABUNDANT *in disturbed soil – often where manured or composted – on roadsides, woodland edges, and in gardens; usually not meadows.*

The ancestor of our common cultivated mushroom, this wild form has a darker, more scaly cap than the smooth, white cap of the store-bought variety. The cap also has an overhanging woolly margin. The Cultivated Mushroom is short and stout, and the cylindrical stem has a narrow, double ring at the top. Its flesh is white with a slight herb-like or mushroomy smell and turns faint pinkish brown when cut or bruised. The spore-producing cells of the Cultivated Mushroom have only two instead of the normal four spores. This species has been widely cultivated giving rise to many commercial varieties, from smooth and white to brown and scaly.

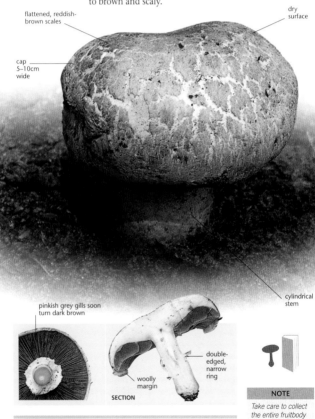

flattened, reddish-brown scales

dry surface

cap 5–10cm wide

pinkish grey gills soon turn dark brown

cylindrical stem

woolly margin

double-edged, narrow ring

SECTION

NOTE

Take care to collect the entire fruitbody with the stem base to avoid confusion with fatal Amanita species that have a volva at the base, while the Cultivated Mushroom does not.

SPORES *Dark brown.*
FRUITING *Summer to late autumn.*
DISTRIBUTION *Rare to occasional in the wild, widespread in temperate Europe down to the Mediterranean.*
EDIBILITY *Edible and tasty.*
SIMILAR SPECIES *A.* bitorquis *has a flattened cap with an inrolled margin and very narrow gills, and a short and thick stem with a collar-like ring.*

Poisonpie ☠

Hebeloma crustuliniforme (Cortinariaceae)

The common name reflects the appearance of this species – it has a pale cream to buff colour like that of uncooked pastry, but is poisonous. Its cap is round to flattened with a central dome, the margin is inrolled, and the surface is smooth and quite sticky when wet. Extremely crowded, the gills are pale brown and exude numerous tiny droplets of clear liquid in damp weather. As they dry around the gill edge, these droplets turn dark brown and trap mature spores within them. The cylindrical stem is white to cream with a very fleecy and granular surface. The flesh is white with a bitter taste and the whole fungus smells strongly of radish.

GROWS *often in small troops, among grass in mixed woods, along woodland paths, parks, and gardens; grows with broadleaf trees and conifers*

pale brown gills

brown spots

NOTE

Use a hand lens to see both the tiny drops of liquid on the gill margin and the woolly-granular stem surface – features specific to this fungus. The sticky cap and smell of radish or cocoa distinguish **Hebeloma** *species in general.*

sticky, rounded young cap

buff cap surface

white cap margin

cap 5–10cm wide

SPORES *Dull brown.*
FRUITING *Summer to late autumn.*
DISTRIBUTION *Common, widespread throughout temperate Europe.*
EDIBILITY *Poisonous, although rarely fatal.*
SIMILAR SPECIES *A number of similar species differ only in microscopic characteristics although their taste may be less bitter, and the smell more akin to cocoa than radish. All* **Hebeloma** *species are regarded as poisonous.*

Spring Fieldcap

Agrocybe praecox (Bolbitiaceae)

GROWS *on roadside verges and in fields and woods, often in grassy or bare places.*

Growing in spring and early summer, this inedible species is pale buff to ivory in all parts. The smooth surface of the rounded to flattened cap may crack as it dries. Often bulbous at the base, the slender stem has a distinct, drooping ring at the top, which may fall off. The gills are pale buff, turning dark brown with age. This fungus has a strong smell and tastes bitter.

cap 2–6cm wide

whitish flesh

torn veil fragments

sturdy, slender stem

SECTION

SPORES *Medium brown.*
FRUITING *Spring to early summer.*
DISTRIBUTION *Rare to occasional, widespread from temperate N. Europe to the Mediterranean.*
EDIBILITY *Inedible.*
SIMILAR SPECIES *Dark Fieldcap (A. erebia), which is dark brown and fruits in the autumn.*

Bearded Fieldcap

Agrocybe molesta (Bolbitiaceae)

OCCURS *on roadside verges and in woodland edges and gardens.*

All parts of this inedible species are very pale ivory-buff to almost white. The rounded cap is smooth but often strongly cracked in dry weather, almost like a mosaic. Pale buff when young, the gills turn dark brown as they mature. The cylindrical stem has a fine, irregular ring-zone at the top and may have fine, root-like cords at the base.

cap 3–7cm wide

gills buff then brown

smooth cap often cracked

slender stem

SECTION

SPORES *Medium brown.*
FRUITING *Summer to late autumn.*
DISTRIBUTION *Occasional to frequent, widespread in temperate regions.*
EDIBILITY *Inedible.*
SIMILAR SPECIES *A. putaminum, which grows on woodchips, has a stem ridged lengthwise, and no ring.*

Trooping Funnel

Clitocybe geotropa (Tricholomataceae)

A very large, edible species, the Trooping Funnel has a funnel-shaped cap, usually with a raised centre. White to pale cream or beige, the cap is dry and smooth. The white gills are crowded and run down the very tall stem, which is club-shaped and fibrous. Its large size and distinctive shape, and its habit of growing in large circles, make this fungus easy to identify. It also has a distinctive, almost rancid smell.

SEEN *in large groups, often in circles, in mixed woods, usually on alkaline soils.*

cap 6–20cm wide

crowded white gills

funnelled cap with central umbo

tall, club-shaped stem

gills run down stem

SECTION

SPORES *White.*
FRUITING *Summer to late autumn.*
DISTRIBUTION *Occasional to frequent, widespread in temperate regions.*
EDIBILITY *Edible.*
SIMILAR SPECIES *Giant Funnel (p.17), which is larger with a short stem; Tawny Funnel (p.105), which is smaller.*

Common Funnel

Clitocybe gibba (Tricholomataceae)

The funnel-shaped cap and stem of this delicate, edible species are pale buff-brown to pinkish beige. The cap often has a small umbo at the centre and its surface is dry and felty. The thin, crowded gills run down the stem, which is slender and fibrous. Faintly smelling of bitter almonds, the flesh has a mild taste.

APPEARS *in small groups, usually in leaf or needle litter in mixed woods, often along paths.*

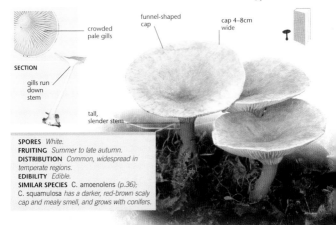

crowded pale gills

SECTION

gills run down stem

funnel-shaped cap

cap 4–8cm wide

tall, slender stem

SPORES *White.*
FRUITING *Summer to late autumn.*
DISTRIBUTION *Common, widespread in temperate regions.*
EDIBILITY *Edible.*
SIMILAR SPECIES *C. amoenolens (p.36); C. squamulosa has a darker, red-brown scaly cap and mealy smell, and grows with conifers.*

Paralysis Funnel ☠

Clitocybe amoenolens (Tricholomataceae)

FOUND *in small troops or circles in needle litter of conifer woods.*

Found originally in Morocco, this species appears to be spreading across parts of France and Italy and has been the cause of some serious poisonings with extreme pain in the extremities and other neurotoxic effects. The pale ivory to buff or brownish cap is usually smooth but may develop a depression at the centre and a cracked or frosted-looking surface. It becomes funnel-shaped with age and has an inrolled margin which may be grooved. The gills of the Paralysis Funnel are cream to pale buff and run down the stem, which is quite short, robust, and coloured whitish brown like the cap. This fungus has a sweet flowery smell of jasmine or overripe pears.

pale yellow-buff gills

NOTE

Take care not to confuse this rare and dangerous fungus with other similar-looking, edible members of the Clitocybe *group. The smell of flowers or ripe pears is a good clue to the identity of this species.*

pale brownish cap

cap 5–15cm wide

cap often depressed at centre

short, stocky whitish brown stem

SPORES *White.*
FRUITING *Autumn to early winter.*
DISTRIBUTION *Rare, known only in France and Italy but spreading.*
EDIBILITY *Highly poisonous.*
SIMILAR SPECIES *Common Funnel (p.35), which has a pinkish beige cap – it is edible but not recommended because of possible confusion; a number of similar* Clitocybe *species such as C. inversa, which has a pale yellow-orange to brick-red cap.*

Dotted Fanvault

Camarophyllopsis atropuncta (Tricholomataceae)

The Dotted Fanvault has a small, domed, dingy grey-brown cap with a lined margin. The grey-brown gills are thick, well spaced, and noticeably arched, running down the stem in a fan-like fashion. The pale grey stem tapers towards the base and has distinctive black flecks at the top.

SEEN *in woodlands and sometimes grassy areas, usually with broadleaf trees, especially hazel, in damp, alkaline soil.*

cap up to 2cm wide

grey-brown domed cap

black flecks on upper stem

widely spaced, arched gills

tapering stem

> **SPORES** *White.*
> **FRUITING** *Autumn.*
> **DISTRIBUTION** *Rare to occasional, mainly N. Europe.*
> **EDIBILITY** *Inedible.*
> **SIMILAR SPECIES** Cedar Waxcap (Hygrocybe russocoriacea), *which has a waxy cap, lacks the black stem flecks, and smells of cedar.*

Cinnamon Navel

Omphalina pyxidata (Tricholomataceae)

This tiny species has a light reddish brown cap deeply depressed at the centre and with radiating darker lines on the surface; the margin may be wavy to toothed. The pale pinkish cream gills are widely spaced and run deeply down the stem. The slender stem is tall, smooth, and shiny, and is often much longer than the cap diameter.

GROWS *in small groups, along paths, often among mosses, mostly on wet, gravelly, or sandy soils.*

cinnamon cap

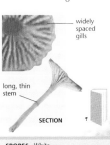

widely spaced gills

long, thin stem

SECTION

cap 1–1.5cm wide

> **SPORES** *White.*
> **FRUITING** *Summer to late autumn.*
> **DISTRIBUTION** *Occasional, widespread in temperate Europe.*
> **EDIBILITY** *Inedible.*
> **SIMILAR SPECIES** O. oniscus *is very dark brown with an unlined cap;* O. sphagnicola, *is darker brown – both grow on moors.*

Fairy Inkcap

Coprinus disseminatus (Coprinaceae)

GROWS, *often in dense clusters, on dead hardwood or on soil by dead trees.*

This tiny species, found growing in huge troops, produces little parachute-like caps, which are yellowish grey and deeply pleated. With a magnifying glass, minute hairs can be seen on the surface. The fairly crowded gills are deep grey-brown to black, and the slender, fragile stems are off-white. Unlike other *Coprinus* species, it hardly melts away when old.

pleated surface to caps

cap 0.5–1.5cm wide

grey gills

tall, smooth stem

SECTION

SPORES *Black.*
FRUITING *Spring to late autumn.*
DISTRIBUTION *Common and widespread, temperate Europe.*
EDIBILITY *Inedible.*
SIMILAR SPECIES *Pygmy Brittlestem (Psathyrella pygmacea) has a smoother cap and is hairless.*

Pleated Inkcap

Coprinus plicatilis (Coprinaceae)

SEEN *in small groups or singly in open meadows, lawns, and other grassy areas.*

A common species in open, grassy areas, the Pleated Inkcap has a smooth, bell-shaped grey-white cap that soon flattens and is pleated with a dark orange-brown disc at the centre. There are no hairs on the cap and the thin blackish gills are attached to a collar around the stem. The tall, very thin and fragile stem is white. This fungus appears overnight and withers by noon.

dark orange-brown disc

cap 1–2cm wide

pleated surface

gills join tiny collar

tall, slender stem

SECTION

SPORES *Black.*
FRUITING *Spring to late autumn.*
DISTRIBUTION *Common and widespread, temperate Europe.*
EDIBILITY *Inedible.*
SIMILAR SPECIES *C. auricomus is slightly larger, browner, and has hairs on the cap.*

Shaggy Inkcap

Coprinus comatus (Coprinaceae)

A popular edible species, this unmistakable fungus has a tall, egg-shaped or elongated cap covered when young in shaggy, recurved white scales – hence the common name. It is also known as the Lawyer's Wig. A narrow ring around the middle of the stem elongates as the fungus matures, lifting the cap upwards. The cap and white gills gradually blacken and dissolve into black ink from the edge upwards, to release the spores – until the cap dissolves entirely and only the stem remains. The Shaggy Inkcap has a delicate flavour, but only when it is young, before it blackens. It is more fleshy than other species of the genus, and popular for its texture. If collected for eating, it should be picked in the daytime and cooked soon after.

FOUND *in small troops in grassy areas and lawns, and on roadsides, often where soil has been disturbed and turfed over.*

recurved white scales

tall, hollow stem

SECTION

cap 4–15cm tall

tall, narrow cap

woolly scales

cap and gills blacken from margin

SPORES *Black.*
FRUITING *Summer to late autumn.*
DISTRIBUTION *Common, widespread in temperate Europe.*
EDIBILITY *Edible and tasty when young.*
SIMILAR SPECIES *Several species are a similar shape when young so cut in half to check for the tall cylindrical shape of the unopened cap, and the ring around the stem; Magpie Inkcap (p.176), which has striking white patches on a black cap.*

NOTE

If collecting for food make sure the gills have not yet started to turn black. Preferably gather before the cap has started to open up at all.

Egghead Mottlegill

Panaeolus semiovatus (Coprinaceae)

GROWS *singly or in small groups on animal dung, straw, or manured grass in fields and meadows.*

Extremely variable in size, the Egghead Mottlegill has a pale ivory to beige cap that is smooth and sticky when wet and shiny when dry. The crowded grey to black gills are mottled with darker shades of grey or black. Rigid but fragile, the tall stem is buff to darker brown with a distinct ring on the stem, which is often stained black from fallen spores. As with many fungi that grow on dung, the size of the fruitbody directly reflects the amount of food available to it. This explains why it can vary from just a few centimetres to over 15cm in height.

grey-black gills

stem 4–15cm tall

SECTION

egg- or bell-shaped cap

cap 1–5cm wide

SPORES *Black.*
FRUITING *Spring to late autumn.*
DISTRIBUTION *Occasional to frequent, widespread in temperate N. Europe.*
EDIBILITY *Inedible.*
SIMILAR SPECIES *A number of smaller, usually darker, species of Panaeolus are found in similar habitats, however none of them has a ring on the stem.*

NOTE

With its sticky cap and ringed stem, Egghead Mottlegill is unlike any other Panaeolus species, so is sometimes placed in its own genus, Anellaria.

Branching Oyster

Pleurotus cornucopiae (Polyporaceae)

The deeply trumpet-shaped caps of this popular edible species are pale cream to buff and very smooth on top. The shallow gills run deeply down the often long stem and are frequently fused into a network of ridges at the bottom. The stem is variable in length depending where the fruitbodies are situated on the host log.

SEEN *often in large numbers with stems fused together, on fallen logs or standing dead trunks of broadleaf trees, especially elm.*

trumpet-shaped cap

cap 4–12cm wide

gills run down stem

gills fused into network at base

SPORES *White.*
FRUITING *Summer to late autumn.*
DISTRIBUTION *Occasional to frequent, widespread in temperate N. Europe.*
EDIBILITY *Edible and tasty.*
SIMILAR SPECIES *Pale Oyster (P. pulmonarius), has a half-rounded, flattened cap, and a shorter or absent stem.*

Silky Rosegill

Volvariella bombycina (Pluteaceae)

This species has a silky, hairy, white to cream or yellowish cap, which is egg-shaped at first then flat with a central umbo. The very broad, free gills are white, then deep pink. The cap and fibrous stem emerge from a tall, thin brown sac or volva. An edible species, it is a relative of the Paddy Straw fungus of oriental cookery.

GROWS *singly or in small clusters on broadleaf trees, notably elm, often high up on the tree.*

cap 10–25cm wide

fibrous stem

silky scales on cap

SECTION solid, off-white flesh

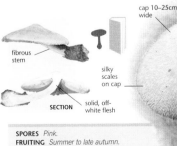

SPORES *Pink.*
FRUITING *Summer to late autumn.*
DISTRIBUTION *Rare to occasional, widespread in N. temperate Europe.*
EDIBILITY *Edible and tasty.*
SIMILAR SPECIES *V. caesiotincta, which is smaller with a more grey-brown cap and greyish volva, and grows on fallen logs.*

Warty Cavalier

Melanoleuca verrucipes (Tricholomataceae)

FOUND *often in large numbers on woodchips, wood mulch, or rotten wood, in woodlands, gardens, and roadsides.*

An easily identified species, the Warty Cavalier, originally from mainland northern Europe, is gradually spreading throughout temperate Europe and Britain. The fleshy white cap has a central umbo, and the gills, which are white when young, grow creamy with age. They are notched where they join the stem. However, it is the white stem with small black flecks or warts all over that is the most distinctive feature of the Warty Cavalier. The white flesh of this inedible species is quite tough, and has a fruity or cheesy smell. Other species of *Melanoleuca* can be found on wood chips, but these are all grey-or brown-capped.

NOTE

Melanoleuca is one of the most difficult genera to identify – this distinctive species with its white cap and white stem with black flecks is an exception.

fleshy cap

central umbo

cap 5–15cm wide

black flecks

gills white when young

SPORES *White.*
FRUITING *Summer to late autumn.*
DISTRIBUTION *Rare to occasional, of late spreading in temperate Europe.*
EDIBILITY *Inedible.*
SIMILAR SPECIES *M. strictipes, M. subalpina, and other white members of the Melanoleuca genus, which all lack the black flecks on the stem and grow in grass or leaf litter.*

Cream Pinkgill

Entoloma sericellum (Entolomataceae)

The pure white to pale yellowish cap of the Cream Pinkgill is domed or bell-shaped when young but eventually flattens when old. The gills are crowded and white when young, but become widely spaced and pink as the fungus matures. They run slightly down the white stem, which is white, silky, and very fragile.

GROWS *in small troops in wet meadows, grassy woodland clearings, and mossy grass in gardens.*

cap 1–2cm wide

pink mature gills

shiny stem

smooth white cap

SPORES *Pink.*
FRUITING *Summer to late autumn.*
DISTRIBUTION *Occasional to frequent, widespread in temperate Europe.*
EDIBILITY *Inedible.*
SIMILAR SPECIES *Some* Volvariella *species, which are small, white, and grow in grass but have a tiny volva at the stem base.*

Greenspored Dapperling

Melanophyllum eyrei (Agaricaceae)

This is one of the few fungi with blue-green gills. They are free from the stem and moderately crowded. The thin, whitish cap has a powdery to minutely granular surface and becomes brownish with age. The very slender, fragile white stem is slightly brownish at the base. It has a matt, powdery or granular surface and does not have a ring.

APPEARS *on rich soil, often in damp areas, especially if the ground has been disturbed – usually singly or in small groups.*

cap 1–2cm wide

powdery white cap surface

thin stem

blue-green gills

stem 2–5cm tall

SPORES *Blue-green.*
FRUITING *Summer to late autumn.*
DISTRIBUTION *Rare to occasional, widespread in temperate Europe.*
EDIBILITY *Inedible.*
SIMILAR SPECIES *None – although there are many small white species from other genera, none has blue-green gills.*

Pearly Powdercap

Cystoderma carcharius (Tricholomataceae)

GROWS *in mossy needle beds in humus and leaf litter, in coniferous woods, on acid soils.*

The domed cap of this inedible species is white at first then soon pinkish grey, darker pink at the centre, with a powdery surface and a fringed margin. Partly joining the stem, the fairly crowded white gills have a strong, earthy smell. The stem is pinkish white, very granular or powdery, with a prominent, flared ring near the top.

pinkish grey cap

cap 2–5cm wide

fringed cap margin

flared ring

pinkish white stem

SPORES *Off-white.*
FRUITING *Summer to late autumn.*
DISTRIBUTION *Rare to occasional, widespread in temperate N. Europe.*
EDIBILITY *Inedible.*
SIMILAR SPECIES *C. ambrosii is almost pure white to slightly brownish when old.*

Coconut Milkcap

Lactarius glyciosmus (Russulaceae)

SEEN *in moss and leaf litter; associated with birch, mainly in wet woods.*

Smelling of dried coconut, this inedible species has a flattened cap depressed at the centre, and is greyish to ochre with a faint pink tinge. The surface is dry and felty, and the crowded, pale pinkish cream gills bleed tiny amounts of mild- to slightly hot-tasting white milk when scratched. The stem is pale pinkish cream.

pink-tinged cap

cap 2–6cm wide

fairly crowded gills

smooth, pale stem

pale pinkish cream gills

SECTION

flattened cap

SPORES *Pale yellow.*
FRUITING *Summer to late autumn.*
DISTRIBUTION *Frequent to common, widespread in temperate N. Europe.*
EDIBILITY *Inedible.*
SIMILAR SPECIES *L. mammosus has a coconut smell, but is rarer, darker, and grows in coniferous woods.*

Garlic Parachute

Marasmius alliaceus (Tricholomataceae)

The strong smell of rotten garlic and tall black stem help to identify this edible species. The cap is domed or flattened, smooth to radially wrinkled, and beige to leather-brown. Crowded and joined to the stem, the gills are pale buff. The slender, stiff stem is blackish brown and smooth to slightly velvety; it is hollow when cut open.

FOUND *in troops on fallen twigs and branches of beech, rarely on leaf litter.*

cap 2–4cm wide

pale buff to brown

radially wrinkled cap

domed to flattened cap

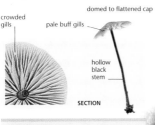

crowded gills

pale buff gills

hollow black stem

SECTION

SPORES *White.*
FRUITING *Summer to late autumn.*
DISTRIBUTION *Frequent to common, widespread in temperate N. Europe.*
EDIBILITY *Edible.*
SIMILAR SPECIES *Foetid Parachute (Micromphale foetidum) is shorter and stouter; M. scorodonius is smaller and paler.*

Horsehair Parachute

Marasmius androsaceus (Tricholomataceae)

A very delicate, inedible species, this fungus has tiny, pale reddish brown caps that are radially furrowed, and depressed at the centre. The pinkish brown gills are very widely spaced and attached to the smooth, shiny black stem, which is wiry and hair-thin. There may be horsehair-like mycelial threads present radiating from the base of the stems.

GROWS *in troops on fallen needles of pine trees in woods and on heaths, often in large numbers.*

radially wrinkled cap surface

widely spaced gills

cap 3–10mm wide

shiny black stem

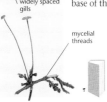

mycelial threads

SPORES *White.*
FRUITING *Summer to late autumn.*
DISTRIBUTION *Frequent to common, widespread in temperate N. Europe.*
EDIBILITY *Edible.*
SIMILAR SPECIES *Collared Parachute (M. rotula) has a whitish cap, a shorter, thicker stem, and white gills attached to a collar.*

Clustered Toughshank

Collybia confluens (Tricholomataceae)

The dense clumps of fruitbodies and an aromatic smell help to identify this inedible species. The cap is pale tan to greyish buff, thin, tough, and domed to flattened. Narrow and crowded, the gills are white to cream. The buff to deep brown stem is hollow, tough and hairy with a dry surface. Several stems are fused together at the base.

FOUND *in dense clusters both in broadleaf and coniferous woods, also in thick leaf litter or needles.*

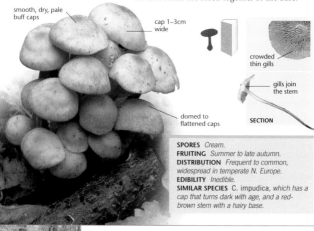

smooth, dry, pale buff caps

cap 1–3cm wide

crowded thin gills

gills join the stem

SECTION

domed to flattened caps

SPORES *Cream.*
FRUITING *Summer to late autumn.*
DISTRIBUTION *Frequent to common, widespread in temperate N. Europe.*
EDIBILITY *Inedible.*
SIMILAR SPECIES C. impudica, *which has a cap that turns dark with age, and a red-brown stem with a hairy base.*

Redleg Toughshank

Collybia erythropus (Tricholomataceae)

The pale caps of Redleg Toughshank combined with its deep red-brown stems are very distinctive. Slightly grooved at the margin, the smooth caps are thin and rounded initially, but soon flatten out. The gills are fairly broad and whitish to deep cream, while the smooth, glossy stems are almost blood-red to deep brown.

GROWS *in small clusters and troops on mossy stumps and buried, very decayed wood in broadleaf forests.*

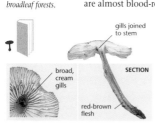

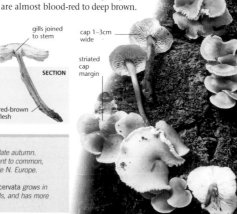

gills joined to stem

cap 1–3cm wide

SECTION

striated cap margin

broad, cream gills

red-brown flesh

SPORES *Cream.*
FRUITING *Summer to late autumn.*
DISTRIBUTION *Frequent to common, widespread in temperate N. Europe.*
EDIBILITY *Inedible.*
SIMILAR SPECIES C. acervata *grows in tufts in coniferous woods, and has more crowded gills.*

Fairy Ring Champignon

Marasmius oreades (Tricholomataceae)

A popular edible species, this Fairy Ring Champignon has very tough, fleshy fruitbodies. The entire fungus is more or less pale buff-tan, darker when wet, much paler when dry and sun-baked. The rounded or domed cap soon expands, becoming flatter with a broad umbo with age, and is smooth. The broad, widely spaced gills are almost free of the stem and are pale cream to buff. The tough, solid stem is dry, slightly powdery to touch, and off-white to pale buff. The mushroom has a pleasant taste and smells faintly of bitter almonds. While the caps are used in cooking, the tough stems are usually discarded.

FORMS *circles or arcs in short turf in meadows, parks, gardens, and near roadsides.*

pale buff cap

rounded or smooth domed cap

cap 2–5cm wide

tough, dry stem

broad, widely spaced gills

gills free of stem

white to buff flesh

SECTION

NOTE
To be certain you have this species, look for the almost free, thick, broadly spaced gills, very tough stem (try bending it), combined with a buff cap.

SPORES *White.*
FRUITING *Spring to late autumn.*
DISTRIBUTION *Common everywhere, widespread in temperate Europe.*
EDIBILITY *Edible and tasty.*
SIMILAR SPECIES *Ivory Funnel (p.20), which also grows in circles, but is highly poisonous – it has a white, frosted-looking cap, and gills that run very slightly down a stem that is not as tough.*

Blueleg Brownie 💀

Psilocybe cyanescens (Strophariaceae)

A recent invader into Europe, this poisonous fungus is spreading widely. The cap is dark brown, drying creamy ochre, often with a darker zone at the margin, and the surface is smooth and slightly greasy when wet. The gills are dark brown and the white stem stains blue when handled or with age. The cap may also have bluish stains on the margin.

GROWS in large clumps or in troops on woodchip mulch in gardens and parks and on forest paths; rarely naturalized on twigs in woodlands.

ochre-brown cap

wavy, upturned cap margin

dark brown gills

cap 3–6cm wide

tough white stem

SECTION

SPORES Purple-brown.
FRUITING Late autumn into early winter.
DISTRIBUTION Occasional to frequent, scattered across Europe.
EDIBILITY Poisonous and hallucinogenic.
SIMILAR SPECIES Olive Brownie (Hypholoma myosotis) grows in boggy areas and does not stain blue – its edibility is unknown.

Dung Roundhead

Stropharia semiglobata (Strophariaceae)

The small cap of this inedible species is convex or hemispherical and does not open out completely flat. It is pale creamy yellow, smooth, and sticky when wet. The gills are very broad, attached to the stem, and dark olive-grey with a white edge. Slender and hollow, the stem is pale yellow, and sticky below a faint ring-zone.

FOUND in small groups in pastures and meadows on a wide range of animal dung.

smooth cap surface

olive-grey gills

convex cap

very deep, broad gills

slender yellow stem

cap 1–3cm wide

hollow stem

SECTION

SPORES Purple-brown.
FRUITING Late spring to late autumn.
DISTRIBUTION Frequent to common, widespread in N. Europe.
EDIBILITY Inedible.
SIMILAR SPECIES S. umbonatescens has a pimple at the centre of its darker, more reddish yellow cap.

Blushing Wood Mushroom

Agaricus sylvaticus (Agaricaceae)

The white flesh of this mushroom stains deep red when cut. Initially rounded, the pale brown cap soon flattens, and has finely pointed, dark brown scales at the centre. The greyish pink, free gills turn dark brown, and the smooth stem is cream to pale brown, with a large, floppy ring.

SEEN *in small troops in both broadleaf and coniferous woods, also along roadsides and in parks and gardens.*

convex cap

dark brown centre

small, pointed scales

grey-pink gills

floppy, fragile ring

cap 5–10cm wide

deep red staining

SECTION

SPORES *Brown.*
FRUITING *Summer to late autumn.*
DISTRIBUTION *Frequent to common, throughout temperate Europe.*
EDIBILITY *Edible and tasty.*
SIMILAR SPECIES *Scaly Wood Mushroom (A. langei) is more robust, has broader scales, larger spores, and stains deeper red.*

Clustered Mushroom ☠

Agaricus vaporarius (Agaricaceae)

This distinctive species has a rounded cap, which may be flattened at the centre and is usually densely covered with broad, flat, dark brown scales, although it may also appear uniformly brown. The gills are pale greyish pink, turning dark brown later. Sometimes tapered or rooting, the stem is thick and tough with a brownish surface below a fragile ring.

OCCURS *in clumps or dense clusters on roadsides, and in parks, gardens, and manured fields.*

pale greyish pink gills

broad, flattened scales

cap 5–15cm wide

brown cap

thick, rooting stem

SPORES *Dark brown.*
FRUITING *Late autumn into early winter.*
DISTRIBUTION *Rare to occasional, temperate N. Europe to the Mediterranean.*
EDIBILITY *Not known, possibly poisonous.*
SIMILAR SPECIES *A. bohusii grows in large clumps, has dense, pointed, and raised cap scales, and is rarer.*

Slender Parasol

Macrolepiota mastoidea (Agaricaceae)

GROWS *singly or in small groups in woodland clearings and parks, and on roadsides, under broadleaf trees.*

An elegant species, the Slender Parasol has an umbonate cap that is pale cream overall and darker brown at the centre. It is covered by fine, bran-like scales that spread out to the margin. The gills are broad and crowded, while the stem is pale buff-brown with fine bands of granular scales, and a thick, double ring at the top. When bruised, the flesh stains red-brown.

cap 5–12cm wide

pale cream gills

thick double ring

tall, slender stem

SECTION

SPORES *White.*
FRUITING *Summer to late autumn.*
DISTRIBUTION *Rare to occasional, temperate N. Europe down to the Mediterranean.*
EDIBILITY *Edible and tasty.*
SIMILAR SPECIES *M. excoriata is shorter and stouter, with a buff cap.*

Shaggy Parasol ☠

Macrolepiota rhacodes (Agaricaceae)

EMERGES *singly, or in clumps or rings, in gardens and mixed woods, and on compost heaps and roadsides.*

Reaching large sizes, the fleshy cap of the Shaggy Parasol has a dark umbo with recurved brown scales on a whitish background. The free gills are white, and the stout, smooth stem is whitish to dull brown, with a bulbous base and thick, double ring. While the gills bruise dark brown, the flesh bruises deep red, then brown.

free, pale cream gills

white flesh bruises red

cap 5–20cm wide

pale buff-brown stem

drumstick shaped fruitbody

dark scales

SPORES *White.*
FRUITING *Summer to late autumn.*
DISTRIBUTION *Frequent to common, temperate N. Europe to the Mediterranean.*
EDIBILITY *Edible, but toxic to some.*
SIMILAR SPECIES *M. olivieri is dark brown overall, less robust, and grows mostly in coniferous woodlands.*

Parasol

Macrolepiota procera (Agaricaceae)

This is a well-known, edible species that often grows very large. The egg-shaped young cap soon expands and flattens with a large central umbo. It has a pale buff-brown surface with very dark, flattened scales radiating out from the centre. The free gills are broad and pale cream, while the tall, club-shaped stem is very firm and pale buff with numerous bands of dark brown scales in a pattern resembling snakeskin. There is a large, double ring on the stem which can be moved up and down when it gets old. The flesh is whitish in colour and bruises to dull yellowish red.

FOUND *in small troops in meadows, fields, and woodland clearings, as well as in dune grasslands and on roadsides.*

dark scales radiate
out from centre

cap 10–30cm
wide

large stem
ring

white to
cream
gills

dark scales on
tall stem

dark
umbo

bulbous
stem base

SPORES *White.*
FRUITING *Summer to late autumn.*
DISTRIBUTION *Frequent to common, widespread throughout temperate N. Europe.*
EDIBILITY *Edible and tasty.*
SIMILAR SPECIES *False Parasol (p.52); The Blusher (p.87); M. fuliginosa has a grey-brown cap with dark brown scales; M. permixta often has pinkish gills and its flesh stains a deeper red-brown.*

NOTE

The Parasol can be easily distinguished by its banded stem. The toxic Blusher (p.87), with which it may be confused, has detachable cap scales.

False Parasol

Chlorophyllum molybdites (Agaricaceae)

RESTRICTED *to artificial habitats such as botanical gardens and hothouses.*

This poisonous, tropical species closely resembles the tasty, edible Parasol (p.51) but fortunately only very rarely occurs in Europe as an exotic alien in hothouses, botanical gardens, and mulch beds. Like the Parasol, it has a rounded creamy cap with concentric brown scales, a cream to brownish stem which bruises reddish, and a double ring which slides along the stem. However, the gills are only creamy white when young and soon become distinctly pale green, giving a greenish grey spore print. It can cause very severe gastric upsets, and is responsible for many poisonings in areas where it grows in the wild.

concentric brown scales

cap up to 15cm wide

pale cream to brown stem

cream gills turn pale green

double ring on stem

SPORES *Olive-green.*
FRUITING *All year round, especially summer to autumn.*
DISTRIBUTION *Extremely rare throughout, in hothouses and gardens.*
EDIBILITY *Poisonous.*
SIMILAR SPECIES *The edible Parasol (p.51) and the mildly poisonous Shaggy Parasol (p.50) also have cream-coloured gills but the spores are never greenish. A spore print could be made on a sheet of white paper for confirmation.*

NOTE

In tropical areas such as Florida, USA, this green-gilled fungus has caused poisoning among European tourists who have mistaken it as the edible Parasol.

Common Cavalier

Melanoleuca polioleuca (Tricholomataceae)

A rather sombre-looking species, this fungus has a smooth, umbonate cap, the whole of which is a dark greyish brown. In contrast, the crowded gills, notched where they join the stem, are white to pale cream. The stem has lengthwise fibres, coloured like the cap and, if cut open, the flesh is usually very dark and blackish brown at the base.

FOUND *singly or in small groups, in grass along paths and roadsides, and in meadows and woodland.*

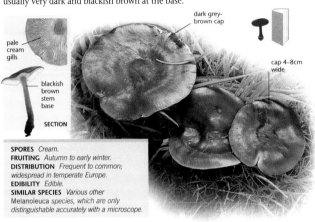

dark grey-brown cap

pale cream gills

blackish brown stem base

SECTION

cap 4–8cm wide

SPORES *Cream.*
FRUITING *Autumn to early winter.*
DISTRIBUTION *Frequent to common; widespread in temperate Europe.*
EDIBILITY *Edible.*
SIMILAR SPECIES *Various other Melanoleuca species, which are only distinguishable accurately with a microscope.*

Pale Brittlestem

Psathyrella candolleana (Coprinaceae)

Very fragile in all its parts, this common fungus has a convex to umbonate, pale buff to ivory-white cap, with thin fragments of white veil on the edge, the margin often splitting with age. The narrow and crowded gills are grey, then lilac, and finally brown when mature. The thin stems are hollow, smooth, and white.

SEEN *in small clumps or dense tufts on old logs or buried wood, in parks, gardens, and woodland.*

crowded gills

fine white veil on cap margin

cap 2–5cm wide

convex to umbonate cap

smooth, fragile stem

SECTION

SPORES *Brown.*
FRUITING *Spring to late autumn.*
DISTRIBUTION *Common in temperate Europe.*
EDIBILITY *Inedible.*
SIMILAR SPECIES *Other similar species of Psathyrella, which are usually much darker brown and quite difficult to identify.*

Poplar Fieldcap

Agrocybe cylindracea (Bolbitiaceae)

An edible species cultivated for centuries in parts of Europe, the Poplar Fieldcap has a convex, pale ivory to buff cap, often wrinkled or cracked. Fused together into large clumps, the long stems may be cylindrical to pointed, with a fragile ring at the top. The upper surface of this ring is often stained dark brown from fallen spores.

EMERGES *in clusters from cracks and knotholes in trees such as poplar, elm, elder, and willow.*

puckered or cracked cap

cap 5–12cm wide

cream to dull brown gills

floppy ring

SECTION

SPORES *Medium brown.*
FRUITING *Summer to late autumn.*
DISTRIBUTION *Rare to occasional, temperate regions.*
EDIBILITY *Edible.*
SIMILAR SPECIES *Some* Pleurotus *species, which all have white or very pale spores and a shorter stem.*

Flowery Blewit

Lepista irina (Tricholomataceae)

One of a group of fungi commonly called blewits, this species has a rounded, greyish buff to pinkish cap, that is smooth to touch, often with a wavy margin. The pale pinkish buff gills are notched where they join the stem, which is sturdy, marked with tough, dark fibres, and pale greyish buff in colour. The white flesh is strongly perfumed when cut, hence the common name.

GROWS *in groups or fairy rings, in gardens, open meadows, and woodland clearings.*

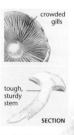

crowded gills

tough, sturdy stem

SECTION

cap 5–15cm wide

greyish buff to pinkish cap

smooth cap surface

SPORES *Pink.*
FRUITING *Autumn to early winter.*
DISTRIBUTION *Locally common, temperate regions.*
EDIBILITY *Edible.*
SIMILAR SPECIES *Field Blewit (L. personata) has a pale beige cap, contrasting violet-lilac stem, and is found in open meadows.*

Rooting Poisonpie

Hebeloma radicosum (Cortinariaceae)

This is a fungus with a strange ecology, since its stem burrows into the soil like a long tap-root, feeding on animal waste. The stem is brown and has irregular scales and a thick ring at the top, while the rounded cap is pale buff-ochre with flattened scales, and is sticky when wet. The fungus smells strongly of bitter almonds.

SEEN *singly on the ground, but the stem starts in the burrow of a small mammal, such as a mole.*

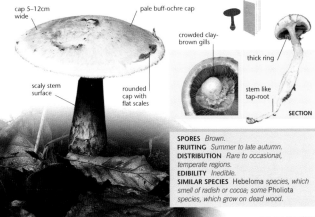

cap 5–12cm wide

pale buff-ochre cap

scaly stem surface

rounded cap with flat scales

crowded clay-brown gills

thick ring

stem like tap-root

SECTION

SPORES *Brown.*
FRUITING *Summer to late autumn.*
DISTRIBUTION *Rare to occasional, temperate regions.*
EDIBILITY *Inedible.*
SIMILAR SPECIES Hebeloma *species, which smell of radish or cocoa; some* Pholiota *species, which grow on dead wood.*

Yellowfoot Brittlestem

Psathyrella cotonea (Coprinaceae)

An attractive fungus, the Yellowfoot Brittlestem has a rounded cap with pointed, dark brown scales on a pale greyish background, sometimes tinged violet. Crowded and pale reddish grey, the gills turn dark chocolate brown with age. The stem is white, with a woolly surface, especially at the base where it is often bright yellow in colour. Similarly, the flesh is white, but bright yellow at the base.

GROWS *in tufts or dense clumps on or around stumps of broadleaf and, more rarely, coniferous trees.*

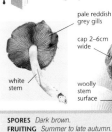

pale reddish grey gills

dark brown scales

cap 2–6cm wide

white stem

woolly stem surface

SPORES *Dark brown.*
FRUITING *Summer to late autumn.*
DISTRIBUTION *Rare to occasional, temperate regions.*
EDIBILITY *Inedible.*
SIMILAR SPECIES Medusa Brittlestem (P. caput-medusae) *is rare, much more scaly and shaggy, and pale buff overall.*

Common Bonnet

Mycena galericulata (Tricholomataceae)

APPEARS *in tufts or dense clumps, on or around the stumps of broadleaf trees.*

This common but inedible fungus differs from other species of *Mycena* in its tough stem and gills that turn pinkish with age. The bell-shaped cap is grey-brown; the pale grey gills are broad, medium-spaced, and have connecting veins. The smooth, shiny stems are tough, and often have a long rooting base.

bell-shaped to convex cap

cap 1–6cm wide

pale to pinkish grey gills

smooth, tough stem

grey-brown cap

SECTION

SPORES *White.*
FRUITING *Summer to early winter.*
DISTRIBUTION *Common, widespread in temperate N. Europe.*
EDIBILITY *Inedible.*
SIMILAR SPECIES *Clustered Bonnet (p.61), which has a rancid smell, and a stem that is deep reddish brown lower down.*

Rooting Shank

Xerula radicata (Tricholomataceae)

SPROUTS *singly or in small groups, around stumps, trees, or on buried wood, especially in beech woods.*

This elegant species has a yellow- to dark brown cap that is smooth, umbonate to flattened, often radially wrinkled, and very sticky when wet. The white gills are widely spaced, broad, and join the stem. They run a little way down the stem and their edges may be brown. The tall, slender stem is deeply rooting. It is fibrous, white at the top, and brown towards the base.

cap 2–10cm wide

twisted stem

flattened cap with umbo

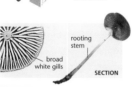

rooting stem

broad white gills

SECTION

SPORES *White.*
FRUITING *Summer to late autumn.*
DISTRIBUTION *Frequent, widespread in temperate N. Europe.*
EDIBILITY *Inedible.*
SIMILAR SPECIES *X. pudens, which is dark brown in colour, has a densely hairy cap and stem, and is rarer.*

Copper Spike

Chroogomphus rutilus (Gomphidiaceae)

Variable in size, this species has a rounded cap that soon becomes flat with a central umbo. The orange-brown to wine-red surface is smooth, and greasy in wet weather. The fungus has thick gills which are olive-brown, then black, with a white edge, and run a long way down the stem. With a faint ring-zone at the top, the stout, fibrous stem is pointed towards the base, where the flesh is coloured wine-red to chrome-yellow.

FOUND singly or in small groups on the ground, mainly associated with pine trees on sandy soils.

cap 3–10cm wide

thick gills

gills run down stem

orange-brown to wine red surface

reddish brown stem

pointed base

SPORES Black.
FRUITING Summer to late autumn.
DISTRIBUTION Frequent, widespread in temperate N. Europe.
EDIBILITY Inedible.
SIMILAR SPECIES Slimy Spike (p.83), which has a whitish to red-grey cap, blackish brown gills, and a bright yellow stem base.

Sooty Milkcap

Lactarius fuliginosus (Russulaceae)

Slightly velvety to the touch, the deep to greyish brown cap of this species has an inrolled margin when young. Cylindrical and smooth, the stem is pale brown. The gills run only a little way down the stem, are moderately spaced, and pale cream to buff. When cut, the gills and flesh bleed a white latex, which slowly stains pink and is slightly hot to taste.

GROWS in small troops on the ground, in leaf litter of broadleaf woods, mainly with oak and beech.

velvety grey-brown surface

cap 5–10cm wide

inrolled margin on young caps

SPORES Ochre.
FRUITING Summer to late autumn.
DISTRIBUTION Rare to occasional in temperate N. Europe.
EDIBILITY Inedible.
SIMILAR SPECIES L. azonites, which has a pale, smoky grey cap and white stem, and flesh that stains bright pink-red.

smooth, pale brown stem

widely spaced gills

SECTION

Brown Rollrim

Paxillus involutus (Paxillaceae)

GROWS *in small troops, associated with a number of trees, mostly broadleaf but conifers also, often in wet, boggy places.*

Although widely eaten in some areas, this controversial species has been implicated in a number of serious poisonings. It has a variable or cumulative toxin, whose effect is poorly understood, so it should definitely not be eaten. The yellow-brown cap, with a strongly inrolled, woolly margin, is slightly domed when young but expands with age and sinks in the centre. It can be very slimy when wet. Yellowish gills run down the short brown stem and bruise deep brown on handling; they are soft, thick, and easily separated from the flesh.

cap 5–15cm wide

inrolled margin

pale yellow-brown flesh

broad, depressed cap

soft, thick gills

thick, usually short stem

deep brown bruising

woolly margin

SECTION

NOTE

When unsure of the identity of a fungus, always try bruising the gills and cutting the flesh. Any colour change can be a helpful pointer in identification. In the case of Brown Rollrim, the gills and stem bruise to deep brown.

SPORES Brown.
FRUITING Spring to late autumn.
DISTRIBUTION Frequent to common, widespread in temperate northern Europe.
EDIBILITY Poisonous.
SIMILAR SPECIES Alder Rollrim (P. filamentosus), which grows only under alders, is usually smaller with a few, flattened, reddish brown scales on the cap, and brighter yellow-ochre gills that bruise red-brown.

Funeral Bell

☠

Galerina marginata (Strophariaceae)

This is a seriously poisonous or even deadly fungus with toxins similar to those of the poisonous *Amanita* species, and its characteristics should be carefully noted to avoid confusion with similar edible fungi. Its small to medium cap is initially convex and then flattened. Rather thin-fleshed, it is rich reddish brown to honey-coloured when dry, and often has a wavy margin. When moist, the cap margin tends to be lined (striate). The narrow, crowded, pale yellow-ochre gills run down the stem slightly. Although similar to the cap in colour, the stem is paler towards the top. It has lengthwise fibres and a delicate ring at the top, which frequently tears and may not be complete. The ring is often stained brown from deposited spores.

FOUND *in small to large clumps on rotten logs and stumps of conifers and broadleaf trees; increasingly common on bark mulch in gardens.*

NOTE

Always examine stems carefully for any signs of a ring. On this, and other species, it is fragile, and may collapse or even be rubbed off with age. Be sure to check all the specimens that you collect.

pale yellow-ochre gills

stem paler on top

smooth cap surface

cap 2–5cm wide

ring at top of stem

margin lined when moist

reddish brown to honey-coloured cap

often wavy cap margin

SPORES *Brown.*
FRUITING *Spring to early winter.*
DISTRIBUTION *Occasional to frequent, widespread in temperate N. Europe.*
EDIBILITY *Highly poisonous – all small* Galerina *species should be treated as poisonous.*
SIMILAR SPECIES *Sheathed Woodtuft (p.60) has scales below the ring and a two-toned cap as it dries; Honey Fungus (p.96) has white spores.*

Sheathed Woodtuft

Kuehneromyces mutabilis (Strophariaceae)

GROWS *in small or large clumps on dead or rotten logs and stumps of broadleaf trees, rarely on conifers.*

The convex date-brown to leathery yellow cap of this popular, edible species soon expands to become umbonate and is fairly thick-fleshed and aromatic. When wet, the surface is smooth or even sticky. However, the Sheathed Woodtuft's most distinctive characteristic is that as the cap dries it becomes much paler ochre from the centre outwards, giving it a two-tone appearance. The medium-spaced gills are ochre-brown, joined to the stem with a slight tooth, and run a little way down the stem. The dark brown stem is distinctly scaly up to a small ring at the top; above this it becomes pale and smooth. The falling spores often stain the ring ochre-brown.

centre turns pale on drying

cap 2–6cm wide

smooth, 2-tone cap

dark, scaly stem

broad gills

pale brown flesh

SECTION

small ring

NOTE

A tasty edible species, this fungus is easily confused with some poisonous species. To make a positive identification, look for the dark brown stem that is covered by pointed scales below the ring.

SPORES *Brown.*
FRUITING *Spring to early winter.*
DISTRIBUTION *Occasional to frequent, widespread in temperate N. Europe.*
EDIBILITY *Edible.*
SIMILAR SPECIES *Funeral Bell (p.59), which is highly poisonous, has fibres and no scales below the ring, and has a mealy taste and smell when crushed; Honey Fungus (p.96), is edible and has white spores.*

Clustered Bonnet

Mycena inclinata (Tricholomataceae)

Growing in dense clumps, the smooth, bell-shaped caps of this pretty species are whitish grey, becoming browner with age, and often have a toothed margin. The white to cream gills are narrow, joined to the stem, and smell of soap or candles. Smooth and shiny, the stems are cream above and deep reddish brown below, often woolly-white at the base.

FOUND *in clumps on dead stumps and logs of broadleaf trees, occasionally on standing trees.*

toothed margin

older fungi turn brown

SECTION

cap 2–4cm wide

red-brown below

gills join stem

stem bases fuse together

SPORES *White.*	

SPORES *White.*
FRUITING *Summer to late autumn.*
DISTRIBUTION *Frequent to common, temperate N. Europe.*
EDIBILITY *Inedible.*
SIMILAR SPECIES *M. maculata has a smooth cap margin, purplish brown stem, and red-brown spots on the cap and gills.*

Clustered Brittlestem

Psathyrella multipedata (Coprinaceae)

Growing in dense clusters, the characteristic rooting stem bases of this species have to be dug out to be seen. The bell-shaped caps are rounded, and date-brown when wet but dry to pale buff. The gills join the stem and are broad, crowded, and deep purple-brown with a whitish edge. Long and white to cream, the stems are fused together at the base into a tap-root.

DEVELOPS *in dense clusters usually in grass or on roadsides, often in urban areas, on loam or clay.*

dense clusters of fungi

cap 1–4cm wide

purple-brown gills

lined margins

long stem

SECTION

SPORES *Blackish.*
FRUITING *Summer to late autumn.*
DISTRIBUTION *Rare to occasional in temperate N. Europe.*
EDIBILITY *Inedible.*
SIMILAR SPECIES *Some Mycena species may look similar but they all have white spore deposits.*

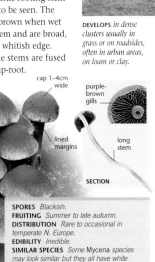

Brown Mottlegill ☠

Panaeolina foenisecii (Coprinaceae)

SCATTERED over lawns, meadows, and turf, often in large numbers; appears very quickly after rain.

One of Europe's most common species, Brown Mottlegill is often found on garden lawns and golf courses. Although poisonous, it is not dangerously so. The rounded, scurfy, dark brown caps dry rapidly to a pale buff from the centre outwards. The gills are deep chocolate, while the stems are brown, fragile, and smooth.

finely scaled cap surface

bell-shaped cap

cap 1–3cm wide

pale brown stem

dark brown gills with white edge

SPORES *Blackish.*
FRUITING *All year round.*
DISTRIBUTION *Common throughout Europe.*
EDIBILITY *Mildly poisonous.*
SIMILAR SPECIES *Some Panaeolus species, which have smooth spores compared to this species' warty ones.*

Wrinkled Shield

Pluteus phlebophorus (Plutaceae)

APPEARS often on the ground, in leaf litter and debris in broadleaf woodlands, especially beech and birch.

The deep brown cap of this species has a distinctly veined and wrinkled surface, which becomes a little paler when dry. The broad, free gills start white then turn pink as they mature. The slender stem is pale buff, fibrous, and darker at the base, while the flesh is very pale, almost white, with an acidic odour.

cap 1–5cm wide

pink mature gills

wrinkled brown cap

white to pale buff stem

pale flesh

SECTION

SPORES *Pink.*
FRUITING *Summer to late autumn.*
DISTRIBUTION *Rare to occasional throughout temperate N. Europe.*
EDIBILITY *Inedible.*
SIMILAR SPECIES *Goldleaf Shield (P. romellii), which has a golden-yellow stem and flesh; P. luctuosus, which is greyer.*

Pearly Webcap

Cortinarius alboviolaceus (Cortinariaceae)

Both the cap and stem of this pretty species are pale
silvery lavender to almost white. The cap is rounded then
expanded with a broad umbo; while the gills start grey-
blue, then become deep rust-brown. The club-shaped
stem is thick-fleshed and fibrous, darkening
to deep violet at the top.

FOUND *in small troops
in broadleaf woods
especially on acid soils;
rarely seen with conifers.*

silky, bell-
shaped cap

gills notched
where they
join stem

cap whiter
when dry

deep violet
flesh in stem
apex

club-shaped
stem

cap 3–8cm
wide

SECTION

SPORES *Rust.*
FRUITING *Autumn.*
DISTRIBUTION *Rare to frequent throughout
temperate N. Europe.*
EDIBILITY *Inedible.*
SIMILAR SPECIES *Gassy Webcap (p.64),
which has deeper violet tones and is
orange-ochre at the stem base.*

Stocking Webcap

Cortinarius torvus (Cortinariaceae)

The rounded cap of the Stocking Webcap is greyish brown
and finely streaked with darker fibres. The broad, widely
spaced gills are rust-brown and smell of ripe pears, while
the robust stem is brown with a cream to buff covering of
veil rather like a nylon stocking. The brownish flesh is
faintly violet at the top of the stem.

GROWS *in small troops
in leaf litter of
broadleaf woods,
especially among
beech and oak.*

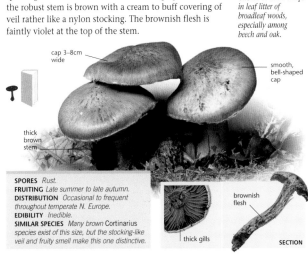

cap 3–8cm
wide

smooth,
bell-shaped
cap

thick
brown
stem

brownish
flesh

SPORES *Rust.*
FRUITING *Late summer to late autumn.*
DISTRIBUTION *Occasional to frequent
throughout temperate N. Europe.*
EDIBILITY *Inedible.*
SIMILAR SPECIES *Many brown Cortinarius
species exist of this size, but the stocking-like
veil and fruity smell make this one distinctive.*

thick gills

SECTION

Bitter Webcap

Cortinarius infractus (Cortinariaceae)

GROWING *in small troops in leaf litter of broadleaf wood, especially beech and oak woods.*

Very variable in colour, the caps of this species range from greyish olive to blue- or clay-grey, with a streaky, blotched appearance, and are sticky when wet. The gills are deep olive-grey maturing to olive-brown. Stout and rather short, the stem is pale brown to buff, and often violet at the top. The flesh is whitish to deep violet at the stem apex and very bitter to taste.

grey-olive gills

rounded, streaky cap

cap 3–8cm wide

violet flesh at the stem top

SECTION

SPORES *Rust.*
FRUITING *Late summer to late autumn.*
DISTRIBUTION *Occasional to frequent throughout temperate N. Europe.*
EDIBILITY *Inedible.*
SIMILAR SPECIES *C. glaucopus, which has a similar streaky cap but a bulbous stem and milder, less bitter taste.*

Gassy Webcap

Cortinarius traganus (Cortinariaceae)

GROWS *singly or in small troops in leaf litter of broadleaf and coniferous woods, especially on acid soils.*

This large species is rather fibrous and scaly, with a pale bluish lilac to ochre cap, darker ochre-brown towards the centre. The broad gills are bright yellow-ochre then deep rust. Swollen and club-shaped, the stem is pale bluish lilac to almost white with a cobwebby zone at the top. The flesh is thick, and deep reddish ochre in the base and smells strongly of acetylene gas or of ripe pears.

domed cap

bluish lilac stem

cap 5–10cm wide

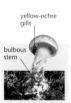

yellow-ochre gills

bulbous stem

SPORES *Rust.*
FRUITING *Late summer to late autumn.*
DISTRIBUTION *Occasional to frequent throughout temperate N. Europe.*
EDIBILITY *Inedible.*
SIMILAR SPECIES *Goatcheese Webcap (C. camphoratus), has a smoother cap, pale lavender stem, and a strong odour of goats.*

Wood Blewit

Lepista nuda (Tricholomataceae)

A popular edible species, Wood Blewit's cap is violet- to grey-brown or pinkish lavender. Smooth and rounded, it soon expands, and has a central umbo and slightly inrolled margin. The crowded gills are pale bluish lilac when young becoming pinker with age. The stout, fleshy stem is very fibrous and a deep bluish violet when young, becoming browner when old, and has a white scurfy appearance towards the top. Pleasantly scented, the flesh is pale lilac-blue in the stem and cap, marbled with buff-ochre.

FOUND *often in large groups or in circles in broadleaf woods, gardens, roadsides, or rich composted areas.*

NOTE

The violet colours of the stem and gills, brownish cap, and pink spores are all characteristic of this species. Wood Blewit often appears very late in the year, sometimes even after winter has set in.

crowded gills

pale lilac-blue flesh

SECTION

smooth violet- to grey-brown cap

cap 4–15cm wide

central umbo on cap

fibrous blue-violet stem

SPORES *Pink.*
FRUITING *Autumn to early winter.*
DISTRIBUTION *Frequent to common, widespread in temperate N. Europe.*
EDIBILITY *Edible and tasty.*
SIMILAR SPECIES *Bruising Webcap (p.66); L. sordida, which is smaller, with much darker, more violet-brown colours overall, and also has smaller spores.*

Bruising Webcap

Cortinarius purpurascens (Cortinariaceae)

GROWS *in leaf litter in a wide range of woodland, both broadleaf and coniferous, usually on acid soils.*

Part of a large group of sticky-capped *Cortinarius* species, the Bruising Webcap has a dark, date- to reddish brown cap. Slightly blue-tinted and rounded when young, the cap is very sticky and greasy when wet and has darker radiating fibres or lines of pigment; it spreads out and flattens with age. The gills are deep blue-violet to lilac-grey before turning rust-brown. Thick and fleshy, the stem is club-shaped or sometimes with a large basal bulb. It is deep violet to pale lilac with darker fibres. All parts of the Bruising Webcap, but especially the stem and gills, bruise deep violet when scratched. Most species of *Cortinarius* have never been tested for edibility and it is best to avoid them all.

rounded young cap

lilac-violet gills

darker fibres on cap

cap 4–8cm wide

bulbous stem base

NOTE

An easy way of assessing if a cap is sticky in dry weather, is to observe whether bits of leaves are stuck to the surface or not.

Fenugreek Milkcap ☠

Lactarius helvus (Russulaceae)

This mildly poisonous fungus smells of curry, fenugreek, or chicory. On expanding, the cap becomes slightly funnel-shaped with a central umbo. Its rich, tawny-ochre surface is dry and felty. The crowded, brittle gills are yellow-ochre with a pinkish tint and hardly change colour when bruised. The stem is smooth and slightly paler than the cap. The gills and flesh bleed a white, watery milk.

FOUND *in scattered groups in damp woods, often in sphagnum moss, associated with birch, pine, and spruce.*

rough surface

cap 5–15cm wide

large, expanded cap

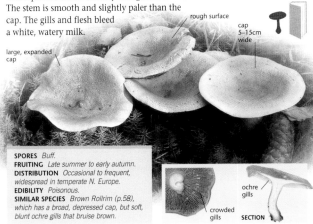

SPORES *Buff.*
FRUITING *Late summer to early autumn.*
DISTRIBUTION *Occasional to frequent, widespread in temperate N. Europe.*
EDIBILITY *Poisonous.*
SIMILAR SPECIES *Brown Rollrim (p.58), which has a broad, depressed cap, but soft, blunt ochre gills that bruise brown.*

crowded gills

ochre gills

SECTION

Oakbug Milkcap

Lactarius quietus (Russulaceae)

The smell of engine or bed bugs, is the clue to identifying the Oakbug Milkcap. Rounded to slightly depressed, the cap is a reddish- to grey-brown with faint but distinct darker zones. The gills are pale brown while the smooth stem is usually darker than the cap and club-shaped. When scratched, the fungus bleeds an unchanging white milk.

ASSOCIATED *with oaks, often in partial fairy-rings around a tree, in leaf litter and grass.*

depressed cap

cap 3–8cm wide

darker spots

pale brown flesh

crowded gills

SECTION

SPORES *Cream.*
FRUITING *Late summer to early autumn.*
DISTRIBUTION *Common to very common, widespread in temperate N. Europe.*
EDIBILITY *Inedible.*
SIMILAR SPECIES *Yellowdrop Milkcap (p.116), which is paler, yellower, and bleeds abundant milk that turns yellow.*

Ringless Honey Fungus

Armillaria tabescens (Tricholomataceae)

GROWS *parasitically in dense clumps on broadleaf trees, especially oak, usually around the roots.*

Particularly common in hot, dry summers, this species grows in dense clusters. The rounded caps, which soon flatten, are pale honey-brown with minute blackish scales at the centre. Moderately crowded, the tawny-buff gills join and run slightly down the slender, fibrous stem, which does not have a ring. Many stems are fused together at the base. The off-white flesh is edible only after cooking.

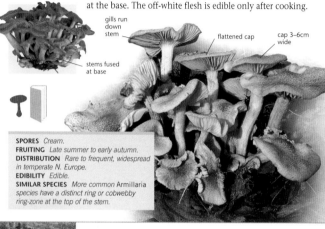

gills run down stem

flattened cap

cap 3–6cm wide

stems fused at base

SPORES *Cream.*
FRUITING *Late summer to early autumn.*
DISTRIBUTION *Rare to frequent, widespread in temperate N. Europe.*
EDIBILITY *Edible.*
SIMILAR SPECIES *More common Armillaria species have a distinct ring or cobwebby ring-zone at the top of the stem.*

Star Fibrecap ☠

Inocybe asterospora (Cortinariaceae)

SEEN *on broadleaf trees, such as beech and hazel, in leaf litter or often on bare soil.*

Inocybe species are difficult to identify but this one is distinctive. Its cap, umbonate at the centre, is red-brown with radiating fibres, paler underneath. The gills are dark brown, while the stem is pale brown with a mealy surface along its entire length. It has a whitish, flattened, rimmed bulb at the base. The fungus has star-shaped spores.

cap 3–6cm wide

dark brown gills

flattened, rimmed bulb at base

mealy, slender brown stem

SECTION

SPORES *Brown.*
FRUITING *Summer to late autumn.*
DISTRIBUTION *Occasional to frequent, widespread in temperate N. Europe.*
EDIBILITY *Poisonous.*
SIMILAR SPECIES *I. margaritispora and I. mixtilis both have a white stem. Most Inocybe species are poisonous.*

Fruity Fibrecap ☠

Inocybe bongardii (Cortinariaceae)

The smell of over-ripe pears is the first clue to this species. Rounded and umbonate, its cap is pale reddish ochre with broad, flattened, dark brown scales. The gills are pinkish ochre ageing to pinkish brown. The fibrous stem, which is club-shaped without a bulb, is whitish above and brown below. When cut, the flesh turns red.

ASSOCIATED *with broadleaf trees, especially beech and oak, in leaf litter, often on clay soils.*

brownish gills

fibrous stem

SECTION

cap 3–6cm wide

rounded cap with darker scales

stem whitish above, brown below

SPORES *Brown.*
FRUITING *Summer to late autumn.*
DISTRIBUTION *Occasional to frequent, widespread in temperate N. Europe.*
EDIBILITY *Poisonous.*
SIMILAR SPECIES *Greenflush Fibrecap (p.136), has green tint in cap centre; Pear Fibrecap (I. pyriodora), has a paler cap.*

Deadly Fibrecap ☠

Inocybe erubescens (Cortinariaceae)

Dangerously poisonous due to high levels of the toxin muscarine, this species is entirely ivory-white with a rounded to strongly umbonate cap, splitting into radial fibres. Its gills, grey-buff then deep brown, are almost free from the stem. The solid, cylindrical stem is fibrous. All parts of the fungus stain deep pinkish red when scratched. This early fruiting species has a pleasant odour and can be easily mistaken for some edible fungi.

GROWS *with broadleaf trees, particularly beech, on warm calcareous soils, especially southern slopes.*

basal bulb with rim

SECTION

greyish gills turn brown

reddish bruising on ivory cap

cap 3–6cm wide

SPORES *Brown.*
FRUITING *Spring to late summer.*
DISTRIBUTION *Rare to occasional, widespread in temperate Europe.*
EDIBILITY *Highly poisonous.*
SIMILAR SPECIES *Silky Fibrecap (I. fibrosa), is larger, whitish and does not stain red, I. godeyi has a distinct basal bulb with a rim.*

Veiled Poisonpie

Hebeloma mesophaeum (Cortinariaceae)

GROWS *with broadleaf trees, in woods, parks, gardens, and along roadsides; sometimes on burnt ground.*

Perhaps the most common *Hebeloma* species, this poisonous fungus has a cap that is date-brown at the centre and paler at the margin, with remnants of a cream veil. The pale buff gills later turn dark clay-brown, and smell of radish or chocolate. Whitish above and brown below, the stem has a cobwebby ring-zone at the top.

brownish centre

pale margin

flakes of veil on cap margin

gills join stem

clay-brown gills

cap 3–5cm wide

stem 3–5cm long

fibrous stem

SECTION

SPORES *Brown.*
FRUITING *Spring to late autumn.*
DISTRIBUTION *Common and widespread in temperate Europe.*
EDIBILITY *Poisonous.*
SIMILAR SPECIES *Several small Hebeloma species, which are only distinguishable if examined under a microscope.*

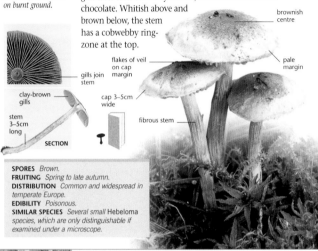

Pinkmottle Woodwax

Hygrophorus russula (Hygrophoraceae)

FOUND *among broadleaf trees, especially oaks, on basic soils.*

The rounded cap of this large, fleshy species sinks in the middle as it expands. Its surface is pale wine-pink, spotted or streaked with purple-red fibres. Thick, widely spaced gills start white, but soon develop pink or red spots. The stout, tapering stem has white spots and purple-red streaks, and eventually it may become entirely wine-red.

cap 5–15cm wide

streaked and spotted cap

white gills stain red

flesh stains pinkish

SECTION

stem tapers at base

thick white flesh

SPORES *White.*
FRUITING *Autumn to early winter.*
DISTRIBUTION *Rare to occasional, widespread in temperate N. Europe.*
EDIBILITY *Edible.*
SIMILAR SPECIES *Matt Woodwax (H. penarius), which is a uniform buff or brown with gills running down the stem.*

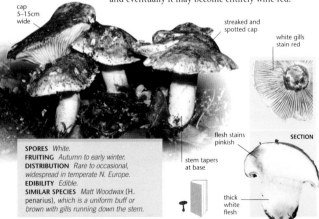

Panthercap ☠

Amanita pantherina (Amanitaceae)

This extremely poisonous species has high concentrations of muscarin and other toxins. Its smooth, rounded cap flattens out with age, has a finely grooved margin, and varies from light to dark brown with numerous rounded or pointed white veil scales on the surface. The gills are free and white. The stem has a bulbous base that has a gutter-like margin and a series of narrow girdles on the upper edge. There is a pendent ring about half way up the stem, and the upper surface is smooth and ungrooved – important features to note.

FRUITS in leaf litter in a wide range of woodlands, both broadleaf and coniferous, usually on alkaline soil.

NOTE

The guttered margin at the stem base and the structure of the ring are vital signs for accurate identification of the Panthercap; another typical feature is the grooved cap margin.

radial grooves along cap margin

ring half way up stem

young cap rounded

bulbous stem base with gutter

cap 5–12cm wide

white veil scales on cap

light to deep brown cap

stem 5–10cm high

flattened mature cap

SPORES White.
FRUITING Summer to autumn.
DISTRIBUTION Rare to frequent, widespread in temperate N. Europe.
EDIBILITY Highly poisonous.
SIMILAR SPECIES Grey Spotted Amanita (A. spissa), which has a grey-brown cap with greyish veil scales, no margin or girdles on the stem bulb, and a ring that is high on the stem and grooved above.

Deer Shield

Pluteus cervinus (Pluteaceae)

FOUND *on dead stumps, logs, branches, and fallen timber, also on sawdust; in woods, parks, and gardens.*

The pale fawn to buff or dark brown cap of the Deer Shield is variable in size as well as colour. It has a felty centre and becomes greasy when wet. The gills are cream, later deep pinkish brown. The club-shaped stem is white with blackish brown fibres. The flesh is white and thick, with a musty, radish-like smell.

smooth cap

cap 5–12cm wide

fine radial fibres

crowded gills

broad, free gills

SECTION

SPORES *Pink.*
FRUITING *Spring to early winter.*
DISTRIBUTION *Common, widespread in temperate N. Europe.*
EDIBILITY *Edible.*
SIMILAR SPECIES *P. pouzarianus, which is greyer and has no smell; P. tricuspidatus, which has dark brown gill edges.*

Giant Knight

Tricholoma colossus (Tricholomataceae)

GROWS *in pine woods, often in sub-mountainous areas, on alkaline soils.*

Giant Knight is a large, rare species. Its dry and felty to slightly fibrous cap is beige-brown to pinkish brown, with a gently inrolled margin, and is sticky when wet. The white to cream gills are notched where they meet the stem, which, coloured like the cap, is finely scaly below a narrow ring zone, white above and fleshy and pointed at the base.

cap 10–20cm wide

bulky stem

notched gills

SECTION

slightly inrolled margin

stout tapering stem

SPORES *White.*
FRUITING *Late summer to autumn.*
DISTRIBUTION *Rare, widespread in temperate N. Europe.*
EDIBILITY *Edible.*
SIMILAR SPECIES *T. ustaloides, which grows in broadleaf woods, has a deep brown cap and distinct stem ring-zone.*

Butter Cap

Collybia butyracea (Tricholomataceae)

This is a common species, producing an umbonate, red-brown to grey-brown cap, with a much darker area at the centre. The greasy feel to the cap is a key feature. The gills are white to pale cream and appear almost free. Slender at the top and swelling to a broad club at the bottom, the stem is dry, fibrous, and darker at the base.

SEEN *in both broadleaf and pine woods in leaf litter, often in large numbers or fairy rings.*

cap 3–6cm wide

almost free white gills

hollow stem

greasy cap surface

SECTION

stem narrows at top

SPORES *White.*
FRUITING *Late summer to early winter.*
DISTRIBUTION *Common, widespread in temperate N. Europe.*
EDIBILITY *Edible.*
SIMILAR SPECIES *Club Foot (p.166), which has gills running down the stem, and is not greasy.*

Cucumber Cap

Macrocystidia cucumis (Tricholomataceae)

This inedible fungus smells of a mixture of herring and cucumber. The slightly velvety, conical or bell-shaped cap is deep red-brown with a yellowish margin. The broad, crowded gills are cream to pale reddish, and the slender, velvety stem is deep brown to almost black at the base.

OCCURS *in woodchip mulch in parks or on roadsides, and on rich soil in woodland.*

cap 2–5cm wide

conical or bell-shaped cap

broad cream gills

stem almost black at base

SECTION

slender, tough stem

SPORES *Ochre.*
FRUITING *Late summer to autumn.*
DISTRIBUTION *Rare to occasional; widespread in temperate N. Europe.*
EDIBILITY *Inedible.*
SIMILAR SPECIES *Some Marasmius species, which have dark stems and smell strongly of garlic or rotten vegetables.*

Blue-girdled Webcap

Cortinarius muscigenus (Cortinariaceae)

GROWS *in damp needle litter, often in large numbers along with spruce trees.*

Both the cap and stem of this species are very sticky and glutinous when wet. The cap is bright reddish brown or orange-brown, while the spindle-shaped stem is pale bluish white to lilac and slimy below the ring-zone at the top. The gills are slightly notched and deep orange-brown while the flesh is pale creamy ochre. There is no apparent smell at the base of the stem.

cap 5–10cm wide

convex, wavy margin

spindle-shaped stem

bluish upper stem

orange-brown gills

pale, creamy ochre flesh

SECTION

SPORES *Rust.*
FRUITING *Late summer to autumn.*
DISTRIBUTION *Uncommon to frequent, widespread in temperate N. Europe.*
EDIBILITY *Inedible.*
SIMILAR SPECIES *Orange Webcap* (C. mucosus) *has white stem; Wrinkled Webcap* (C. livido-ochraceus) *base smells of honey.*

Burnt Knight

Tricholoma ustale (Tricholomataceae)

FOUND *in small, scattered groups in leaf litter along with beech trees.*

The tough, convex to flattened cap of the Burnt Knight is smooth, sticky in wet weather, and rich red-brown. Its notched gills are cream with russet-red spots. Cylindrical to club-shaped, the tough stem is white at the top and pale brown towards the base, lacking a ring-zone. The slightly bitter white flesh has a faint smell and darkens with age.

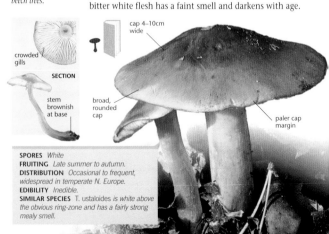

crowded gills

SECTION

stem brownish at base

cap 4–10cm wide

broad, rounded cap

paler cap margin

SPORES *White*
FRUITING *Late summer to autumn.*
DISTRIBUTION *Occasional to frequent, widespread in temperate N. Europe.*
EDIBILITY *Inedible.*
SIMILAR SPECIES *T. ustaloides is white above the obvious ring-zone and has a fairly strong mealy smell.*

Goliath Webcap

Cortinarius praestans (Cortinariaceaea)

The cap of this large *Cortinarius* species is massive, rounded, and sticky when wet. Deep purple-brown, it has flakes of white veil around the wrinkled margin. Its crowded gills are pale grey-blue. The bulbous stem is whitish, ringed with pale lavender veil fragments. There is a narrow ring-zone dusted with spores at the top.

GROWS *under broadleaf trees, especially oak and beech, in chalky soil.*

veil fragments

bulbous stem

SECTION

cap 10–22cm wide

purple-brown cap

wrinkled margin

SPORES *Rust-brown.*
FRUITING *Autumn.*
DISTRIBUTION *Rare to occasional in temperate N. Europe.*
EDIBILITY *Edible.*
SIMILAR SPECIES C. cumatilis, *which is smaller, has a lilac-blue cap without a wrinkled margin or veil flakes.*

Conifer Roundhead

Stropharia hornemanii (Strophariaceae)

The sticky-capped Conifer Roundhead varies from yellowish white to violet-tinted tawny brown. The gills are greyish violet and the narrow stem ring is dappled black with spores. Fragments of veil can be seen around the cap margin. The white stem below the ring is scurfy with shaggy scales.

OCCURS *in conifer woods, on old stumps and litter; occasionally with birch.*

greyish violet gills

cap up to 20cm wide

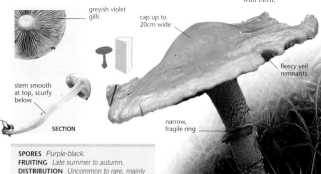

fleecy veil remnants

stem smooth at top, scurfy below

SECTION

narrow, fragile ring

SPORES *Purple-black.*
FRUITING *Late summer to autumn.*
DISTRIBUTION *Uncommon to rare, mainly northern but in mountains further south.*
EDIBILITY *Inedible.*
SIMILAR SPECIES *Burgundy Roundhead* (S. rugosoannulata), *has darker cap and gills, and a thick, grooved ring; it is edible.*

Snakeskin Grisette ☠

Amanita ceciliae (Amanitaceae)

SEEN *mainly with broadleaf trees in woodlands, parks, or plantations, often on chalky clay soils.*

A distinctive, often tall species, this poisonous fungus has a tawny to dark grey-brown cap, covered in separable, fleecy grey patches. The cap edge, often paler than the centre, is noticeably grooved. Moderately spaced and not attached to the stem, the gills are white. The stem is zoned with mouse- to smoke-grey zig-zags and darkens on handling. At the base is a fragile grey volva.

cap up to 15cm wide

stem up to 20cm high

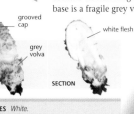

grooved cap

grey volva

white flesh

SECTION

SPORES *White.*
FRUITING *Summer to autumn.*
DISTRIBUTION *Occasional to locally common, widespread.*
EDIBILITY *Poisonous.*
SIMILAR SPECIES *A. submembranacea, which is more olive-brown with a paler stem, and grows in broadleaf and conifer woods.*

Hotfoot Webcap

Cortinarius bulliardii (Cortinariaceae)

ASSOCIATED *with beech and oak, sometimes hazel, on alkaline soils.*

The cap of this species is chestnut brown to violet-brown and the gills are deep purplish brown, but it is the stem which is most colourful. It is brown with a bright red covering of veil over the base, while the top is bluish. The mycelium at the base of the stem is also brilliant red.

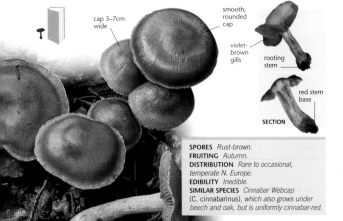

cap 3–7cm wide

smooth, rounded cap

violet-brown gills

rooting stem

red stem base

SECTION

SPORES *Rust-brown.*
FRUITING *Autumn.*
DISTRIBUTION *Rare to occasional, temperate N. Europe.*
EDIBILITY *Inedible.*
SIMILAR SPECIES *Cinnabar Webcap (C. cinnabarinus), which also grows under beech and oak, but is uniformly cinnabar-red.*

Girdled Webcap

Cortinarius trivialis (Cortinariaceae)

The deep reddish brown to olive-brown cap and stem of this species become extremely glutinous when wet. It is the stem which is most distinctive, with bands or girdles of slimy veil spread over the lower half all the way up to a cobwebby ring-zone. The gills and upper stem have a pale lilac hue when young.

GROWS *in wet, boggy areas; associated with willow, birch, poplar, or even beech and oak.*

slimy cap surface

SECTION

bluish flesh in stem base

rings of slimy veil on stem

cap 3–10cm wide

SPORES *Rust-brown.*
FRUITING *Summer to late autumn.*
DISTRIBUTION *Occasional to common, widespread in temperate N. Europe.*
EDIBILITY *Inedible.*
SIMILAR SPECIES *None – although all Cortinarius species have sticky caps and stems, none has the distinctive stem girdles.*

Scaly Knight

Tricholoma vaccinum (Tricholomataceae)

The expanded, bell-shaped, red-brown cap of this species is noticeably scaly. It often has a central umbo and its margin is inrolled, but without grooves. In contrast to the cap, the gills are whitish, becoming russet-spotted with age. The fibrous stem is usually pale at the top and brown at the base. The pale flesh stains pink with age and can be bitter tasting.

GROWS *singly or in troops among needle litter, with conifers, especially spruce.*

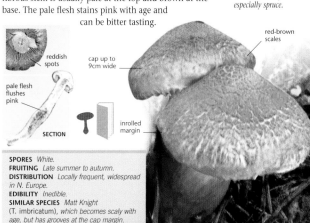

reddish spots

cap up to 9cm wide

pale flesh flushes pink

SECTION

inrolled margin

red-brown scales

SPORES *White.*
FRUITING *Late summer to autumn.*
DISTRIBUTION *Locally frequent, widespread in N. Europe.*
EDIBILITY *Inedible.*
SIMILAR SPECIES *Matt Knight (T. imbricatum), which becomes scaly with age, but has grooves at the cap margin.*

Blushing Dapperling ☠

Leucoagaricus badhamii (Agaricaceae)

The poisonous Blushing Dapperling can be very variable in appearance since its main characteristic is that it rapidly discolours to nearly black with handling and age. When fresh it can be almost white with a concentric pattern of flattened, pale brown scales on the cap. These become more obvious as they darken and the cap is often completely blackish brown at the centre. The gills are also white when fresh and are free from the pale, velvety stem. The fragile stem ring, when present, is turned upwards. All parts of the Blushing Dapperling become reddish on handling, finally darkening to blood-red, and eventually almost black.

gills free from stem

flesh stains blood-red

SECTION

cap up to 5cm wide

brown scales at centre

cap whitish when fresh

fragile, upturned ring

stem darkens with age

NOTE

Cut specimens in half and rub the flesh to check for reddening. The reaction may take several minutes to occur in older, dried out specimens.

SPORES *White to yellowish.*
FRUITING *Summer to autumn.*
DISTRIBUTION *Occasional, widespread throughout.*
EDIBILITY *Poisonous.*
SIMILAR SPECIES *Several other Leucoagaricus species, which are toxic and darken with age, including the Yellowing Dapperling (L. bresadolae), which turns yellow then black and is mainly found in compost heaps or hothouses.*

Chestnut Dapperling ☠

Lepiota castanea (Agaricaceae)

One of the deadliest of all fungi species, the Chestnut Dapperling, along with other closely related small to medium *Lepiota* fungi, contains toxins similar to those of the Death Cap (p.133) that cause delayed liver and kidney damage. The Chestnut Dapperling is characterized by brown scales on both the cap and stem, which contrast with its whitish to russet gills. Although the scales, as with most *Lepiota* species, are darkest and most concentrated at the centre, the general appearance of the cap is brownish throughout. The cap margin is often uplifted with age, while the stem ring is fragile, indistinct and is frequently absent. Like the Stinking Dapperling (*L. cristata*), the pale flesh has a strong and unpleasant odour.

APPEARS *singly or in small troops, in humus-rich sites, in woods, coppices, ditches, wasteland, and along roadsides.*

whitish to russet gills

free gills

pale or ochre flesh

SECTION

chestnut-brown cap

dark brown scales at centre

cap up to 4cm wide

chestnut-brown stem scales

SPORES *White.*
FRUITING *Late summer to autumn.*
DISTRIBUTION *Occasional to common, widespread in the south of the region.*
EDIBILITY *Highly poisonous.*
SIMILAR SPECIES *Several similar small Lepiota species, which can be told apart under a microscope, among them the Tawny Dapperling (L. fulvella) which is larger and more orange-brown.*

NOTE

Any small- to medium-sized species with an umbo on the cap and brownish concentric scales on a paler background (features of Lepiota), should be treated as poisonous.

Spindle Toughshank

Collybia fusipes (Tricholomataceae)

GROWS *usually in fused clusters around the base of broadleaf trees, mainly oak and sometimes beech.*

The greasy cap of this distinctive, clustered fungus is varied in shape from umbonate to irregular. Reddish brown, often with darker brown spots, it is paler at the edges and dries out to a lighter colour. The gills are beige, spotting reddish brown with age. Contorted and fibrous, the stem tapers to the clustered base, which is often deeply rooted in the ground. It is so tough that it can be twisted without snapping, this feature is true of most of the toughshank, as their common name indicates. The fruitbodies usually push up from below the root buttresses of trees. They are so durable that they may last for many days or even weeks, the old blackened caps persisting longer. Although not poisonous, Spindle Toughshank is too tough to be digested and best avoided.

mottled, reddish brown cap

fused clusters

cap up to 8cm wide

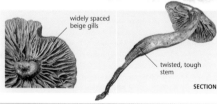

widely spaced beige gills

twisted, tough stem

SECTION

SPORES *White.*
FRUITING *Early summer to autumn.*
DISTRIBUTION *Rare in north, very common in south.*
EDIBILITY *Inedible.*
SIMILAR SPECIES *Spectacular Rustgill (p.108), which is large and clustered on wood but is more orange with a stem ring; other clustered Collybia species such as C. erythropus, which are paler and more delicate.*

NOTE

Like many other groups of fungi, toughshank have caps which become two tone in colour as they dry out. But very few fungi have such tough and rooting stems, combined with clustered growth and white spores.

Golden Gilled Bolete

Phylloporus pelletieri (Boletaceae)

Unusual and attractive, this bolete has gill-like golden pores. The dry, velvety cap is reddish brown, with thick "gills" running down the stem. These are interveined, forking, and easily separated from the edible flesh. When young they are bright golden-yellow becoming more rusty-ochre with age. The tapering stem is also yellowish at the top; becoming reddish brown below.

OCCURS *singly or in small numbers, associated with broadleaf trees, especially oak.*

young yellow pores

tapering stem

"gills" with interlinking veins

NOTE

Boletes such as Suede Bolete *(p.198) and* **Boletus ferrugineus** *look similar from above, but have spongy pores below instead of soft gills.*

---

cap up to 8cm wide

velvety reddish brown cap

SPORES *Ochre-yellow.*
FRUITING *Late summer to autumn.*
DISTRIBUTION *Rare to occasional, widespread except in the north.*
EDIBILITY *Edible.*
SIMILAR SPECIES *Bay Bolete (p.193), which has slot-like veined "gills" that are distinctive; several other velvety brown-capped boletes, which are superficially similar from above, but have conventional pores.*

Rufous Milkcap ☠

Lactarius rufus (Russulaceae)

GROWS *in groups, sometimes in large numbers, in conifer woods – mainly with pine, but also birch – in acidic soils.*

An eye-catching, bright russet red or rufous brown, the Rufous Milkcap has a dry cap with a felty to velvety texture. There is usually a characteristic dip and central pimple-like bump on the cap. The cream to brownish gills are crowded and may run slightly down the stem. Similar in colour, the stem often develops a white base and becomes hollow with age. The flesh is crumbly, exuding a white milky substance, which does not change colour but is burning hot to the taste after a 30 second delay. This feature accounts for its toxicity, although it is commonly eaten in Nordic countries after being rinsed and cooked, or pickled in salt.

NOTE

Cut the gills to make the milk ooze out, and check there is no change in colour by dropping some on a white tissue. Rufous Milkcap can be safely eaten when well rinsed and cooked.

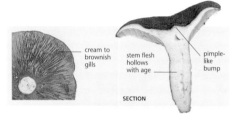

cream to brownish gills

stem flesh hollows with age

pimple-like bump

SECTION

bright, rufous brown cap

felty surface

cap up to 10cm wide

rufous brown stem

SPORES *Off-white.*
FRUITING *Summer to autumn.*
DISTRIBUTION *Common and widespread throughout.*
EDIBILITY *Poisonous unless correctly cooked.*
SIMILAR SPECIES *Various reddish brown* Lactarius *species in a similar habitat; Liver Milkcap (*L. hepaticus*) is the most similar with a liver-coloured cap and white milk which dries to yellow. Curry Milkcap (*L. camphoratus*) has a furrowed cap margin and smells of curry.*

Slimy Spike

Gomphidius glutinosus (Gomphidiaceae)

This large, edible species has an especially sticky or slimy cap with a pointed umbo. It is brownish grey with wine coloured streaks. The gills are widely spaced and arched, turning from light grey to black as the spores mature. The greyish stem is yellow at the base with an indistinct ring zone blackened by falling spores. It is sticky when young.

FOUND *singly or in troops among needle litter in coniferous forests and plantations only with spruce.*

cap up to 13cm wide

brownish grey cap

widely spaced gills

yellow stem base

SECTION

blackish ring zone

SPORES *Black.*
FRUITING *Late summer to late autumn.*
DISTRIBUTION *Occasional to common, widespread throughout Europe.*
EDIBILITY *Edible.*
SIMILAR SPECIES *Blackening Spike (G. maculatus), which grows with larch; Rosy Spike (G. roseus), which grows with pine.*

Herald of Winter

Hygrophorus hypothejus (Hygrophoraceae)

This rounded to funnel-shaped, inedible species fruits even in winter. Its brown to olive-brown cap has a thick, slimy layer. The gills are sulphur-yellow becoming more intense with age, and run down the stem. There is a bulging ring zone, above which the stem is dry and white, while below it is slimy and pale yellow.

SEEN *singly, but often in troops in needle litter among conifers, especially pine.*

cap up to 5cm wide

yellowish cap margin

white upper stem

SPORES *White.*
FRUITING *Late autumn to winter.*
DISTRIBUTION *Common and widespread throughout.*
EDIBILITY *Inedible.*
SIMILAR SPECIES *Date Waxcap (p.84), which has similar colouring but grows in open grassland.*

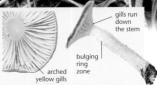

gills run down the stem

bulging ring zone

arched yellow gills

Date Waxcap

Hygrocybe spadicea (Hygrophoraceae)

This rare, inedible species has a greasy date-brown cap that is conical at first, then flattish with a central umbo, and splits at the margin. The cap and stem are fibrous – the stem is yellow when young, later streaked brown, and fairly brittle. The gills are yellow, occasionally orange, with a serrated margin.

GROWS *in unimproved grassland, prefering warm, southerly sites, with basic soil, including meadows, banks, and lawns.*

cap up to 8cm wide

yellow gills

waxy, date-brown cap

brown fibres on yellow stem

SPORES *White.*
FRUITING *Summer to autumn.*
DISTRIBUTION *Very rare to occasional, widespread in S. Europe.*
EDIBILITY *Inedible.*
SIMILAR SPECIES *Blackening Waxcap (p.162), can resemble a young Date Waxcap but otherwise blackens with age.*

Velvet Rollrim

Tapinella atrotomentosa (Paxillaceae)

This fungus is easy to identify with its stout, off-centre, cigar-brown stem, covered in blackish velvet. The cap is cinnamon-brown, sometimes with olive and black tones, and has a tightly inrolled margin. The gills are orange-yellow when young, darker with age, and easily separated from the bitter yellowish flesh.

OCCURS *singly or in large numbers, in coniferous forests, at ground level or on rotting stumps and roots.*

cap up to 20cm wide

inrolled margin

off-centre stem

velvety black covering

yellowish flesh

SECTION

SPORES *Rusty brown.*
FRUITING *Late summer to early winter.*
DISTRIBUTION *Common and widespread throughout N. Europe.*
EDIBILITY *Inedible.*
SIMILAR SPECIES *Olive Oysterling (p.231) grows with broadleaf trees; Oyster Rollrim (T. panuoides) is smaller.*

Scaly Webcap

Cortinarius pholideus (Cortinariaceae)

The cap of this unusual *Cortinarius* species is densely covered with tiny, pointed brown scales. The broad gills are violet-blue at first, maturing to violet-brown, while the brown stem is ringed with bands of woolly, fibrous veil. The flesh in the stem apex is violet but brown elsewhere. Scaly Webcap smells of fresh tangerines.

FOUND *in wet, boggy areas, associated with birch, and occasionally other trees, mostly on acid soils.*

pointed umbo

cap 3–8cm wide

dry, scaly cap

flesh violet at top of stem

woolly brown veil rings

SECTION

SPORES *Rust-brown.*
FRUITING *Summer to late autumn.*
DISTRIBUTION *Rare to occasional; widespread in temperate N. Europe.*
EDIBILITY *Inedible.*
SIMILAR SPECIES *Numerous small brown Cortinarius species, but almost none has a combination of scaly cap and banded stem.*

Tiger Sawgill

Lentinus tigrinus (Polyporaceae)

The clustering Tiger Sawgill is trumpet-shaped and white, with creamy yellow gills that run deeply down the stem. Its funnel-shaped cap has an inrolled margin and is patterned with dark brown scales. The stem is similarly striped with dark brown scales and has occasional veil remains. The flesh is tough and so only edible when young.

CLUSTERS *in groups on living or dead broadleaf trees, mainly willow and poplar.*

cap up to 10cm wide

brown scales

creamy yellow gills

gills run down stem

SPORES *White.*
FRUITING *Summer to autumn.*
DISTRIBUTION *Occasional to common, widespread throughout Europe.*
EDIBILITY *Edible.*
SIMILAR SPECIES *Scaly Sawgill (L. lepideus) and Veiled Oyster (Pleurotus dryinus), which both have a ring-zone.*

Silky Webcap

Cortinarius evernius (Cortinariaceae)

This is an elegant species with contrasting cap and stem colours. The cap is rich purple-brown when wet and paler buff-brown when dry. The tall, pointed, cylindrical stem is pale lavender-violet, very silky, with a whitish band of veil remains at the top. Broad and widely spaced, the gills are violet-brown. When cut, the flesh smells of radish.

FOUND *in wet, boggy areas, often in sphagnum moss; associated with spruce on acid soils.*

cap 3–10cm wide

smooth, deep brown cap

long, tapering stem

broad gills

SECTION

pale violet flesh

violet brown gills

SPORES *Rust-brown.*
FRUITING *Summer to late autumn.*
DISTRIBUTION *Locally common; widespread in temperate N. Europe.*
EDIBILITY *Poisonous.*
SIMILAR SPECIES *C. scutulatus, which has a finely scaled cap and stem with several whitish bands.*

Scaly Fibrecap

Inocybe hystrix (Cortinariaceae)

Although the fungi from the *Inocybe* group are difficult to distinguish without a microscope, this is one of the more distinctive species. Both the cap and stem are covered in bristly-looking, curved, dark brown scales on a paler ochre background. The hazel cap has an expanded bell shape, with contrasting pale gills. The flesh has a spermatic smell, especially when rubbed.

SEEN *singly or in small numbers in litter, especially in broadleaf but also conifer woods.*

curved, erect dark brown scales

cap up to 5cm wide

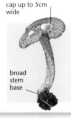

broad stem base

scaly cap and stem

SPORES *Tobacco-brown.*
FRUITING *Late summer to autumn.*
DISTRIBUTION *Uncommon to rare, widespread with broadleaf trees.*
EDIBILITY *Poisonous.*
SIMILAR SPECIES *Blackenfoot Fibrecap (I. atripes) has a blackening stem; Greenfoot Fibrecap (I. calamistrata) smells aromatic.*

The Blusher ☠

Amanita rubescens (Amanitaceae)

The domed, pinkish brown cap of The Blusher can be mottled with lighter, pale pink areas with age, after heavy rain, or even if the weather has been particularly hot. The grey to pink cap scales can be dense and warty or more fleecy and sparse, making this species difficult to identify at first. The gills are off-white and crowded, and the stem ring, which may be yellow, is broad and drooping with grooves on the upper side. White to pinkish grey, the stem is often stout with a broad swollen base that has remains of volval bands. Where damaged, rubbed, or broken, the flesh gradually turns pink, becoming more brown with time.

GROWS *singly and in groups, in all types of woodland – both broadleaf (especially birch, beech and oak) and conifer (especially pine and spruce).*

scaly, pinkish brown cap

cap 6–18 cm wide

white to pinkish grey stem

large floppy, furrowed ring on stem

crowded off-white gills

swollen stem base

SECTION

NOTE

The changing colour of the damaged flesh is a way to identify this species. Rub the stem and wait for the slow pinkening.

SPORES *White.*
FRUITING *Early summer to late autumn.*
DISTRIBUTION *Very common and widespread.*
EDIBILITY *Poisonous when raw, edible on being cooked.*
SIMILAR SPECIES *Panthercap (p.71), which is poisonous, has a grooved cap edge, distinctly rimmed volva, white cap scales, and does not turn pink when damaged; A. franchetii and Grey Spotted Amanita (A. spissa), which also do not change colour.*

White Webcap

Leucocortinarius bulbiger (Cortinariaceae)

GROWS *singly or in small groups among litter with conifers, often in mountainous areas.*

The White Webcap is a large but rare, edible species found with conifers. Its usually beige to ochre-brown cap can sometimes be reddish in colour. It is convex or domed and opens out with age, retaining a broad umbo at the centre. When moist, the cap is slightly sticky, and its margin is fleecy with fibrous veil remnants. The white gills become brownish with age or if bruised, and the white flesh smells of celery. The fibrous stem is also white with a fairly persistent ring-zone and a bulbous base with a rim. This is the only webcap with white spores – all the others have brown or rust-coloured spores and gills.

white gills become brownish

bulbous stem base

NOTE

If collecting for consumption, check features such as suitability of habitat and spore colour. Also check for a ring zone and veil remains on the cap, or a cobwebby veil on the caps of immature specimens.

white flesh

SECTION

reddish beige cap

cap up to 15cm wide

slightly sticky surface

SPORES White.
FRUITING Summer to autumn.
DISTRIBUTION Very rare to occasional and locally common; widespread across Europe but very rare in Britain.
EDIBILITY Edible.
SIMILAR SPECIES The Blusher (p.87), which is much more common and can have similar cap colours, but has membranous cap patches and a persistent ring and stem volva.

Wrinkled Webcap

Cortinarius elatior (Cortinariaceae)

This species has a large, conical, slimy cap, which is dark honey-brown with a strongly wrinkled and violet-tinged margin. Its dark brown gills are broad and either very wavy or wrinkled. The deeply rooting, pointed stem is slimy and violet below the ring-zone and smells of honey at the base.

SEEN *in mature broadleaf woodlands, especially with beech; more rarely under conifers, usually on acid soils.*

large, central umbo

cap 3–12cm wide

thin ring-zone

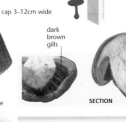

dark brown gills

orange-buff flesh at base of stem

SECTION

SPORES *Rust-brown.*
FRUITING *Summer to late autumn.*
DISTRIBUTION *Occasional to frequent, widespread in temperate N. Europe.*
EDIBILITY *Inedible.*
SIMILAR SPECIES *Purple Stocking Webcap (C. stillatitius), which has a less wrinkled cap and a thick, slimy violet veil on stem.*

Stinking Brittlegill

Russula foetens (Russulaceae)

One of a group of similar *Russula* species, the Stinking Brittlegill has a rancid, oily smell and is greasy to the touch. The domed cap is a tawny orange-brown with pronounced grooves and wart-like bumps at the margin, while the gills are cream, spotted brown. The white stem is hollow with chambered sections and stains brown at the base.

APPEARS *singly or in groups in litter with broadleaf and conifer trees.*

gills discoloured brown

large, rounded cap

cap up to 15cm wide

hollow, chambered stem

SECTION

warts on cap margin

SPORES *Cream.*
FRUITING *Summer to late autumn.*
DISTRIBUTION *Common to very common; widespread throughout.*
EDIBILITY *Inedible.*
SIMILAR SPECIES *R. illota, which has dark gill edges; R. inamoena, which grows with oak; R. subfoetens has yellowing flesh.*

The Gypsy

Rozites caperatus (Cortinariaceae)

A fairly distinctive species, The Gypsy has a honey-brown, wrinkled cap, often with a pale frosting of lilac veil especially at the centre. When young, the caps are egg-shaped, gradually expanding to become convex but retaining an umbonate centre. The pale brown gills are serrated and the similarly coloured stem has a firm, lilac-tinged white ring like a sheath. The off-white flesh is mild to the taste, dense, and fibrous. A good edible species, The Gypsy is widely collected.

FOUND *singly or in groups in coniferous woods, and sometimes also with beech.*

gills with toothed edge

SECTION

off-white to brown flesh

white stem ring

NOTE

Check for the presence of a true membranous ring attached to the stem and not just a cobwebby ring-zone as with Cortinarius *species. The Gypsy's spores are pale brown, unlike the rusty spores of* Cortinarius *species.*

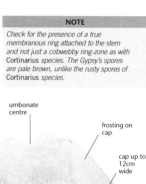

umbonate centre

frosting on cap

cap up to 12cm wide

lilac-white stem

SPORES *Pale brown.*
FRUITING *Summer to autumn.*
DISTRIBUTION *Locally common and widespread; very rare in Britain.*
EDIBILITY *Edible.*
SIMILAR SPECIES *Gassy Webcap (p.64), which has similar colours but smells strongly of pears and gas; Spectacular Rustgill (Gymnopilus junonius), which lacks any lilac tones and grows clustered on wood.*

Variable Webcap

Cortinarius anomalus (Cortinariaceae)

One of a large group of similar, silky, dry brown *Cortinarius* species, the Variable Webcap is difficult to identify with certainty. The brown-ochre cap often has a slight umbo in the centre and a pale, silvery blue sheen especially at the edges. The gills are close together, beginning bluish and becoming rusty ochre with age. Generally whitish, the stem has a bluish tinge above the ring-zone, and is pale whitish ochre below with silvery ripples.

SEEN *usually singly, sometimes in small groups, in a variety of dense woodland, but also on more open woodland edges.*

dome at cap centre

cap up to 7cm wide

silver sheen on margin

rusty ochre gills

bluish grey stem flesh

SECTION

SPORES Rusty brown.
FRUITING Late summer to autumn.
DISTRIBUTION Occasional to common, widespread.
EDIBILITY Inedible.
SIMILAR SPECIES Gassy Webcap (p.64), which has a strong smell of gas; C. caninus, which lacks the blue tint on cap or stem.

Bitter Poisonpie ☠

Hebeloma sinapizans (Cortinariaceae)

The sticky, domed, tawny beige cap of this fungus often has a thin, paler margin. The gills are a uniform pale- then tobacco-brown colour, and are not spotted or weeping as with some *Hebeloma* species. The stem is paler than the cap, often slightly scaly, and hollow when mature. If cut in half, the cap and stem display a distinct hanging wick of flesh. The whole fungus smells of radish.

GROWS *in deciduous woods, although is occasionally seen with conifers, singly or in small numbers in leaf litter or grass.*

uniform gills

stout stem

paler cap margin

tobacco-brown gills

cap up to 12cm wide

SPORES Tobacco-brown.
FRUITING Late summer to autumn.
DISTRIBUTION Common and widespread.
EDIBILITY Poisonous.
SIMILAR SPECIES Poisonpie (p.33), which is smaller, paler, and with weeping or dotted gills; H. edurum, which smells sweet and prefers chalky pine woods.

Common Rustgill

Gymnopilus penetrans (Cortinariaceae)

This medium-sized, inedible, orange-brown fungus has a brightly coloured and fibrous cap which can be slightly sticky when young. The stem is dull yellow with pale, bitter flesh. The gills are also yellowish but tend to develop distinctive rusty brown spots with age.

GROWS *singly or in numbers on fallen woody debris of conifers but very occasionally broadleaf trees.*

cap up to 8cm wide

fibrous yellowish orange stem

gills age to rusty brown

SECTION

pale yellow flesh

orange-brown cap

SPORES *Rust-brown.*
FRUITING *Autumn.*
DISTRIBUTION *Common to very common, widespread.*
EDIBILITY *Inedible.*
SIMILAR SPECIES *None – several Cortinarius species have similar colours but do not grow on wood.*

Weeping Widow

Lacrymaria lacrymabunda (Coprinaceae)

With its ring-zone blackened by spores and its black gills oozing clear droplets, it is easy to see why this edible species is called Weeping Widow. The domed cap, brown in the centre and greyish at the margin, has a distinctive felted, fleecy texture. The pale stem is girdled in veil fragments and is usually blackened by spores.

SEEN *usually in numbers, often growing close together in nutrient-rich places in leaf litter, along roadsides, paths, and waste ground often near nettles.*

cap up to 10cm wide

gills grey then black

pale stem

SECTION

veil remnants blackened by spores

SPORES *Black.*
FRUITING *Autumn.*
DISTRIBUTION *Common to very common, widespread.*
EDIBILITY *Inedible.*
SIMILAR SPECIES *Rusty Widow (L. pyrotricha) has a bright rusty orange cap; Coprinus species have black spores but no ring-zone.*

Glistening Inkcap

Coprinus micaceus (Coprinaceae)

An egg-shaped, bright tan to brown, clustering, inedible fungus, the Glistening Inkcap is often found in large groups. The caps appear pleated, and are darker in the centre with a pale cream line at the edge. They are covered in fine, powdery granules which make the cap surface

OCCURS *often in dense clusters on and around the base of rotting trees and fallen broadleaf wood of all kinds.*

glisten, though these can rub off with age. The brittle stems are pale by contrast and the gills turn inky black with age.

brown gills edged white

silvery stem

SECTION

cap up to 4cm wide

'pleated' egg-shaped caps

SPORES *Black.*
FRUITING *Late spring to early winter.*
DISTRIBUTION *Common and widespread.*
EDIBILITY *Inedible.*
SIMILAR SPECIES C. domesticus, *which has a yellow mat around the base;* Psathyrella *clusters, which have no granules or pleats on the cap.*

Split Fibrecap ☠

Inocybe fastigiata (Cortinariaceae)

Members of the genus *Inocybe* are notoriously difficult to identify. A good clue to this species is its distinctly pointed cap which often has an upturned margin that splits easily, giving it a torn appearance. The cap surface is covered by coarse radial fibres; the stem is off-white to yellow and often scurfy looking. The gills have a spermatic smell.

FOUND *singly or in small troops associated with broadleaf trees, often in disturbed soil of woodland edges, paths, and banks.*

cap up to 7cm wide

margin flared upwards

yellow-grey gills

SECTION

off-white stem

SPORES *Tobacco-brown.*
FRUITING *Summer to autumn.*
DISTRIBUTION *Common and widespread.*
EDIBILITY *Poisonous.*
SIMILAR SPECIES *Frosty Fibrecap (*I. maculata*), which is a darker chestnut-brown, sometimes with a bulb at the base of the stem.*

Magic Mushroom ☠

Psilocybe semilanceata (Strophariaceae)

FOUND *singly or scattered in large numbers in pastures, upland fringes, commons, and heaths.*

NOTE

There are a number of small brown fungi with central raised bumps; however, none has a blue-green stem base.

This poisonous fungus is well known for its hallucinogenic properties. It is also popularly known as the Liberty Cap. When fresh and moist, the bell-shaped cap is olive grey and lined, with a characteristic central nipple. It becomes honey–cream in colour with a smooth surface as it dries out. The gills are grey when young, maturing to dark brown with a violet tint, they are virtually free from the stem. The wavy stem is very slender and smooth, and is a similar honey-cream to the cap, but often has a distinctive blue-green base.

cap up to 2cm wide

cap olive-grey when fresh

nipple at centre of cap

bell-shaped cap

lilac-brown gills

thin stem

SECTION

SPORES *Purplish black.*
FRUITING *Late summer to late autumn.*
DISTRIBUTION *Locally very common; widespread throughout.*
EDIBILITY *Poisonous.*
SIMILAR SPECIES *Mealy Horsedung Brownie (P. fimetaria), which has a white veil and grows on horse dung; P. atrobrunnea, which has a broad umbo, smells mealy, and grows in boggy places. Other similar genera include Galerina, Corocybe, and Hypholoma.*

Red Banded Webcap

Cortinarius armillatus (Cortinariaceae)

This Webcap has a dry orange-brown cap covered in fine fibres and with reddish brown veil scales along the edge. It remains domed, and has thick brown flesh in the centre when it is cut in half. Its gills are pale beige, later becoming cinnamon. The stem is club-shaped, with attractive coral-red veil girdles below the ring zone.

GROWS *with birch especially in damp situations; sometimes found with other broadleaf trees.*

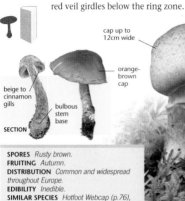

cap up to 12cm wide

orange-brown cap

beige to cinnamon gills

bulbous stem base

SECTION

zig-zag coral-red girdles

SPORES *Rusty brown.*
FRUITING *Autumn.*
DISTRIBUTION *Common and widespread throughout Europe.*
EDIBILITY *Inedible.*
SIMILAR SPECIES *Hotfoot Webcap (p.76), which has a fiery red base; C. paragaudis, which has duller girdles.*

Shaggy Scalycap

Pholiota squarrosa (Strophariaceae)

An easily recognizable species, the Shaggy Scalycap has dense, dark brown scales on its light yellow cap and stem. The upturned, pointed scales cover both the rounded cap and the lower part of the tough stem below the ring-zone. Its crowded gills are straw-yellow when young, later becoming brown, and the pale yellow flesh smells of radishes.

FOUND *clustered at the base of broadleaf trees, especially beech and ash.*

yellow gills turn brown

rounded, scaly cap

scaly stem

cap up to 15cm wide

upturned brown scales

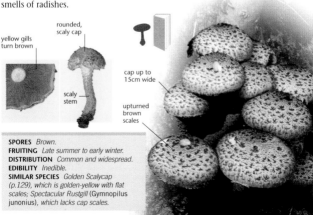

SPORES *Brown.*
FRUITING *Late summer to early winter.*
DISTRIBUTION *Common and widespread.*
EDIBILITY *Inedible.*
SIMILAR SPECIES *Golden Scalycap (p.129), which is golden-yellow with flat scales; Spectacular Rustgill (Gymnopilus junonius), which lacks cap scales.*

Honey Fungus

Armillaria mellea (Tricholomataceae)

FORMS *large, dense clusters in woods, parks, and gardens. Parasitic mainly on broadleaf trees, especially beech and oak. Also known to attack garden shrubs.*

This common, edible fungus is one of the most confusing for the beginner to identify as it has such a variable appearance. It is now reclassified as a group of closely related separate species. Growing in clusters, the fruitbodies are firmly joined together at the base. The cap can be domed, flattened, or funnel-shaped and wavy, and varies in colour from honey-brown, to yellowish or olive, with a darker brown centre covered in sparse brownish scales. The gills are white, becoming spotted brown. Often tapering, the brownish stem is darker towards the base, sometimes with lighter fibres. It has a thick, woolly, cream or yellow-tinged ring. The young, fresh caps should be cooked well.

well-spaced gills

darker stem base

cap 3–15cm wide

tapering stems

NOTE

Look out for black "bootlaces", or rhizomorphs, on the ground or along logs and a dusting of white spores on the fruitbodies from the caps above. Eat only young, fresh caps and cook well.

SPORES *White.*
FRUITING *Autumn.*
DISTRIBUTION *Very common and widespread.*
EDIBILITY *Edible but can cause gastric upset.*
SIMILAR SPECIES *A. ostoyae has more scales, a brown-tinged ring, and is most likely to cause stomach upsets; A. cepistipes has darker greyish scales with a more fragile ring; A. gallica, is less clustered with a bulbous stem base.*

Earthy Powdercap

Cystoderma amianthinum (Tricholomataceae)

The small yellow to orange-brown cap of this inedible fungus is initially domed, then flattish and even wavy at the edges. It can dry out much paler and the surface can be wrinkled, dusted with fine powdery granules, and have a tattered skirt of veil at the cap edge. The gills and flesh are white when young, becoming more yellowish with age. The stem is brownish with a fragile ring and powdered with granules below.

APPEARS *singly or in troops, but in a variety of habitats including dense woodland and open grassland, parks, and gardens. Often where moss is present.*

tattered cap margin

cap up to 4cm wide

granular lower stem

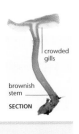

crowded gills

brownish stem

SECTION

SPORES *Off-white.*
FRUITING *Late summer to late autumn.*
DISTRIBUTION *Common and widespread.*
EDIBILITY *Inedible.*
SIMILAR SPECIES C. jasonis *has a darker cap and flesh. Various Dapperlings (Lepiota) have scattered cap fragments, white spores and scaly stem with ring.*

Yellowfoot Dapperling ☠

Lepiota magnispora (Agaricaceae)

The key identifying characteristic for this *Lepiota* species is that its stem has no ring-zone but is covered in fleecy fibres. The stem is white at the top but orange-yellow below. Like most of its relatives, its cap has a central brown disc, with minute ochre scales on a felted to fleecy orange-ochre background. The gills are white and free from the stem.

brown central disc

ochre scales

cap up to 7cm wide

fleecy fibres

yellowish stem base

SINGLY *or in small numbers in litter in conifer and broadleaf woods, often at wood margins, along paths and on banks.*

rounded young cap

SPORES *White.*
FRUITING *Late summer to autumn.*
DISTRIBUTION *Occasional to common and widespread.*
EDIBILITY *Poisonous.*
SIMILAR SPECIES *Shield Dapperling (p.28), which has a whiter cap, no yellow on the stem, and a ring-zone.*

The Prince

Agaricus augustus (Agaricaeae)

A large, beautiful species with a finely scaly, tawny-brown cap. The Prince has a tall white stem with a woolly-scaly surface below a floppy ring. The cap scales may vary from straw-yellow to gold or reddish brown over a much paler, almost white background. When cut, the flesh turns a pale yellow to orange-brown and smells pleasantly of aniseed.

GROWS on roadsides, woodland edges, and gardens, on sandy or clayey soils.

cap 9–22cm wide

flattened, yellow-brown scales

large, floppy, delicate ring

pinkish grey gills

woolly scales below stem ring

SECTION

SPORES *Dark brown.*
FRUITING *Summer to late autumn.*
DISTRIBUTION *Occasional to frequent, temperate N. Europe to the Mediterranean.*
EDIBILITY *Edible.*
SIMILAR SPECIES *A. sylvaticus, which is smaller with finely pointed, brown scales. Its flesh stains bright red when cut.*

Spring Cavalier

Melanoleuca cognata (Tricholomataceae)

This species has pink-flushed, golden-ochre gills and a brown cap. It is one of the more typical *Melanoleuca* fungi, which can only be distinguished by microscopic differences. All have smooth, dry, flat caps with a central umbo. Spring Cavalier is found in woodlands, parks, gardens, alongside paths and in mulch beds.

FOUND singly or in small scattered numbers in nitrogen-rich, disturbed sites.

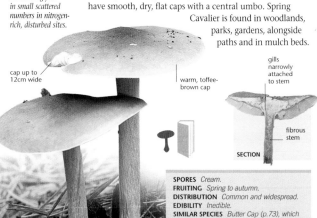

cap up to 12cm wide

warm, toffee-brown cap

gills narrowly attached to stem

fibrous stem

SECTION

SPORES *Cream.*
FRUITING *Spring to autumn.*
DISTRIBUTION *Common and widespread.*
EDIBILITY *Inedible.*
SIMILAR SPECIES *Butter Cap (p.73), which has a waxy cap and pale free gills. Other Melanoleuca species are varying shades of white, grey, beige, or brown.*

Aniseed Cockleshell

Lentinellus cochleatus (Auriscalpiaceae)

As one might expect from the common name, one of the key identifying features of this species is its strong smell of aniseed. The other is the shape of its cap, whose margin is curled somewhat like a cockleshell. The mature caps of Aniseed Cockleshell are trumpet-shaped and red-brown and most often grow in layered clusters. The leathery stems are off-centre and the cream to pale brown gills have a serrated edge and run deeply down the stem. Despite its sweet, pleasant smell, the flesh of the Aniseed Cockleshell is bitter and inedible.

SEEN *in clustered groups on the ground on rotting wood, roots, or stumps of broadleaf trees; sometimes among mosses and leaf-litter.*

NOTE

Various species have trumpet-shaped fruitbodies which grow in clusters; this species is distinct with its serrated gill edge and delicate smell of aniseed.

serrated edge

cap up to 6cm wide

cream to pale brown gills

gills run down stem

off-centre stem

curled, red-brown caps

SPORES *White.*
FRUITING *Late summer to autumn.*
DISTRIBUTION *Occasional to locally common, widespread.*
EDIBILITY *Inedible.*
SIMILAR SPECIES *Branching Oyster (p.41), which is pale with a central stem; Jack O'Lantern (p.106), which is more orange, and is poisonous. Neither smells of aniseed. Other* Lentinellus *species lack stems.*

Tawny Grisette

Amanita fulva (Amanitaceae)

This species has a conical to umbonate, smooth, dull tawny-brown cap with few, if any, scaly patches and a grooved margin. Its smooth, pale to light brown stem is ringless and at its base, which is often buried in soil, has a thick persistent off-white and tan-brown volva. The Tawny Grisette has white to cream gills, which are crowded and free from the stem.

GROWS *singly or in small troops, mainly in broadleaf woods but occasionally with conifers; associated with birch, sometimes beech and oak.*

crowded free gills

white to cream gills

hollow stem

SECTION

cap up to 8cm wide

pale to light brown stem

dull tawny-brown cap

off-white and brown volva

SPORES White.
FRUITING Summer to autumn.
DISTRIBUTION Common and widespread throughout N. temperate Europe to the Mediterranean.
EDIBILITY Edible only when cooked.
SIMILAR SPECIES Orange Grisette (p.115) is orange; Grisette (p.169) is grey-brown.

Birch Knight

Tricholoma fulvum (Tricholomataceae)

This common fungus has a tawny orange-brown cap, often darker at the centre, with a furrowed margin. Sticky when moist, it expands flat, sometimes becoming upturned and wavy with age, but always retains its low central umbo. The gills are pale yellow when young, becoming brown spotted with age. The yellow flesh is bitter and smells mealy.

FOUND *singly or in troops on the ground or in litter; associated with birch and sometimes conifers, especially spruce.*

cap up to 10cm wide

orange-brown cap

pale yellow gills

broad central umbo

furrowed margin

SECTION

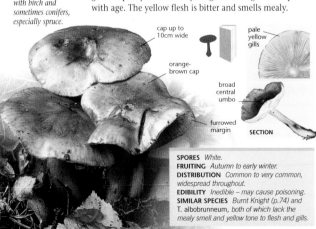

SPORES White.
FRUITING Autumn to early winter.
DISTRIBUTION Common to very common, widespread throughout.
EDIBILITY Inedible – may cause poisoning.
SIMILAR SPECIES Burnt Knight (p.74) and T. albobrunneum, both of which lack the mealy smell and yellow tone to flesh and gills.

Wood Woollyfoot

Collybia peronata (Tricholomataceae)

This small and tough species has a yellow-brown cap, which when fresh is radially streaked with dark brown, becoming pale and wrinkled with age. The yellowish brown gills are widely spaced. Similarly pale, the stem can be easily twisted without breaking. Often buried in leaf litter, the stem base is covered in felty yellow fibres. The leathery flesh is peppery.

GROWS *singly or in small groups among leaf or needle litter, in both conifer and broadleaf woods.*

cap up to 6cm wide

widely spaced, pale yellowish brown gills

woolly fibres at base

leathery stem

domed, yellow-brown cap

SPORES *Pale cream.*
FRUITING *Autumn.*
DISTRIBUTION *Very common throughout.*
EDIBILITY *Inedible.*
SIMILAR SPECIES C. fuscopurpurea, *which has a darker brown stem and prefers basic soils; Russet Toughshank (*C. dryophila*) is more orange brown and has a smooth stem.*

Girdled Dapperling ☠

Lepiota boudieri (Agaricaceae)

The radially fibrous, orange-brown cap and the zig-zag stem girdles make this an attractive species. Like many *Lepiota* species, its cap has a dark centre which can be almost black-brown. In contrast, the gills are white to cream. The stem has orange-brown veil remnants in girdles and the white flesh has a pleasant smell.

OCCURS *singly or in small numbers in nutrient-rich alkaline soil in woodlands and coppices.*

crowded white gills

black-brown centre

cap up to 3cm wide

orange-brown stem girdles

slender stem

orange-brown cap

SPORES *Cream.*
FRUITING *Summer to autumn.*
DISTRIBUTION *Occasional but widespread.*
EDIBILITY *Poisonous.*
SIMILAR SPECIES Chestnut Dapperling (p.79) *has a more scaly cap, a shorter stem, and a strong, unpleasant smell. Many small* Lepiota *species require expert identification.*

Deadly Webcap ☠

Cortinarius rubellus (Cortinariaceae)

An important and deadly poisonous species, the Deadly Webcap has caused numerous deaths and poisonings throughout Europe. It causes severe damage to the liver and central nervous system. The cap is umbonate, with very fine radial fibres or scales. The club-shaped stem has yellowish belts of veil. All parts of the fungus are tawny orange to reddish brown and smell faintly of radish.

FOUND *often in moss, such as sphagnum, in coniferous woodlands, especially pine or spruce, on acid soils.*

broad, widely-spaced gills

pale orange flesh

SECTION

umbonate, scaly cap

cap 3–8cm wide

SPORES *Rust-brown.*
FRUITING *Summer to late autumn.*
DISTRIBUTION *Rare, but widespread in temperate N. Europe.*
EDIBILITY *Highly poisonous.*
SIMILAR SPECIES *Fool's Webcap (right), Sunset Webcap (C. limonius) has a rounded cap, pointed stem, and an oily smell.*

Golden Bootleg

Phaeolepiota aurea (Tricholomataceae)

An attractive edible species with bright golden-brown colours and contrasting ruff-like cream stem ring, its cap is domed, granular, and wrinkled, with a fringed margin. The lower stem is covered in a similar golden granular sheath like a boot, hence its common name. The gills are whitish, becoming russet.

GROWS *singly or in small groups in humus-rich, disturbed sites along woodland edges, tracks, and in nettles.*

cap up to 25cm wide

margin with torn remains of veil

golden granular sheath

cream ring becomes rusty with spores

pale flesh

SECTION

SPORES *Ochre-brown.*
FRUITING *Autumn.*
DISTRIBUTION *Locally common and widespread.*
EDIBILITY *Edible and tasty.*
SIMILAR SPECIES *Spectacular Rustgill (p.108) is toxic, has a smooth cap, and lacks the bootleg sheath.*

Fool's Webcap ☠

Cortinarius orellanus (Cortinariaceae)

This is a fatally poisonous fungus, with similar late-onset symptoms of kidney failure as with the Death Cap (p.133). The domed red-brown cap flattens out but retains its central umbo. It has radial fibres and may be felty to the touch. The rusty yellow-brown gills are widely spaced and do not run down the stem, which is yellow-brown and cylindrical. The tapering stem has traces of yellow threads along its length but no stem girdles. Smelling of radish or turnip, Fool's Webcap favours acid oak woodlands. Because of the difficulties in identifying webcaps accurately, it is best to regard them all as poisonous and take spore prints to avoid confusion with the Chanterelle (p.118).

OCCURS *singly or in small groups on the ground in broadleaf and conifer woods, on basic and acid soils.*

rusty yellow-brown gills

yellow fibres along stem length

cap up to 6cm wide

domed, red-brown cap

SPORES *Rust-brown.*
FRUITING *Summer to late autumn.*
DISTRIBUTION *Common and widespread, less common in north.*
EDIBILITY *Highly poisonous.*
SIMILAR SPECIES *Deadly Webcap (left) which has a club-shaped stem with stem girdles; edible Chanterelle species are yellow and trumpet-shaped, with veins rather than gills underneath; inedible Gymnopilus species are of similar colours but grow on wood.*

NOTE

Observe the gills by cutting specimens in half – they should be widely spaced and not run down the stem; the colour should be rusty brown and not pale or spotted.

Copper Brittlegill

Russula decolorans (Russulaceae)

The pine-loving Copper Brittlegill has a smooth, coppery orange to brick-coloured, convex cap that expands with age, and cream to ochre gills that often have a black edge. Its greying stem is relatively tall and often wrinkled. A key feature of this species is that the flesh of the entire fruitbody discolours to strong grey or almost black when it is cut or bruised.

GROWS *singly or in troops among needle litter or moss in coniferous woods, especially with pine.*

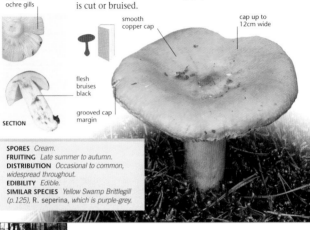

cream to ochre gills

smooth copper cap

cap up to 12cm wide

flesh bruises black

grooved cap margin

SECTION

SPORES *Cream.*
FRUITING *Late summer to autumn.*
DISTRIBUTION *Occasional to common, widespread throughout.*
EDIBILITY *Edible.*
SIMILAR SPECIES *Yellow Swamp Brittlegill (p.125),* R. seperina, *which is purple-grey.*

Booted Knight

Tricholoma focale (Tricholomataceae)

The Booted Knight is named after the boot-like, fibrous sheath, banded with orange-red that covers the lower portion of the stem. Its domed cap is orange-brown, streaked with red to brick-coloured fibres. The stem has a thick ring, above which it is white. Below the ring, it has a sheath of orange-red bands. The cream flesh is mild to taste and smells of meal or cucumber.

FOUND *singly or in groups with conifers, especially pines, in sandy soils*

cap up to 12cm wide

orange-red streaks

orange-red bands

cream flesh

creamy white gills

thick white ring

SECTION

SPORES *White.*
FRUITING *Autumn.*
DISTRIBUTION *Rare to occasional, widespread.*
EDIBILITY *Inedible.*
SIMILAR SPECIES *T. caligatum, which is very rare, has a less orange tone, and is scaly with a fruity smell.*

Tawny Funnel

Lepista flaccida (Tricholomataceae)

True to its name, this funnel-shaped species has a tawny, orange-brown cap and stem. It may develop darker blotches as it gets old, and its margin, which usually remains inrolled, is slightly wavy. The gills run deeply down the stem and are white when young, becoming yellow-orange and later tawny. The stem hollows out with age and often has a woolly base. The edible Tawny Funnel is found in large numbers in woods of all kinds and continues to fruit into the winter. *L. gilva*, which is more yellow in colour and has brownish spots at the cap margin, is regarded by some as a form of the Tawny Funnel.

OCCURS *in large numbers, often among deep litter in both coniferous and broadleaf woods.*

white gills become tawny with age

gills run down stem

woolly stem base

SECTION

NOTE

Although the Tawny Funnel is edible, it has a poor flavour. If it is being eaten, great care should be taken with its identification as several other funnel fungi are highly poisonous. Its very thin flesh, deeply funnelled cap, and slender stem are characteristic.

dry, funnel-shaped cap

inrolled margin

cap up to 12cm wide

SPORES *Cream.*
FRUITING *Summer to early winter.*
DISTRIBUTION *Common to very common; widespread throughout the region.*
EDIBILITY *Edible.*
SIMILAR SPECIES *Common Funnel (p.35), which is paler with thinner cap flesh; Clitocybe sinopica, which has a mealy smell. Both are edible.*

Jack O'Lantern ☠

Omphalotus illudens (Paxillaceae)

CLUSTERS, *sometimes in dense tufts, at the base of dead and decaying broadleaf trees and stumps, especially oak and chestnut.*

This very poisonous, clustering species has gills that glow in the dark, hence its common name. Its reddish to orange-brown cap is smooth and shaped like a trumpet, while its margin is slightly inrolled and split. The widely spaced gills are golden orange, running some distance down the stem. The stem itself is reddish orange, tends to taper, and may be off-centre. The flesh is yellow and firm. Commonly found in North America, the Jack O'Lantern may have been introduced from there to Europe. It is a common cause of poisoning in the USA, but is rarely fatal. A related species, *O. olearius*, grows in southern Europe, especially on old olive trees.

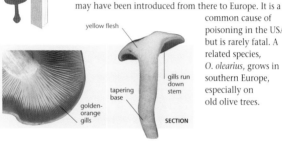

yellow flesh

golden-orange gills

tapering base

gills run down stem

SECTION

trumpet-shaped cap

cap up to 14cm wide

SPORES Off-white.
FRUITING Summer to autumn.
DISTRIBUTION Rare to occasional; widespread, but absent in far north.
EDIBILITY Highly poisonous.
SIMILAR SPECIES Spectacular Rustgill (p.108), which clusters on broadleaf trees but is more domed and has a ring; O. olearius, which has a vivid orange cap and a longer stem, but occurs only in the far south. Both are toxic.

NOTE

Do not confuse this highly toxic species with the edible Chanterelle (p.118), which is yellow and not orange-brown, and does not grow in tufts or on wood.

Surprise Webcap ☠

Cortinarius semisanguineus (Cortinariaceae)

A prominent feature of this species is its bright yellow-brown to olive cap, which contrasts sharply with the vivid red gills, in old as well as young specimens. The dry, domed cap has a central umbo and radial fibres, and the stem is paler yellow-brown with few fibres. The flesh is yellowish, tinged reddish brown at the stem base, and smells faintly of radish or sometimes iodine. Species of *Cortinarius* with vivid orange or red colours, especially on the gills, belong to the *Dermocybe* group and are often used for dyeing. The poisonous Surprise Webcap is sometimes used to dye wool.

FOUND *singly, but more often in large troops, in coniferous woods of all types, especially spruce, on acid soils.*

cap up to 7cm wide

yellow-brown cap

narrow yellow-brown stem

NOTE

To identify this fungus, check whether it has a dry, felty feel, and look out for the following characteristic colour sequence: yellow cap, followed by red gills and a yellow-brown stem.

bright red gills

umbonate cap

SECTION

SPORES *Rust-brown.*
FRUITING *Late summer to late autumn.*
DISTRIBUTION *Common to very common; widespread throughout.*
EDIBILITY *Poisonous.*
SIMILAR SPECIES *Bloodred Webcap (C. sanguineus) and C. phoeniceus, which both have redder caps and may occur with broadleaf trees.*

Splendid Webcap ☠

Cortinarius splendens (Cortinariaceae)

GROWS *singly or in small numbers; associated with broadleaf trees, especially beech, on warm chalky sites.*

This attractive but deadly poisonous, bright yellow fungus has sulphur-yellow veil speckles on the sticky cap. The cap centre may be orange-yellow and have a slight umbo. Though bright yellow when young, the gills become more rusty yellow with age. The stem may be coated with a few cobweb-like threads; its base is noticeably bulbous with a distinct rim to the margin.

rusty yellow gills

bulbous base

yellow flesh

SECTION

orange-yellow veil speckles

cap up to 7cm wide

SPORES *Rust-brown.*
FRUITING *Summer to autumn.*
DISTRIBUTION *Rare to occasional, widespread in southern regions.*
EDIBILITY *Highly poisonous.*
SIMILAR SPECIES *Yellow Knight (p.125); C. citrinus, which is more greenish; C. elegantissimus, has straw and bluish flesh.*

Spectacular Rustgill ☠

Gymnopilus junonius (Cortinariaceae)

CLUSTERED, *often in large numbers, at base of trees and on fallen wood – especially broadleaf but occasionally coniferous.*

A large, spectacular orange-brown fungus, the cap of this species is domed and dry, sometimes with a central umbo, covered in radial fibres, and may have a tattered margin of veil fragments. The gills become progressively more rust-brown with age as does the large, floppy ring on the stem. This bitter-tasting fungus is sometimes reported as being hallucinogenic.

orange-brown fibrous cap

cap up to 20cm wide

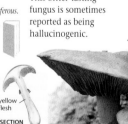

floppy stem ring

yellow flesh

SECTION

SPORES *Rust-brown.*
FRUITING *Late summer to late autumn.*
DISTRIBUTION *Occasional to common, widespread.*
EDIBILITY *Poisonous.*
SIMILAR SPECIES *Shaggy Scalycap (p.95) and Golden Scalycap (p.129) have scaly caps or stems; Golden Bootleg (p.102).*

Meadow Waxcap

Hygrocybe pratensis (Hygrophoraceae)

This stout orange waxcap has a dry to greasy cap, which is domed when young and expands with age, becoming wavy, often with a central umbo. The arched cream gills run down the similarly coloured, dry, fibrous stem, which tapers towards the base. The peachy-orange colour of this well-known edible species gradually fades to buff. It also has a pure white form.

SEEN *singly, but often in large troops, in unimproved grassland; occasionally in woodland, especially grassy clearings.*

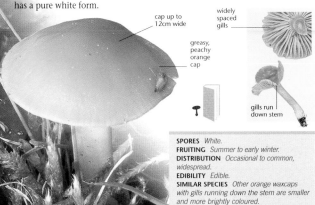

cap up to 12cm wide

widely spaced gills

greasy, peachy orange cap

gills run down stem

SPORES *White.*
FRUITING *Summer to early winter.*
DISTRIBUTION *Occasional to common, widespread.*
EDIBILITY *Edible.*
SIMILAR SPECIES *Other orange waxcaps with gills running down the stem are smaller and more brightly coloured.*

Brick Tuft

Hypholoma lateritium (Strophariaceae)

Smooth, brick-red caps, darker at the centre and sometimes with pale, fleecy scales at the margin, make this large woodland species distinctive. The young gills are grey, and become purplish brown with age. Pale yellow above and a darker reddish brown below, the stem lacks a ring zone.

OCCURS *usually in tufts, rarely alone, on broadleaf wood.*

cap up to 10cm wide

brick-red caps, darker at centre

crowded, broadly attached gills

reddish brown base

SPORES *Purple-brown.*
FRUITING *Autumn to early winter.*
DISTRIBUTION *Occasional to common, widespread.*
EDIBILITY *Inedible.*
SIMILAR SPECIES *Sheathed Woodtuft (p.60), Honey Fungus (p.96), Velvet Shank (p.110), and Sulphur Tuft (p.130).*

Velvet Shank

Flammulina velutipes (Tricholomataceae)

FOUND *clustered in tufts on a variety of broadleaf trees, especially elm and willow. Prefers decaying wood or old, standing trees.*

This widely eaten species grows clustered on wood. It has a smooth, sticky, orange-brown cap, which is domed and inrolled at the margin. Very rarely, a white form of this species also occurs. The gills are yellowish and moderately spaced, producing white spores. Tapering to the base, the stem is smooth and yellow at the top and distinctly velvety and black towards the base. The flesh is pale yellow with an indistinct mushroomy smell. Velvet Shank has a good flavour and is cultivated and marketed under various Japanese names, including Inotake. It is stimulated to fruit by cold and even frosty weather.

orange-brown cap

cap up to 6cm wide

yellow gills

smooth yellowish stem

SPORES *White.*
FRUITING *Late autumn to early spring.*
DISTRIBUTION *Occasional to common, widespread.*
EDIBILITY *Edible.*
SIMILAR SPECIES *Sulphur Tuft (p.130), which has purplish green gills and purple spores, and is poisonous; Common Rustgill (p.92) and Spectacular Rustgill (p.108), which have spotted orange-brown gills and brown spores.*

Orange Milkcap

Lactarius aurantiacus (Russulaceae)

This species has a smooth to slightly sticky, orange to russet cap that is gently funnel-shaped, with a sometimes persisting umbo. The gills are pinkish buff becoming cinnamon, while the salmon-coloured stem is smooth and palest at the top. A white milk, which does not change colour, oozes from the gills. The flesh is mild and smells of rubber.

GROWS *singly, but more often in troops, in litter from broadleaf and coniferous trees; or sometimes with dwarf willow in sand dunes.*

pinkish buff gills

orange cap

cap up to 5cm wide

pale orange-brown flesh

SECTION

salmon-coloured stem

SPORES *Cream.*
FRUITING *Late summer to autumn.*
DISTRIBUTION *Common to very common, widespread.*
EDIBILITY *Inedible.*
SIMILAR SPECIES *Tawny Milkcap (L. fulvissimus), which has a pale cap margin, and milk that dries pale yellow.*

Fishy Milkcap

Lactarius volemus (Russulaceae)

The flat, velvety orange-brown cap of the Fishy Milkcap, as with all *Lactarius* species, often has a central dip; its margin is paler and often cracks. The crowded cream gills become spotted brick-red when bruised and ooze a white milk that smells of fish. Its finely velvety stem is a paler, creamy orange with a tendency to bruise brick red.

APPEARS *singly or in small numbers on the ground in broadleaf woods, at times with conifers.*

dry, velvety cap

cap up to 12cm wide

SPORES *Off-white.*
FRUITING *Autumn.*
DISTRIBUTION *Rare but widespread.*
EDIBILITY *Edible.*
SIMILAR SPECIES *Velvet Rollrim (p.84); Velvet Shank (left), which grows in tufts. Both have more velvety stems, lack a fishy smell, and grow on wood.*

cream gills spotted red

stem stains red

SECTION

Fibrous Waxcap

Hygrocybe intermedia (Hygrophoraceae)

FOUND *in unimproved, particularly basic grassland including meadows, parks, lawns, and cemeteries.*

This waxcap has a pointed cap that is streaked with red, orange, and yellow. Both the cap and stem are dry and covered in coarse fibres, which are scarlet to orange on a yellow backround, and fade with age. The cap remains inrolled at the margin, often splitting into uneven lobes, while the pale yellow to orange gills have a serrated edge. The stem, which may stain greyish slowly, may be twisted, and has a white base.

radial fibres on cap

cap up to 7cm wide

cap splits with age

SPORES *White.*
FRUITING *Summer to autumn.*
DISTRIBUTION *Rare to occasional, but widespread.*
EDIBILITY *Inedible.*
SIMILAR SPECIES *Persistent Waxcap (H. persistens), which is yellow; Crimson Waxcap (p.161), which is blood-red.*

Saffrondrop Bonnet

Mycena crocata (Tricholomataceae)

GROWS *on the ground in small groups on leaf litter and twigs, almost totally restricted to beech, especially on alkaline soils.*

This distinctive *Mycena* species is very easily damaged, exuding a bright saffron-yellow juice which gives it its common name. The delicate, bell-shaped grey-brown cap has a lined, paler margin. The gills and upper stem are pale, while the lower stem is more brownish, often rooting and with tiny hairs at the base. The whole fungus tends to spot bright orange-yellow with age or damage.

gills almost free from stem

stem paler at top

SECTION

cap up to 3cm wide

orange-yellow stain

slender brownish stem

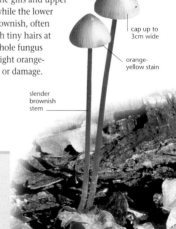

SPORES *Pale cream.*
FRUITING *Late summer to autumn.*
DISTRIBUTION *Locally common and widespread throughout.*
EDIBILITY *Inedible.*
SIMILAR SPECIES *Bleeding Bonnet (M. sanguinolenta), Burgundydrop Bonnet (M. haematopus) – both exude dark red latex.*

Red Swamp Brittlegill

Russula aquosa (Russulaceae)

This is an attractive species with the cap in shades of cherry-red or purplish red, darker at the centre. The surface can be quite glossy when young, and the skin of the cap can be peeled off almost completely. The gills and the club-shaped, fragile stem are white, but the stem rapidly becomes very soft and waterlogged and can discolour slightly greyish.

APPEARS *in wet boggy areas, often in sphagnum moss, in coniferous or mixed woodland.*

cherry-red cap

cap up to 7cm wide

white stem

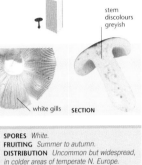

stem discolours greyish

white gills

SECTION

SPORES *White.*
FRUITING *Summer to autumn.*
DISTRIBUTION *Uncommon but widespread, in colder areas of temperate N. Europe.*
EDIBILITY *Edible.*
SIMILAR SPECIES *R. sphagnophila, which has a grooved margin to the cap and is more greenish brown.*

Redlead Roundhead

Stropharia aurantiaca (Strophariaceae)

All roundheads have domed and sticky caps. This bright vermillion species is no exception. The cap margin with scattered scales often has the ragged remains of a fleecy, pale veil. The gills are pale olive at first later becoming brown- or crimson-grey, while the fibrous, pale stem has a fragile ring.

OCCUR *in large groups and singly in humus-rich sites such as mulch beds, sawdust heaps, and straw piles.*

cap up to 6cm wide

bright orange-red cap

brown-grey gills

white edge on gills

SECTION

pale, fibrous stem

SPORES *Purplish brown.*
FRUITING *Summer to autumn.*
DISTRIBUTION *Occasional to locally common; becoming increasingly widespread.*
EDIBILITY *Inedible.*
SIMILAR SPECIES *Psilocybe thrausta, which has an orange cap and orange-brown stem, grows with beech and not on woodchips.*

Caesar's Amanita

Amanita caesarea (Amanitaceae)

FOUND *in broadleaf woods, especially with oak and chestnut, on sandy soils.*

This fungus is widely eaten in Mediterranean countries but careful identification is needed as it can be confused with poisonous species of *Amanita*. The rounded golden orange cap expands to become convex or flat, with a furrowed margin. Veil fragments on the cap surface are infrequent, more often absent. The stem, gills, and drooping stem ring are all pale golden yellow, as is the flesh. There is a white bag-like stem ring at the stem base.

convex cap

yellow gills

white volva

SECTION

ridged margin

golden orange cap

cap up to 20cm wide

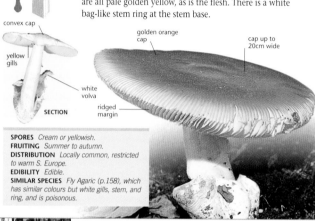

SPORES *Cream or yellowish.*
FRUITING *Summer to autumn.*
DISTRIBUTION *Locally common, restricted to warm S. Europe.*
EDIBILITY *Edible.*
SIMILAR SPECIES *Fly Agaric (p.158), which has similar colours but white gills, stem, and ring, and is poisonous.*

Flaming Scalycap

Pholiota flammans (Strophariaceae)

APPEARS *in small clusters, or singly, on decaying conifer wood, seldom on broadleaf.*

This scaly, bright orange-yellow species has a preference for rotting conifer wood. Both the rounded cap and the stem below the ring-zone are covered in upturned, pointed, fleecy, bright yellow scales – the cap ground colour is more tawny while the stem is yellowish. The flesh too is bright yellow and the gills salmon-yellow becoming rusty brown.

upturned scales

cap up to 7cm wide

tawny cap

bright yellow flesh

fleecy stem below ring-zone

yellow stem

SECTION

SPORES *Brown.*
FRUITING *Autumn.*
DISTRIBUTION *Occasional to common and widespread.*
EDIBILITY *Inedible.*
SIMILAR SPECIES *Sulphur Tuft (p.130) lacks scales and has grey-green gills; other Pholiota species, which are paler or lack scales.*

Orange Grisette

Amanita crocea (Amanitaceae)

The bright orange-brown or apricot cap of this species is smooth with few, if any, scaly patches and a grooved, paler margin. The ringless stem has indistinct orange-brown zig-zag lines, with a persistent, thick, whitish volva that is yellowish inside. The crowded white gills are free from the stem. Orange Grisette may be eaten if cooked well.

GROWS on soil, in coniferous and broadleaf woodland, with a preference for birch and beech.

crowded off-white gills

bright orange to apricot cap

white volva at stem base

cap 6–12cm wide

zig-zag lines on stem

SPORES *White.*
FRUITING *Early summer to autumn.*
DISTRIBUTION *Rare to occasional, widespread.*
EDIBILITY *Edible.*
SIMILAR SPECIES *Tawny Grisette (p.100), which has a russet cap and no zig-zag markings on the stem.*

Tawny Webcap ☠

Cortinarius callisteus (Cortinariaceae)

The Tawny Webcap has a rounded golden brown cap with radial tawny-orange fibres and scales. The gills are orange to yellow-brown, while the stem is a similar colour with tawny scales and a bulbous base. Vivid orange-yellow, the flesh has a peculiar smell of ozone or hot motor oil. Like many others in this group, the Tawny Webcap is fluorescent in ultraviolet light.

SEEN *singly, or more often in large troops, among conifers, especially spruce.*

cap up to 8cm wide

orange-brown fibres

yellowish brown gills

bulbous yellow stem

SECTION

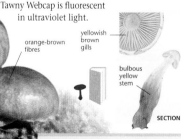

SPORES *Rust-brown.*
FRUITING *Autumn.*
DISTRIBUTION *Rare to occasional, mainly found in northernmost regions.*
EDIBILITY *Poisonous.*
SIMILAR SPECIES *Sunset Webcap (C. limonius), which has a fleecy stem; C. tophaceous, grows with broadleaf trees.*

Two Spored Milkcap

Lactarius acerrimus (Russulaceae)

FOUND *singly or in small groups on the ground in leaf litter or grass; associated with oak.*

This is the only milkcap species with spores produced in groups of two rather than four. Its funnel-shaped cap is heavily zoned, yellowish to russet, and rather sticky. The pinkish cream gills are branched near the stem which is short, tapering, and off-centre.

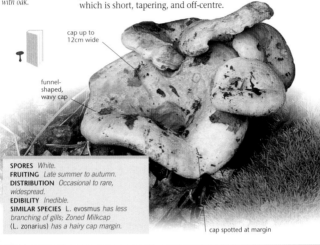

cap up to 12cm wide

funnel-shaped, wavy cap

cap spotted at margin

SPORES *White.*
FRUITING *Late summer to autumn.*
DISTRIBUTION *Occasional to rare, widespread.*
EDIBILITY *Inedible.*
SIMILAR SPECIES L. evosmus *has less branching of gills; Zoned Milkcap* (L. zonarius) *has a hairy cap margin.*

Yellowdrop Milkcap ☠

Lactarius chrysorrheus (Russulaceae)

GROWS *singly or in small numbers, scattered in leaf litter or grass; associated mainly with oak.*

This poisonous species has a funnel-shaped cap, which is pinkish buff to salmon with distinctly darker circular zones. It has white milk and flesh which turns slowly bright sulphur-yellow. Although mild initially, the flesh slowly becomes acrid. The gills are cream then pinkish buff. The relatively smooth cap and bright sulphur-yellow milk makes this species easy to recognise.

funnel-shaped cap

pinkish to salmon zones

cap up to 8cm wide

unforked gills

smooth, paler stem

SPORES *Cream.*
FRUITING *Summer to autumn.*
DISTRIBUTION *Common to very common, widespread.*
EDIBILITY *Poisonous.*
SIMILAR SPECIES Oakbug Milkcap (p.67) *lacks pink cap tones; Lemon Milkcap* (L. citriolens) *has a distinctly hairy cap.*

False Saffron Milkcap

Lactarius deterrimus (Russulaceae)

One of the most brightly coloured milkcap species, the cap, gills, and stem of this fungus are all a rich salmon-orange becoming mottled green with age, frost, or bruising. Its gills exude carrot-orange milk which may slowly darken. Sticky when moist, the cap may be funnel-shaped with a curved margin and faint, darker concentric zones. The smooth stem easily bruises green, and becomes hollow with age. False Saffron Milkcap is a good edible species retaining a carroty texture, although it has the alarming but harmless side-effect of turning the urine red.

GROWS *usually in rings or troops; associated solely with spruce in all types of locations, including parks and roadsides.*

NOTE

Species within this group are not always easy to separate unless habitat is clear. However, all milkcaps with orange milk are thought to be edible, although some, like the False Saffron Milkcap, are tastier than others.

gills produce bright orange milk

fruitbody bruises green

cap up to 12cm wide

funnel-shaped, sticky cap

smooth stem

SPORES *Off-white.*
FRUITING *Late summer to autumn.*
DISTRIBUTION *Common to very common, widespread.*
EDIBILITY *Edible and tasty.*
SIMILAR SPECIES *Saffron Milkcap (L. deliciosus) has strong cap zones, a spotted stem, and hardly any green discolouration; L. quieticolor has buff, cinnamon, and greenish blue tones; L. salmonicolor has fewer cap zones and its flesh stains wine-red.*

Chanterelle

Cantharellus cibarius (Cantharellaceae)

FOUND *often in moss, it is associated with pines and spruce but also with oak, beech, and birch.*

The smooth cap of the bright golden yellow Chanterelle forms a broad, flattened trumpet, often slightly depressed in the middle, with a wavy margin. On the underside, the pale apricot-yellow surface is strongly wrinkled, with gill-like veins running down the short, pointed stem. The flesh is thick, white to pale yellow, and bruises orange to red. Edible and tasty, the Chanterelle has a pleasant apricot smell and is widely available in markets.

NOTE

Although the Chanterelle is edible, it has some highly poisonous look-alikes. Some are more scaly and may have a violet flush on the scales. Others are paler and bruise reddish brown. If in doubt, do not consume.

gill-like blunt veins

wavy, cap margin

white to pale yellow flesh

SECTION

depressed cap centre

cap 2–12cm wide

short, solid stem

SPORES *Ochre-yellow.*
FRUITING *Summer to late autumn.*
DISTRIBUTION *Occasional to common; widespread throughout N. hemisphere but becoming rarer in places.*
EDIBILITY *Edible and tasty.*
SIMILAR SPECIES *Deadly Webcap (p.102) and Fool's Webcap (p.103) have reddish orange caps, rusty brown gills, and are highly poisonous. Amesthyst Chanterelle (C. amesthystus) has a pale violet cap.*

Birch Webcap

Cortinarius triumphans (Cortinariaceae)

A striking species, the Birch Webcap has a greasy, rounded, orange-yellow to tawny cap, often with small fragments of veil round the margin, and with large rings or girdles of darker veil round the stout, pointed stem. The gills are pale lavender when young and rust-brown when old. Although it has a pleasant smell, the pale yellow-cream flesh tastes bitter.

OCCURS *in small groups; associated with birch in woods and parks.*

cap 5–15cm wide

belts of yellow veil around stem

lavender to blue-grey gills

greasy, golden-orange cap

pointed stem base

stout yellow stem

SPORES *Rust-brown.*
FRUITING *Summer to late autumn.*
DISTRIBUTION *Locally common, widespread in temperate N. Europe.*
EDIBILITY *Inedible.*
SIMILAR SPECIES *C. cliduchus, which has a darker, olive-ochre to ochre-brown cap and grows with oak or spruce.*

Contrary Webcap

Cortinarius varius (Cortinariaceae)

The smooth, rounded, sticky cap of this fungus is tawny brown, with a darker (almost red-brown) centre, while the crowded gills are pale lilac-blue when young. The club-shaped stem is white with a white veil forming a faint girdle. The cobwebby veil is usually stained rust-brown with spores and the flesh is white.

SEEN *in mountainous areas on chalky soils, only with spruce.*

rounded, tawny yellow cap

red-brown cap centre

cap 5–10cm wide

SPORES *Rust-brown.*
FRUITING *Summer to late autumn.*
DISTRIBUTION *Occasional to common, widespread in temperate N. Europe.*
EDIBILITY *Inedible.*
SIMILAR SPECIES *C. variiformis, which has more prominent veil girdles and grows with oak.*

smooth cap surface

lilac-blue gills

club-shaped stem

Blueleg Webcap

Cortinarius amoenolens (Cortinariaceae)

SEEN *in groups or rings in beech woods on chalky soils, often in deep leaf litter.*

The domed or rounded, pale clay-yellow to ochre cap of this species becomes sticky when wet. The violet-lilac stem is rounded and bulbous at the base with a distinct margin to the bulb. The gills are pale lilac-blue. Violet in the stem, the flesh has a sweet, plum-like odour but it is not edible.

rounded cap

cap 5–10cm wide

pale lilac-blue gills

violet stem with flattened bulb

SECTION

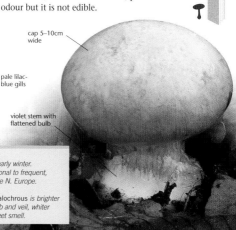

SPORES *Rust-brown.*
FRUITING *Autumn to early winter.*
DISTRIBUTION *Occasional to frequent, widespread in temperate N. Europe.*
EDIBILITY *Inedible.*
SIMILAR SPECIES *C.* calochrous *is brighter yellow with yellower bulb and veil, whiter flesh, and lacks the sweet smell.*

Geranium Brittlegill

Russula fellea (Russulaceae)

GROWS *under beech trees only and blends well with fallen leaves.*

The Geranium Brittlegill can be identified by the overall honey colour of all its parts. The rounded, smooth cap soon expands and flattens and the margin may become slightly grooved. Moderately spaced, the gills join the cylindrical and smooth stem. The flesh of the fungus has the distinct smell of pelargoniums.

cap 3–8cm wide

pale honey-yellow gills

smooth stem 4–8cm high

stem hollow and brittle

SECTION

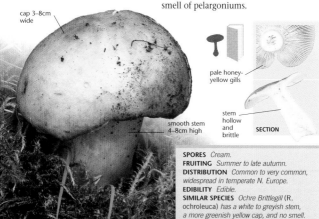

SPORES *Cream.*
FRUITING *Summer to late autumn.*
DISTRIBUTION *Common to very common, widespread in temperate N. Europe.*
EDIBILITY *Edible.*
SIMILAR SPECIES *Ochre Brittlegill (R.* ochroleuca*) has a white to greyish stem, a more greenish yellow cap, and no smell.*

Yellow Fieldcap

Bolbitius vitellinus (Bolbitiaceae)

This delicate fungus has a sticky, egg-yolk-yellow cap, which is oval when young. With age it flattens out and becomes cream coloured with only a hint of yellow left at the centre. The cap edge has tiny grooves and the bright rusty gill colour often shows through. Pale yellow when young, the narrow stem becomes white as it matures.

ASSOCIATED *mostly in man-made habitats, especially manure and compost piles; also seen in grass in woods and fields.*

cap up to 6cm wide

pale yellow stem

sticky yellow cap

delicate stem

rusty gills

SECTION

SPORES *Rusty brown.*
FRUITING *Late summer to autumn.*
DISTRIBUTION *Frequent and widespread.*
EDIBILITY *Inedible.*
SIMILAR SPECIES *Yellowleg Bonnet (p.122), which also has a sticky yellowish cap, but the stem is usually a more vivid yellow and the gills are creamy, never turning rusty.*

Lion Shield

Pluteus leoninus (Pluteaceae)

The rounded cap of this delicate species is golden yellow to tawny and minutely fibrous or even slightly scaly, with a grooved margin. Its bright colours tend to fade with age. The gills are salmon pink with a yellow edge, while the stem is white with yellow tones, especially towards the base.

SEEN *on stumps and rotten wood, including the fallen trunks of broadleaf trees.*

pink gills with yellow edge

cap up to 5cm wide

cap easily separated from stem

smooth stem

SECTION

SPORES *Pale pink.*
FRUITING *Late summer to autumn.*
DISTRIBUTION *Occasional to common, and widespread.*
EDIBILITY *Inedible.*
SIMILAR SPECIES *Aromatic Pinkgill (Entoloma pleopodium) has pink gills; P. aurantiorugosus has a bright orange cap.*

Yellowleg Bonnet

Mycena epipterygia (Tricholomataceae)

This is an easily recognizable bonnet fungus, with its delicate, slimy, bell-shaped cap and vivid yellow stem with a darker base. The ochre-yellow cap, often with a brown centre, has a grooved margin and cuticle that can be peeled away. Although fairly tough, the slender stem is slimy so is often covered with plant or soil debris. The pale gills are widely spaced and narrowly attached to the stem. The Yellowleg Bonnet may have a mealy, rancid smell, especially if crushed.

GROWS *in troops, often in large numbers, in litter with broadleaf and conifer trees.*

NOTE
There are a large number of different bonnet fungi, all of which have slender stems, delicate bell-shaped caps, and white spores. The only way to distinguish them accurately is by examination under a microscope.

delicate, domed cap

cap up to 2.5cm wide

stem up to 8cm tall

almost free gills

yellow cap with brown tones

thin yellow stem

SECTION

SPORES *Cream.*
FRUITING *Summer to early winter.*
DISTRIBUTION *Common to very common; widespread throughout.*
EDIBILITY *Inedible.*
SIMILAR SPECIES *Orange Bonnet (M. acicula), which has a dry, orange-yellow cap; Ivory Bonnet (M. flavoalba), is dry and pale yellow; Dripping Bonnet (M. rorida), which is slimy but typically much smaller, with a brownish cap.*

False Deathcap

Amanita citrina (Amanitaceae)

The smooth-edged cap of this fungus can either be lemon-yellow or pure white, and when young is covered in a map-like mosaic of detachable white or beige scales. The crowded gills are whitish yellow. There is a drooping ring at the top of the stem and a rounded bulb with a distinct rim at the base. The flesh smells strongly of raw potatoes, especially when rubbed.

FOUND *singly or in troops in woodland, on acidic soil; grows with conifers as well as broadleaf trees such as beech, oak, and birch.*

off-white to yellow gills

beige scales on cap

cap 5–10cm wide

bulbous stem base

drooping ring

SECTION

SPORES *Off-white.*
FRUITING *Late summer to autumn.*
DISTRIBUTION *Common and widespread.*
EDIBILITY *Inedible.*
SIMILAR SPECIES *Destroying Angel (p.15) has an irregular cap; Jewelled Amanita (below); Deathcap (p.133) has a sickly smell – all three species are poisonous.*

Jewelled Amanita ☠

Amanita gemmata (Amanitaceae)

The cap of the Jewelled Amanita varies from cream to bright yellow. It has white veil patches and grooves at the edge and often becomes flat or depressed. The off-white gills are crowded and the white stem has a fragile ring, which is often missing. The narrow volva sometimes has a rim, with crumbly belts above.

OCCURS *singly or in small groups, in natural woodland and plantations, mainly with conifers but also broadleaf trees.*

white veil patches

cap up to 10cm wide

SPORES *White.*
FRUITING *Early summer to late autumn.*
DISTRIBUTION *Rare to locally common, widespread mainly in southern regions.*
EDIBILITY *Poisonous.*
SIMILAR SPECIES *False Deathcap (above), which smells of raw potato; A. eliae, which is taller and more beige.*

crowded gills

off-white flesh

off-white to yellow gills

SECTION

Vinegar Brittlegill

Russula acetolens (Russulaceae)

A small edible species, the Vinegar Brittlegill has a smooth, bright yellow cap, which is often sticky, and a slender, pure white stem. With age, the cap becomes grooved at the margin and the broad orange-ochre gills deepen in colour. The mature fungus also develops a strong vinegary or sour smell.

GROWS, *usually with birch, occasionally other broadleaf trees, on acidic soils in damp areas.*

widely spaced orange gills

thin white stem

cap 2–5cm wide

clear yellow cap

SPORES *Orange.*
FRUITING *Summer to late autumn.*
DISTRIBUTION *Rare to occasional, widespread in temperate N. Europe.*
EDIBILITY *Edible.*
SIMILAR SPECIES *Golden Brittlecap* (R. risigallina), *which has pink or apricot tones on the cap and smells fruity or of old roses.*

Velvet Brittlegill

Russula violeipes (Russulaceae)

The key feature of the Velvet Brittlegill is its violet stem, which is signified by the word *violeipes* in Latin. The rounded cap varies from pale lemon-yellow to greenish yellow or purple, or even a mix of all three shades. The cream gills are narrow and crowded while the edible white flesh smells faintly of Jerusalem artichokes.

ASSOCIATED *with both broadleaf and coniferous trees; especially with beech, on rich soils.*

cap 3–8cm wide

crowded cream gills

stem flushed lilac

greasy stem surface

SPORES *Cream.*
FRUITING *Summer to late autumn.*
DISTRIBUTION *Rare to occasional, widespread in temperate N. Europe.*
EDIBILITY *Edible.*
SIMILAR SPECIES *R. amoenicolor, which has a greener or dark purple cap, often depressed, with a grooved margin.*

Yellow Swamp Brittlegill

Russula claroflava (Russulaceae)

This species has a striking yellow cap, with yellowish cream gills that turn grey at the edges. The white stem soon becomes greyish, and if scratched the flesh turns deep grey-black within 5–15 minutes. It may momentarily turn red before turning black. The edible flesh has a pleasant smell and is mild to taste.

FOUND *very often in sphagnum and other mosses; commonly associated with birch trees in wet, swampy areas.*

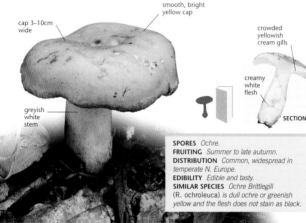

smooth, bright yellow cap

cap 3–10cm wide

greyish white stem

crowded yellowish cream gills

creamy white flesh

SECTION

SPORES *Ochre.*
FRUITING *Summer to late autumn.*
DISTRIBUTION *Common, widespread in temperate N. Europe.*
EDIBILITY *Edible and tasty.*
SIMILAR SPECIES *Ochre Brittlegill (R. ochroleuca) is dull ochre or greenish yellow and the flesh does not stain as black.*

Yellow Knight

Tricholoma equestre (Tricholomataceae)

The cap of this species is bronze- to orange-yellow, sometimes with scales, especially at the centre. It has bright yellow gills, even when young. The stem, which is also yellow, has a slightly fibrous texture and the whitish yellow flesh has a mealy smell. The Yellow Knight varies considerably in stature from slender to robust.

OCCURS *singly or in troops on the ground with conifers, especially pine; also broadleafs such as beech.*

scales on cap

yellow-brown cap

SPORES *White.*
FRUITING *Autumn to early winter.*
DISTRIBUTION *Locally common and widespread; less so in Britain.*
EDIBILITY *Edible and tasty.*
SIMILAR SPECIES *Plums and Custard (p.146); Soapy Knight (p.168); T. bufonium which has an unpleasant gassy smell.*

cap up to 14cm wide

Sulphur Knight ☠

Tricholoma sulphureum (Tricholomataceae)

GROWS *singly or in groups, on the ground, with broadleaf trees and conifers.*

This poisonous *Tricholoma* species is unmistakable because of its strong, unpleasant gassy smell, like coal-tar, produced by a chemical known as scatol. The dry, sulphur-yellow cap is sometimes tinged with brown. It is convex, with a broad umbo and a smooth margin. The gills, stem, and flesh are also sulphur yellow. The stem is slightly fibrous with a paler base and the gills are well spaced, and notched where they join the stem. *T. bufonium* with its contrasting reddish brown cap but otherwise similar features, is considered by some to be a form of the Sulphur Knight – it occurs mainly with conifers.

broad umbo

smooth cap margin

cap up to 8cm wide

well spaced gills

hollow stem

entire fruitbody sulphur-yellow

SECTION

stem up to 10cm tall

SPORES *White.*
FRUITING *Autumn to early winter.*
DISTRIBUTION *Common to very common, widespread throughout.*
EDIBILITY *Poisonous.*
SIMILAR SPECIES *Plums and Custard (p.146), which has a wine-red to reddish brown cap, lacks the gassy smell and grows on wood; Aromatic Knight (T. lascivum), which has a slightly gassy to sweet smell and whitish fruitbody.*

Golden Waxcap

Hygrocybe chlorophana (Hygrophoraceae)

This small yellow waxcap has pale whitish to lemon-
coloured gills. It is waxy to the touch and so slimy on
the cap that when wet, it is often difficult to hold. The
compressed yellow stem may have a groove along its
length. The stem base is whitish while the upper portion,
near the gills, is often
finely powdery.

FOUND *singly or often
in some numbers, in
grassland, especially
short mossy patches
free from chemical
fertilizers.*

flattened, lemon-
yellow cap

cap up to
7cm wide

whitish yellow
gills

flattened,
yellow stem

yellow
flesh

SECTION

SPORES *White.*
FRUITING *Late summer to early winter.*
DISTRIBUTION *Occasional to common,
widespread throughout.*
EDIBILITY *Edible.*
SIMILAR SPECIES H. ceracea *has a dry stem
and gills;* H. glutinipes *has a sticky cap and
stem;* H. persistens *has a dry cap.*

Larch Woodwax

Hygrophorus lucorum (Hygrophoraceae)

A bright lemon cap with a central umbo and a slippery
texture when wet, make this species easy to recognize. The
white to pale yellow gills are arched and run down the
stem. There is an indistinct ring-zone on the stem, above
which the apex is white and dry. Below it, the stem is
sticky with zig-zag yellow bands on a yellow background.

APPEARS *singly or in
groups in needle litter
with larch.*

central umbo

cap up to
6cm wide

arched
yellow gills

bulging
ring
zone

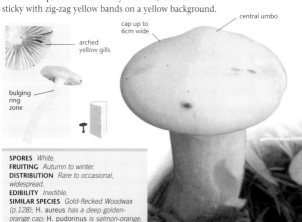

SPORES *White.*
FRUITING *Autumn to winter.*
DISTRIBUTION *Rare to occasional,
widespread.*
EDIBILITY *Inedible.*
SIMILAR SPECIES *Gold-flecked Woodwax
(p.128);* H. aureus *has a deep golden-
orange cap;* H. pudorinus *is salmon-orange.*

Blackening Chanterelle

Cantharellus melanoxeros (Cantharellaceae)

GROWS *in fused clusters in leaf litter with broadleaf trees, especially beech and oak.*

This rare but distinctive chanterelle has a trumpet-shaped cap tapering to a narrow, compressed stem. There are branching, ridge-like veins on the underside. The whole fungus is yellow when young, becoming increasingly ochre to brownish yellow with age. The stem is generally a more intense yellow. The species blackens on bruising, hence the common name. Though edible, it should not be eaten because of its conservation status.

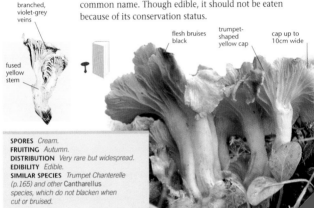

branched, violet-grey veins

fused yellow stem

flesh bruises black

trumpet-shaped yellow cap

cap up to 10cm wide

SPORES *Cream.*
FRUITING *Autumn.*
DISTRIBUTION *Very rare but widespread.*
EDIBILITY *Edible.*
SIMILAR SPECIES *Trumpet Chanterelle (p.165) and other* Cantharellus *species, which do not blacken when cut or bruised.*

Gold-flecked Woodwax

Hygrophorus chrysodon (Hygrophoraceae)

This attractive, edible species looks its best when young and white. It is very slippery, with bright yellow scales fringing the cap and gill edges and the stem apex. The white gills are widely spaced and arched when young, running down the stem; the flesh is white or lemon-yellow.

FOUND *singly or in small troops in broadleaf and occasionally conifer woods, on basic sites.*

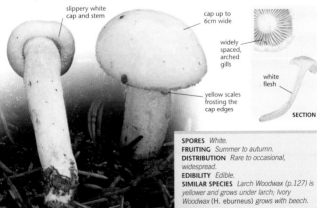

slippery white cap and stem

cap up to 6cm wide

widely spaced, arched gills

white flesh

yellow scales frosting the cap edges

SECTION

SPORES *White.*
FRUITING *Summer to autumn.*
DISTRIBUTION *Rare to occasional, widespread.*
EDIBILITY *Edible.*
SIMILAR SPECIES *Larch Woodwax (p.127) is yellower and grows under larch; Ivory Woodwax (*H. eburneus*) grows with beech.*

Golden Scalycap

Pholiota aurivella (Strophariaceae)

This species has a sticky, golden- to rust-yellow cap with dark brown, sometimes blackening, scales scattered across it. These are easily shed in rain and with age, leaving the cap smooth. The stem is also greasy to sticky with more persistent scales. The crowded gills are pale yellow, becoming rusty brown.

GROWS *in tufts on broadleaf trees, especially beech, but also willow, poplar, and ash.*

cap up to 15cm wide

rusty gills

broadly attached gills

SECTION

sticky cap with loose scales

smooth cap margin

SPORES *Brown.*
FRUITING *Late summer to autumn.*
DISTRIBUTION *Occasional to locally common, widespread.*
EDIBILITY *Inedible.*
SIMILAR SPECIES Spectacular Rustgill (p.108); *P. jahnii grows mainly on beech, and P. limonella mainly on birch, alder, and fir.*

False Chanterelle

Hygrophoropsis aurantiaca (Hygrophoropsidaceae)

Frequently mistaken for the genuine – and edible – Chanterelle (p.118), this inedible fungus differs in its thin-fleshed, yellow to orange-brown cap with a felty, inrolled margin. The gills are soft, crowded, often forked and not like the irregular wrinkles of the true Chanterelle. The smooth stem is fairly thin and hollow, with pale orange flesh.

GROWS *in needle or leaf litter, on sawdust or woodchip piles, or even on rotten wood.*

soft, felted-furry cap surface

cap 3–10cm wide

yellowish cream gills, with grey edges

flesh stains blackish

SECTION

slender stem

SPORES *White.*
FRUITING *Summer to late autumn.*
DISTRIBUTION *Common and widespread throughout temperate N. Europe.*
EDIBILITY *Inedible.*
SIMILAR SPECIES *Chanterelle (p.118), is thicker fleshed with blunt wrinkles rather than gills on the cap underside.*

Sulphur Tuft

Hypholoma fasciculare (Strophariaceae)

SEEN *in tufts, often in large numbers, growing on the rotting wood of both conifers and broadleaf trees.*

NOTE

Check specimens for their green to purple-black gills to rule out similar edible species such as Sheathed Woodtuft (p.60), Honey Fungus (p.96), and Velvet Shank (p.110), all of which grow in tufts on wood but have different-coloured gills.

Although it is easy to spot this poisonous, sulphur-yellow fungus clustered on wood, sometimes in dense tufts, its variable appearance sometimes makes it difficult to identify. The yellow-edged caps are more orange at the centre. Domed when young, they become funnel-shaped and undulating when older. Also yellow and fibrous, the stem is darker at the base. It has a ring-zone which becomes brownish purple with fallen spores. The gills are a garish yellow-green when young, becoming increasingly purplish black with age. The flesh of the Sulphur Tuft is very bitter and can cause severe stomach upsets.

cap up to 7cm wide

sulphur-yellow cap

darker centre on caps

green and purplish black gills

stem yellow at top

darker stem base

SPORES *Purple-brown.*
FRUITING *Summer to autumn.*
DISTRIBUTION *Common to very common, widespread.*
EDIBILITY *Poisonous.*
SIMILAR SPECIES *Brick Tuft (p.109) and Snakeskin Brownie (H. marginatum), which both have whitish gills and a silky white stem layer when young; Conifer Tuft (H. capnoides), which does not have any greenish tint in its greyish violet to purple-brown gills.*

Plantpot Dapperling

Leucocoprinus birnbaumii (Agaricaeae)

Outside the tropics, the occurance of this unusual species is restricted to indoor habitats, such as plant pots. It is very distinctive with its finely scaled bell-shaped, bright golden to orange-yellow cap, pale yellow gills, and stem with a fleeting ring. The very fragile fruitbody shrivels rapidly in just a few hours.

OCCURS *singly or in small clusters in hot-houses, garden centres, and greenhouses.*

finely scaly cap

cap up to 5cm wide

lined cap margin

crowded, free gills

slightly swollen stem base

SPORES *White.*
FRUITING *All year round.*
DISTRIBUTION *Occasional and widespread.*
EDIBILITY *Inedible.*
SIMILAR SPECIES L. denudatus, *found in plant pots, has a central umbo and lacks cap scales; Flaming Scalycap (p.114), which grows in the wild on wood.*

Citrine Waxcap

Hygrocybe citrinovirens (Hygrophoraceae)

This medium-sized waxcap has a dry, fibrous, lemon-yellow to greenish cap and stem. The cap remains conical, flaring out with age, often with large splits in the margin. The compressed, silky stem is white at the base with a groove along its length. This waxcap has gills which are free from the stem, beginning white and later taking on a greenish tinge.

FOUND *singly, or in small troops, in fertilizer-free grassland, including fields, parks, lawns, and cemeteries.*

white to greenish gills

yellow to lime-coloured cap

cap up to 9cm wide

yellowish flesh

SECTION

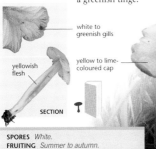

SPORES *White.*
FRUITING *Summer to autumn.*
DISTRIBUTION *Rare to occasional, widespread.*
EDIBILITY *Inedible.*
SIMILAR SPECIES Death Cap (p.133) *has a ring and volva; Parrot Waxcap (p.135) and* H. laeta *are sticky and domed.*

Green Brittlegill

Russula aeruginea (Russulaceae)

This is a common *Russula*, with a cap that varies from deep grass-green to yellowish green and often has tiny, scattered red-brown spots. The crowded, crumbly gills are cream and the spongy, brittle stem is white, often spotted rust-brown. The flesh is slightly hot to the taste. The fungus has no distinctive smell.

GROWS *with birch trees, often in damp woodland in grass and leaf litter.*

rounded, depressed cap

cap 3–8cm wide

crowded white to cream gills

rusty spots often on stem

SPORES *Cream.*
FRUITING *Summer to late autumn.*
DISTRIBUTION *Common to very common, widespread throughout temperate N. Europe and the Mediterranean.*
EDIBILITY *Edible.*
SIMILAR SPECIES *Greasy Green Brittlegill (R. heterophylla) has fine radial wrinkles.*

Greencracked Brittlegill

Russula virescens (Russulaceae)

The cap surface of this mint- or blue- to yellow-green species is broken up into fine cracks and scales rather like a mosaic. The fleshy cap is rounded, becoming flattened and slightly depressed. The brittle, crowded gills are white, as is the pointed stem. Firm and mild to taste, the flesh does not have a noticeable smell.

MOST *commonly found with beech and sometimes oak, often on clay soils.*

crowded gills

cap 4–10cm wide

white flesh

SECTION

stout white stem

SPORES *White.*
FRUITING *Summer to late autumn.*
DISTRIBUTION *Occasional to frequent, widespread throughout temperate N. Europe and the Mediterranean.*
EDIBILITY *Edible and tasty.*
SIMILAR SPECIES *R. cutefracta, which is darker green and more finely cracked.*

Death Cap

Amanita phalloides (Amanitaceae)

Variability in colour makes this poisonous fungus tricky to identify at first, and has led to its confusion with edible species. The cap can vary from yellowish green to bronze, greyish, and even, though rarely, white. It is always radially streaked with a smooth cap margin, and can be slightly greasy. The gills and stem are white, though the stem is sometimes flushed with the cap colour and banded with faint zig-zag marks. The stem has a white, drooping, slightly grooved ring, which may fall off, and the base has a white membranous volval bag which may be greenish inside. The Death Cap has a sweet sickly smell, strongest with age. It is highly poisonous – if consumed it will cause vomiting, then slow liver and kidney failure.

GROWS *in woodlands of all types, including grassy fringes or parks; associated with broadleaf trees, such as beech, oak, and hazel, on rich soils.*

cap 5–9cm wide

streaky cap surface

veil patches on cap

banded stem

immature, green-capped fruitbody

white gills

large, baggy white volva

SECTION

SPORES *White.*
FRUITING *Summer to autumn.*
DISTRIBUTION *Widespread with host trees.*
EDIBILITY *Highly poisonous.*
SIMILAR SPECIES *False Deathcap (p.123) and Grey-veiled Amanita (p.164), which both smell of raw potato; Deceiving Knight (p.134), which lacks a stem ring and volva; Stubble Rosegill (p.172), which has pink spores and is edible.*

NOTE

If in any doubt about identification, do not eat wild fungi as it can be fatal. Make sure you collect the whole specimen, including the stem base.

Olive Webcap

Cortinarius atrovirens (Cortinariaceae)

GROWS *with conifers, especially firs, in mountainous or upland areas, on alkaline soils.*

The cap of this species is a striking, deep olive- to brownish green, becoming paler, more sulphur-yellow at the margin. It is sticky with slightly fibrous streaks. The gills are greenish lemon when young as is the stout, bulbous stem. There is a cobwebby veil at the top of the stem. The flesh is bright yellow and has a peppery smell.

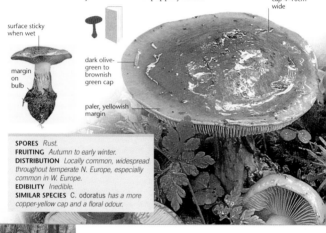

cap 4–10cm wide

surface sticky when wet

margin on bulb

dark olive-green to brownish green cap

paler, yellowish margin

SPORES *Rust.*
FRUITING *Autumn to early winter.*
DISTRIBUTION *Locally common, widespread throughout temperate N. Europe, especially common in W. Europe.*
EDIBILITY *Inedible.*
SIMILAR SPECIES *C. odoratus has a more copper-yellow cap and a floral odour.*

Deceiving Knight

Tricholoma sejunctum (Tricholomataceae)

FOUND *singly or in groups on the ground with conifers, and also among broadleaf trees.*

Though always fibrous to streaky in appearance, the colour of this species' cap can vary from the more common greenish yellow tones to brown. It is conical to convex with a low umbo, and a smooth, splitting margin. Both the gills and the stem are whitish, although the latter flushes yellow with age. The pale flesh tastes slightly bitter.

streaky surface

cap up to 10cm wide

notched, wavy, pale gills

smooth margin splits apart

mealy, off-white flesh

SECTION

SPORES *White.*
FRUITING *Autumn.*
DISTRIBUTION *Occasional to common, widespread.*
EDIBILITY *Edible but can cause gastric upset.*
SIMILAR SPECIES *Death Cap (p.133); Soapy Knight (p.168); Yellow-grey Knight (T. portentosum), which has a grey-streaked cap.*

Parrot Waxcap

Hygrocybe psittacina (Hygrophoraceae)

A small, bell-shaped, brightly coloured waxcap with a very slimy cap, this species has a vivid mixture of colours. It is predominantly green, yellow, and orange but sometimes also blue, lilac, and pink. With darker bands at the margin, the cap glistens when wet, becoming shiny as it dries out. Coloured like the cap, the gills often have a paler edge. The stem is also slimy with a rippled surface and nearly always has a hint of green at the top. This inedible fungus is almost odourless. The variety *H. psittacina* var. *perplexa* has a dark, brick-red cap but is otherwise similar.

APPEARS *singly or in troops in grassland or, less often, in woods with moss.*

gills free from stem

fragile white flesh

SECTION

cap a mix of green, pink, or orange

cap up to 4cm wide

slimy cap with bands at edge

stem greenish at top

SPORES *White.*
FRUITING *Early summer to winter.*
DISTRIBUTION *Common and widespread throughout.*
EDIBILITY *Inedible.*
SIMILAR SPECIES *Heath Waxcap (H. laeta), which has similar, though duller colours, a slimy gill edge, and smells of burnt rubber; green Stropharia species, which have brown spores and a stem ring.*

NOTE

Check the top of the stem for hints of bright green, and look at the gill edge with a hand lens to confirm that there is a pale, opaque margin.

Mousepee Pinkgill ☠

Entoloma incanum (Entolomataceae)

GROWS *in unimproved grassland, including wood edges and lawns, especially on basic soil; prefers short, mossy turf.*

This is a small, poisonous fungus of basic, unimproved grassland. When young, the cap colour is vibrant grass green but rapidly fades to yellow-brown with only a hint of olive. The domed cap has a central depression, and is dry, with streaks at the margin, which is sometimes wavy. Smooth and hollow, the stem is green, bruising bright blue-green at the base, while the gills are yellowish, turning pink. The species smells strongly of mouse droppings, especially if kept enclosed.

medium-spaced gills

streaks at cap margin

cap up to 3cm wide

hollow stem

SECTION

SPORES *Pale pink.*
FRUITING *Summer to autumn.*
DISTRIBUTION *Rare to occasional, widespread.*
EDIBILITY *Poisonous.*
SIMILAR SPECIES *Aromatic Pinkgill (E. pleopodium) smells of bubble gum; Parrot Waxcap (p.135), which is orange.*

Greenflush Fibrecap

Inocybe corydalina (Cortinariaceae)

The Greenflush Fibrecap is mainly greyish in colour but with varying amounts of green. More white at first, the convex greyish green cap has a fibrous to scaly texture, and an umbo that is often olive-coloured. The gills are whitish becoming grey, while the stem is pale cream. The flesh smells sweet and aromatic, like pear drops.

FOUND *singly or, occasionally, in small groups, in leaf litter or bare ground in broadleaf woods.*

greenish olive umbo

cap up to 8cm wide

fibrous to scaly cap

whitish gills turn grey

white flesh

SECTION

SPORES *Clay-brown.*
FRUITING *Autumn.*
DISTRIBUTION *Occasional, widespread.*
EDIBILITY *Inedible.*
SIMILAR SPECIES *Willow Shield (p.168), which grows on wood and has pink spores and gills; I. haemacta, which has similar colouring but flushes reddish with age.*

Green Dapperling ☠

Lepiota grangei (Agariaceae)

This is one of the few Dapperlings with greenish tints. The pale brown, conical cap flattens out with a distinct umbo. It is covered with dark green to greenish brown scales, especially when young. Darkest at the centre, it becomes orange at the margin with age. The cream gills develop rust spots. The stem is whitish above the ring-zone, covered with greenish granular scales below, and orange at the base.

SEEN *singly or in small groups with broadleaf trees in disturbed places such as coppices, roadsides, and waste places.*

large central disc

cap up to 3cm wide

light brown background

gills become rust spotted

greenish granular scales

orange-brown base

SECTION

SPORES *Creamy yellow.*
FRUITING *Late summer to autumn.*
DISTRIBUTION *Occasional to common, widespread.*
EDIBILITY *Inedible; possibly poisonous.*
SIMILAR SPECIES L. griseovirens *has smaller spores;* L. pseudofelina *is greyer. Both need microscopic evaluation.*

Ringed-blue Roundhead

Stropharia aeruginosa (Strophariaceae)

The distinctive blue-green domed cap of this species has fleecy white scales at the margin when young, which fade to yellowish ochre. The gills are brownish violet with a frosted white edge. There is a prominent though fragile ring on the stem, which is whitish above the ring and pale blue-green below, with fleecy scales.

GROWS *singly or in small groups on debris in broadleaf and coniferous woods, or among moss in pasture or on roadsides.*

white edge on dark gills

grey-brown gills

SECTION

glutinous cap

white scales at margin

cap up to 7cm wide

SPORES *Dark brown.*
FRUITING *Autumn.*
DISTRIBUTION *Common to very common.*
EDIBILITY *Inedible.*
SIMILAR SPECIES *Blue Roundhead (*S. cyanea*), which lacks the white gill edge; Peppery Roundhead (*S. pseudocyanea*), which smells of pepper.*

Aniseed Funnel

Clitocybe odora (Tricholomataceae)

Not many fungi are blue-green and this unusual colour, along with a strong smell of aniseed, distinguishes this edible fungus. The rounded cap is often inrolled at the margin and becomes flat to slightly depressed with age. It also fades to grey-green and rarely white. The creamy yellow gills run slightly down the stem.

APPEARS *singly but more often in troops or rings, sometimes in large numbers among leaf litter in woods, especially with conifers.*

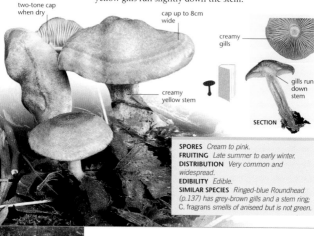

two-tone cap when dry

cap up to 8cm wide

creamy gills

gills run down stem

creamy yellow stem

creamy yellow stem

SECTION

SPORES Cream to pink.
FRUITING Late summer to early winter.
DISTRIBUTION Very common and widespread.
EDIBILITY Edible.
SIMILAR SPECIES Ringed-blue Roundhead (p.137) has grey-brown gills and a stem ring; C. fragrans smells of aniseed but is not green.

Mealy Bigfoot Webcap

Cortinarius caerulescens (Cortinariaceae)

The cap, stem, and gills of this species are all coloured greyish violet-blue. Finely fibrous and streaked, the cap is discoloured yellowish at the centre. The gills are crowded and violet when young, while the stem is very stout and bulbous at the base, with a cobwebby veil between the cap margin and the stem.

FOUND *commonly with beech, oak, hazel and other broadleaf trees on alkaline soils.*

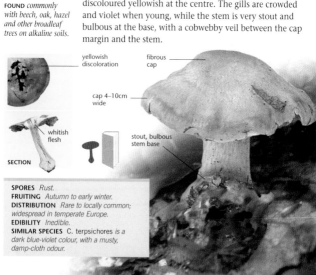

yellowish discoloration

fibrous cap

cap 4–10cm wide

whitish flesh

stout, bulbous stem base

SECTION

SPORES Rust.
FRUITING Autumn to early winter.
DISTRIBUTION Rare to locally common; widespread in temperate Europe.
EDIBILITY Inedible.
SIMILAR SPECIES C. terpsichores is a dark blue-violet colour, with a musty, damp-cloth odour.

Big Blue Pinkgill

Entoloma bloxamii (Entolomataceae)

This attractive, robust blue species of chalky grasslands has a bell-shaped cap that flattens out but retains a nearly pointed umbo. Bright grey-blue to blue when young, the cap and stem fade deceptively dull with age. Both are dry and covered in fine fibres, giving the fungus a slightly felty texture. Very variable, the stem may retain the blue colour longer than the cap and may be yellowish at the base. The stem height is about equal to that of the cap width. The gills are white and later become pink with age; the flesh is white with a hint of blue below the cap cuticle and it has a mealy smell. Relatively rare, the Big Blue Pinkgill has been given conservation status. It is not an edible species.

GROWS *in unimproved grassland, including dunes, meadows, and lawns, but with a preference for alkaline soil.*

white to pink gills

yellowish stem base

white flesh

SECTION

NOTE

A fairly distinctive species when young and blue, older specimens may be faded grey, so check for a pink spore print and mealy smell.

blue cap covered in fibres

cap up to 7cm wide

cap width equal to stem height

SPORES *Pale pink.*
FRUITING *Summer to autumn.*
DISTRIBUTION *Rare to occasional, widespread.*
EDIBILITY *Inedible.*
SIMILAR SPECIES Entoloma nitidum, *which is a woodland species with the stem taller than its cap width. Other blue* Entoloma *species, which are much smaller, and sometimes have blue gill edges.*

Blue Edge Pinkgill ☠

Entoloma serrulatum (Entolomataceae)

GROWS *in all types of unimproved grassland, in fields, road margins, lawns, and parks, often in short grass with moss.*

A small blue-black grassland species, this fungus has a dry, felted to scaly cap with a central depression like a navel. Fading to grey-black with age, it sometimes develops splits at the edges. The stem is narrow with similar colours and texture to the cap when young, although it fades to olive-grey-brown, with a white base. The gills are bluish white when young, later becoming pinkish blue, with a distinctive blue-black serrated edge.

cap up to 2.5cm wide

pinkish blue mature gills

blue-black cap

smooth stem

hollow stem

serrated gill edge

SECTION

SPORES *Pale pink.*
FRUITING *Early summer to autumn.*
DISTRIBUTION *Rare to common, widespread.*
EDIBILITY *Poisonous.*
SIMILAR SPECIES *E. chalybaeum, which has blue gills with brown edges; E. caesiocinctum, which has a more brownish cap.*

Lilac Pinkgill

Entoloma porphyrophaeum (Entolomataceae)

GROWS *in unimproved grassland, including fields, short-cropped mossy lawns, parks, and woodland edges.*

This tall and pointed fungus grows in grassland that has not been treated with chemicals. The cap is greyish with strong violet tones when young, and fades brownish with age. It is inrolled at the margin and has a dry felty texture with very visible radial fibres. The gills are pale pink, while the stem has a similar colour and texture to the cap, often with its violet tones remaining longest at the top.

pointed centre

inrolled margin

cap up to 8cm wide

violet-grey cap

stem up to 15cm tall

SECTION

SPORES *Pale pink.*
FRUITING *Late summer to autumn.*
DISTRIBUTION *Rare to occasional and widespread.*
EDIBILITY *Inedible.*
SIMILAR SPECIES *Big Blue Pinkgill (p.139); E. elodes has a strong, mealy smell; Sepia Pinkgill (E. jubatum) is smaller.*

Charcoal Burner

Russula cyanoxantha (Russulaceae)

The cap of this very variable species is usually shades of purple, lavender, or violet; however, it may also be partly or entirely green. The cap surface is dry, smooth, and tough. Rounded at first, it becomes flattened when mature. The crowded white gills are very flexible and feel greasy or oily when touched, unlike the brittle and dry gills of most *Russula* species. The sturdy stem is white to dull cream in colour. Quite tough, it turns brittle when old. The flesh of the edible Charcoal Burner is mild to slightly hot to taste and has a crunchy texture.

OCCURS *singly, or in small groups, in broadleaf woods, especially beech but also under conifers, on acid soils.*

crowded white gills

NOTE

Only two or three Russula species have gills that are flexible – the Charcoal Burner being one of them. To confirm identity, test with iron sulphate which turns the flesh greenish unlike most species, which become pink.

cap rounded when immature

SECTION

white to cream flesh

cap 5–15cm wide

cap with shades of violet or purple

smooth, dry cap surface

sturdy, tough white stem

SPORES *White.*
FRUITING *Summer to late autumn.*
DISTRIBUTION *Common throughout temperate N. Europe.*
EDIBILITY *Edible and tasty.*
SIMILAR SPECIES *Oilslick Brittlegill (R. ionochlora), which is a brighter lilac-lavender with a greenish yellow centre when mature; Charcoal Burner, its gills are brittle rather than flexible, and cream not white in colour.*

Olive Brittlegill

Russula olivacea (Russulaceae)

FOUND in large groups, mostly with beech and oak, usually on clay or acid soils.

As with many *Russula* species, the cap colour of the Olive Brittlegill is variable. Its surface is matt and dry with minute concentric cracks. When mature, the broad gills are deep ochre-orange. Immediately below the gills, the white stem top has a faint flush of purple.

rounded young cap

purple to olive green cap

cap 8–15cm wide

concentrically cracked, matt surface

stout white stem

SPORES *Yellow.*
FRUITING *Summer to autumn.*
DISTRIBUTION *Occasional to locally common, widespread in temperate Europe.*
EDIBILITY *Edible and tasty.*
SIMILAR SPECIES *R. alutacea is slightly smaller, and has a purple flush at the base of the stem, not the top.*

Yellowing Brittlegill

Russula puellaris (Russulaceae)

SEEN in wet broadleaf and coniferous woods, also in heaths and sand dunes.

The common name describes this species well; all parts of the fungus stain ochre-yellow when old. Its cap is fragile with a grooved margin and is wine-red to purple-brown with a darker centre. The gills are deep cream, while the fragile stem is white but rapidly yellowing. Lacking any distinctive smell, the flesh is mild to taste.

cap 3–5cm wide

broad gills

fragile white stem

purple-brown to wine-red cap

soft, fragile flesh

SECTION

SPORES *Cream.*
FRUITING *Summer to autumn.*
DISTRIBUTION *Frequent to common, widespread from S. Europe to the subarctic.*
EDIBILITY *Edible.*
SIMILAR SPECIES *Variable Brittlegill (R. versicolor) also stains yellow but much paler, is larger, and has a slightly hot taste.*

Purple Brittlegill

Russula atropurpurea (Russulaceae)

This sturdy, fleshy species has a smooth, rounded then depressed cap, which varies from wine-red to blackish purple, often irregularly blotched with yellow. Its white to cream gills are narrow and crowded. Similarly coloured, the stem turns greyish or pale brown with age or when wet. The flesh is slightly hot to taste.

GROWS *in broadleaf and coniferous woodlands, under a wide variety of trees, usually on acid soils.*

crowded, white to cream gills

smooth cap, depressed at centre

purple to wine-red cap

cap 5–10cm wide

white stem

SECTION

SPORES *Cream.*
FRUITING *Summer to autumn.*
DISTRIBUTION *Common throughout, widespread from S. Europe to the subarctic.*
EDIBILITY *Edible.*
SIMILAR SPECIES R. viscida *is much larger, and the base of the stem has a yellowish colouring.*

Fragile Brittlegill

Russula fragilis (Russulaceae)

A variable species, this brittlegill's cap is violet to deep purple-red or greenish purple, often of mixed colours. The stem is white. The gills are broad, crowded, and white, usually with a minute saw-toothed margin. The fungus tastes very hot and smells of fruit.

SEEN *in broadleaf and coniferous woodlands, under a wide variety of trees, usually on wet, acid soils.*

dark cap centre

smooth, fragile cap

white gills

fragile stem

SECTION

cap 2–5cm wide

SPORES *White.*
FRUITING *Summer to autumn.*
DISTRIBUTION *Common throughout, widespread from S. Europe to the subarctic.*
EDIBILITY *Inedible.*
SIMILAR SPECIES R. knauthii, *which is larger, uniformly purple-red, and lacks the serrated gill margins.*

Humpback Brittlegill

Russula caerulea (Russulaceae)

This beautiful species is easily identified by its smooth, domed, deep blue-purple cap, which has a distinct hump at the centre. When old, the broad gills are deep ochre-orange. The fungus has a club-shaped stem which is white and fragile. Its flesh is mild to taste, although the skin of the cap is bitter.

ASSOCIATED *with pines, and is seen pushing up through needle litter.*

purple cap

cap 3–6cm wide

club-shaped white stem

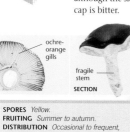

ochre-orange gills

fragile stem

SECTION

SPORES *Yellow.*
FRUITING *Summer to autumn.*
DISTRIBUTION *Occasional to frequent, widespread in N. Europe to the subarctic.*
EDIBILITY *Inedible.*
SIMILAR SPECIES *R. amethystina, which lacks the domed centre and has a vaguely zoned cap surface.*

Primrose Brittlegill

Russula sardonia (Russulaceae)

SEEN *often growing in very large numbers; associated with pine trees.*

This inedible species is striking to look at, but fiercely hot to taste. Its red-purple to violet cap is broadly domed, smooth, and shiny. The gills run a little way down the stem and are pale primrose-yellow. The flesh smells faintly of stewed fruit, and has the unusual property of turning pink if exposed to ammonia. The sturdy stem is purple to wine-red with a whitish base.

smooth, broadly domed cap

cap 3–6cm wide

crowded pale yellow gills

red-purple cap

wine-red stem

SPORES *Yellow.*
FRUITING *Summer to autumn.*
DISTRIBUTION *Occasional to frequent, widespread in N. Europe to the subarctic.*
EDIBILITY *Inedible.*
SIMILAR SPECIES *R. torulosa, which is darker, has a shorter stem, and smells strongly of stewed fruit or geraniums.*

Pig's Ear

Gomphus clavatus (Gomphaceae)

This unusual fungus is hard to spot, partly because of its relative scarcity, partly because it is well camouflaged among the leaf litter in which it grows. When young, it is a striking pinkish purple, with contrasting purplish yellow veins beneath. As it ages, it fades to brown. The cap is shaped like a spinning top, the underside has forked and wrinkled folds, rather than gills. Although this species occurs mainly in coniferous forests, it also grows in broadleaf woods, particularly beech, and its overall colour and texture, especially in mature specimens, resemble those of beech leaves on the woodland floor. The spores are yellow-ochre and the flesh is pale and edible, although gathering such a rare species is not recommended.

GROWS *singly and in troops, mainly with conifers but also with broadleaf trees, particularly beech; found in warm, basic sites, especially in mountains.*

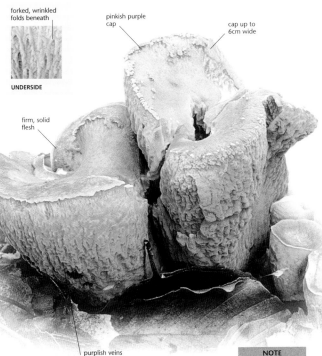

forked, wrinkled folds beneath

UNDERSIDE

pinkish purple cap

cap up to 6cm wide

firm, solid flesh

purplish veins tinged yellow

NOTE

Older brown specimens of this well camouflaged fungus are hard to spot and you will need keen eyes to detect the pinkish purple tinges underneath that fade away with age.

SPORES *Yellow-ochre.*
FRUITING *Summer.*
DISTRIBUTION *Rare to occasional, widespread throughout Europe.*
EDIBILITY *Edible.*
SIMILAR SPECIES *Blackening Chanterelle (p.128),*
Cantharellus amethysteus, and other chanterelles with similar pale lilac tones are generally more yellow with distinct stems.

Powdery Brittlegill

Russula parazurea (Russulaceae)

GROWS *with broadleaf trees, especially oak, lime, and chestnut, in grass and leaf litter.*

This species is characterized by its attractive blue- to greenish grey cap which has a powdery bloom, like a fresh grape. Initially rounded, the cap then broadly expands. The pale cream gills are crowded. The white to dull cream stem is cylindrical and firm. The flesh is crumbly and has a mild taste.

white bloom on blue-grey cap

crowded, pale cream gills

cap 3–6cm wide

broadly domed cap

white stem

SPORES *Cream.*
FRUITING *Summer to late autumn.*
DISTRIBUTION *Frequent to common; widespread in warmer areas of N. Europe.*
EDIBILITY *Edible.*
SIMILAR SPECIES *R. grisea, which is more lilac-violet without the bloom on the cap and has much tougher flesh.*

Plums and Custard

Tricholomopsis rutilans (Tricholomataceae)

A common species, Plums and Custard is very easily identifiable by its custard-yellow cap streaked with plum-coloured fibres. The cap fades to purplish brown with age and contrasts sharply with the bright yellow gills and stem. The cap margin is slightly inrolled and usually has grooves.

FOUND *commonly in small clusters on decaying conifer wood, especially pine and spruce.*

cap up to 10cm wide

plum-coloured fibres dense at centre

grooved margin

egg-yolk-yellow gills

dense yellow flesh

SECTION

SPORES *White*
FRUITING *Late summer to late autumn.*
DISTRIBUTION *Common to very common, widespread.*
EDIBILITY *Inedible.*
SIMILAR SPECIES *Prunes and Custard (T. decora), which has blackish brown fibres on the cap.*

Violet Webcap

Cortinarius violaceus (Cortinariaceae)

This magnificent, but unfortunately uncommon edible fungus is easily distinguished from all other *Cortinarius* species by its intense violet colours. All parts of the Violet Webcap are dark to blackish violet. The convex to umbonate cap has a fibrous, slightly scaly, dry surface. The cylindrical and club-shaped stem is fibrous with a web-like veil at the top that joins the stem to the cap margin and is easy to see on young specimens. Also deep violet in colour, the flesh has a smell that is reminiscent of cedar wood or leather. It turns blood-red if tested with a drop of any strong alkaline solution, such as caustic soda. The form which grows in broadleaf woods is usually larger, and has smaller spores than the one that grows in coniferous woodland. The latter is known as *C. violaceus* subspecies *hercynicus*. In all other respects, the two forms are identical.

OCCURS *usually in small groups in both broadleaf and coniferous woods, especially birch and pine.*

club-shaped stem

fibrous violet flesh

SECTION

cap 5–15cm wide

violet to dark purple cap

dry, scaly surface

SPORES *Rust-brown.*
FRUITING *Summer to late autumn.*
DISTRIBUTION *Locally common, widespread in temperate N. Europe.*
EDIBILITY *Edible.*
SIMILAR SPECIES *Bruising Webcap (p.66) which is brown with violet darkening flesh and gills. All other violet* Cortinarius *species may be paler, smoother, or more sticky, but no other species has this intense violet-back colour with a scaly dry cap and brown spores.*

Bitter Bigfoot Webcap

Cortinarius sodagnitus (Cortinariaceae)

Smooth and sticky when wet, the cap of this species is bright violet, becoming ochre when old, with bitter skin. The gills are pale lilac, then rust-brown. The stem has a rounded bulb with a distinct upper margin and is pale lilac with a cobweb veil at the top. The flesh is also pale lilac.

GROWS *singly or in small groups, sometimes in circles, with beech trees on chalky soils.*

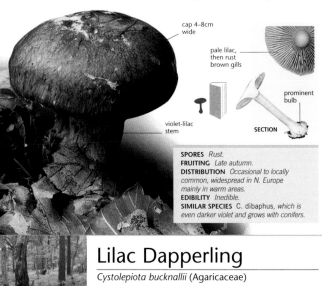

cap 4–8cm wide

pale lilac, then rust brown gills

violet-lilac stem

prominent bulb

SECTION

SPORES *Rust.*
FRUITING *Late autumn.*
DISTRIBUTION *Occasional to locally common, widespread in N. Europe mainly in warm areas.*
EDIBILITY *Inedible.*
SIMILAR SPECIES *C. dibaphus, which is even darker violet and grows with conifers.*

Lilac Dapperling

Cystolepiota bucknallii (Agaricaceae)

This species stands out, both for its beautiful colour and for its unusual smell. The cap and stem are pale lilac-violet and very powdery and scurfy to the touch. Contrasting with the cap, the narrow gills are pale lemon yellow. The Lilac Dapperling has a very strong, pungent odour of coal gas. Its colours fade to buff-yellow with age.

FOUND *singly or in small groups, in woods or along woodland edges, often in damp, disturbed sites, on alkaline soils.*

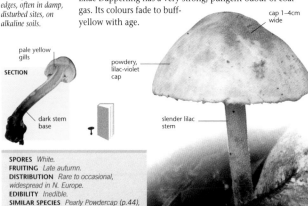

cap 1–4cm wide

pale yellow gills

SECTION

powdery, lilac-violet cap

dark stem base

slender lilac stem

SPORES *White.*
FRUITING *Late autumn.*
DISTRIBUTION *Rare to occasional, widespread in N. Europe.*
EDIBILITY *Inedible.*
SIMILAR SPECIES *Pearly Powdercap (p.44), Earthy Powdercap (p.97), and Bearded Dapperling (Lepiota sistrata) lack lilac tones.*

Violet Domecap

Calocybe ionides (Tricholomataceae)

This is a beautiful species, with both its cap and stem a deep lilac-violet. The cap is broadly domed, with radial fibres or wrinkles. Contrasting with the violet stem, the gills are crowded and pale cream. The flesh of the Violet Domecap is cream and has a strong smell and taste of new-ground meal.

OCCURS *in small groups in both broadleaf and coniferous woods, in open areas, on rich soils.*

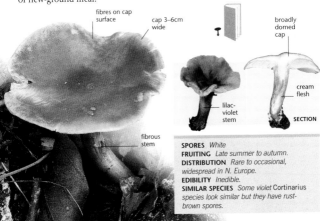

fibres on cap surface

cap 3–6cm wide

broadly domed cap

cream flesh

lilac-violet stem

SECTION

fibrous stem

SPORES *White*
FRUITING *Late summer to autumn.*
DISTRIBUTION *Rare to occasional, widespread in N. Europe.*
EDIBILITY *Inedible.*
SIMILAR SPECIES *Some violet* Cortinarius *species look similar but they have rust-brown spores.*

White Fibrecap ☠

Inocybe geophylla (Cortinariaceae)

This small, poisonous species has two main colour forms, white and pale violet; the latter is known as Lilac Fibrecap (*I. geophylla v. lilacina*). The domed, pointed cap is smooth to finely fibrous. The gills are narrowly attached to the stem and pale brown. Scurfy at the top, the slender stem is finely fibrous. The flesh has a musty smell.

GROWS *in small troops, in open areas, in both broadleaf and coniferous woods.*

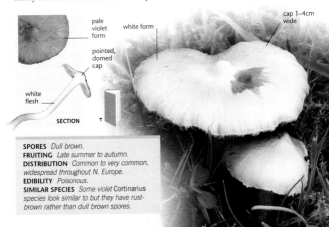

pale violet form

white form

pointed, domed cap

white flesh

SECTION

cap 1–4cm wide

SPORES *Dull brown.*
FRUITING *Late summer to autumn.*
DISTRIBUTION *Common to very common, widespread throughout N. Europe.*
EDIBILITY *Poisonous.*
SIMILAR SPECIES *Some violet* Cortinarius *species look similar to but they have rust-brown rather than dull brown spores.*

Amethyst Deceiver

Laccaria amethystina (Hydnangiaceae)

OCCURS *usually in small troops in both broadleaf and coniferous woods, especially in wet areas.*

When fresh and moist, the Amethyst Deceiver's cap, stem, and gills are an intense, almost luminous, amethyst-violet, making it one of the most attractive woodland fungi. The cap is dry to felty, with a central navel, and paler marginal stripes. As the fungus dries, it turns a drab greyish-violet and is difficult to recognise. The gills are thick and widely spaced, while the stem is slender, tough, and very fibrous. The stem usually has a white, cottony-felty base. This edible species does not have a distinctive taste or smell.

cap 2-5cm wide

thick, widely spaced gills

violet-amethyst in all parts

hollow stem centre

SECTION

slender, fibrous stem

SPORES *White.*
FRUITING *Summer to late autumn.*
DISTRIBUTION *Common to very common; widespread throughout temperate N. Europe.*
EDIBILITY *Edible.*
SIMILAR SPECIES *Bicoloured Deceiver* (L. bicolor), *which has a brownish cap with lavender-blue gills and a brownish stem with a violet base.*

NOTE

At first sight, you might think this species has violet spores, but as the gills mature they are clearly dusted with white spores.

Lactarius lilacinus

Lactarius lilacinus (Russulaceae)

The depressed cap of this fungus is a soft shade of wine- to lilac-pink. Dry and felty, it has a small umbo when fully expanded. The cream-ochre gills run slightly down the stem. When scratched, they bleed a scanty, watery milk, which is mildly hot to taste. Similarly coloured as the cap, the smooth stem has a whitish base and is often hollow when old.

GROWS *in small groups in wet, boggy alder woods, often among other woodland plants.*

pale ochre gills

cap 3-6cm wide

slightly decurrent gills

depressed cap

hollow stem

SECTION

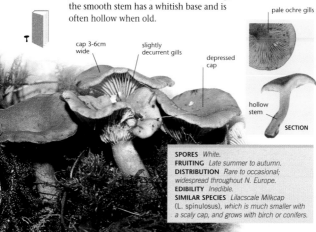

SPORES *White.*
FRUITING *Late summer to autumn.*
DISTRIBUTION *Rare to occasional; widespread throughout N. Europe.*
EDIBILITY *Inedible.*
SIMILAR SPECIES *Lilacscale Milkcap (L. spinulosus), which is much smaller with a scaly cap, and grows with birch or conifers.*

Blackedge Bonnet

Mycena pelianthina (Tricholomataceae)

The rather drab-looking cap of the Blackedge Bonnet is a dull pinkish grey to purplish brown, drying to pale grey-lilac. Its gills are broad, widely spaced, and purplish-grey with a dark, serrated, almost black edge that can be seen better through a hand lens. The slender, hollow stem is pale purple and the moist flesh has a strong smell of radish.

FOUND *in small troops on thick, damp leaf litter in beech woods, mainly on chalky soil.*

black gill margin

hollow stem

SECTION

striated margin

smooth, bell-shaped cap

cap 3-6cm wide

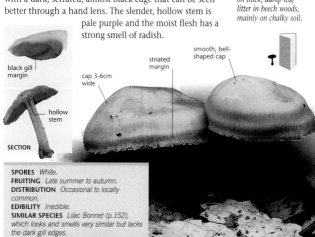

SPORES *White.*
FRUITING *Late summer to autumn.*
DISTRIBUTION *Occasional to locally common.*
EDIBILITY *Inedible.*
SIMILAR SPECIES *Lilac Bonnet (p.152), which looks and smells very similar but lacks the dark gill edges.*

Lilac Bonnet ☠

Mycena pura (Tricholomataceae)

This is an extraordinarily variable species, its bell-shaped to rounded cap ranging from lilac, violet, and pink to grey, and even yellowish white. Some of these colour forms are considered separate species or varieties. The similarly coloured gills are fairly crowded, and broadly join the stem or may be notched where they meet it. The stem itself is slender, smooth, hollow, and is coloured like the cap or paler. There is a strong smell of radish from the gills and flesh. This species is known to be poisonous.

GROWS *in small groups in leaf litter and humus in woods, parks, and open areas.*

varying cap colour

fairly crowded gills

slim, smooth stem

SECTION

bell-shaped to flattened cap

cap 2–6cm wide

lined margin

hollow stem

NOTE

Always take careful note of any smell a fungus has, and of fine details like coloured gill edges or colour changes; such characteristics will help distinguish between other similar-looking species.

SPORES White.
FRUITING Summer to late autumn.
DISTRIBUTION Frequent to very common, widespread from temperate northern countries to the Mediterranean.
EDIBILITY Poisonous.
SIMILAR SPECIES *Blackedge Bonnet (p.151) has dark gill edges; M. diosmus is dark violet-brown with a darker marginal zone, and smells strongly of tobacco.*

Woolly Milkcap

Lactarius torminosus (Russulaceae)

An extremely woolly-hairy cap makes this a striking species. Broadly depressed in the centre, the cap is pinkish white to flesh-pink with darker pink zones and an inrolled, very hairy margin. The gills are very crowded, narrow, white to pale pink, and run a little way down the stem. Rather short and hollow, the stem is smooth and paler than the cap, with brittle white flesh. When broken, the gills and flesh exude a white milk which is very hot to taste. Although often considered poisonous, this species is widely eaten in Scandinavia cooked or pickled.

ASSOCIATED *with birch trees, often in open, grassy areas, along roads and paths.*

NOTE

To distinguish between Lactarius *species, note whether the milk is thick or watery, and if it changes colour on a white handkerchief or like this species, stays the same.*

crowded, pale pink gills

hollow stem

SECTION

pale pink cap with darker pink zones

depressed cap

hairy, inrolled margin

cap 5–12cm wide

short, smooth stem

SPORES *White.*
FRUITING *Summer to late autumn.*
DISTRIBUTION *Common to very common, widespread in temperate N. Europe up to subarctic areas.*
EDIBILITY *Poisonous raw; edible when correctly cooked.*
SIMILAR SPECIES *Bearded Milkcap* (L. pubescens), *which also grows under birch, is smaller, and much paler in colour, varying from very pale pinkish yellow to almost white.*

Pink Domecap

Calocybe carnea (Tricholomataceae)

Small and edible, the Pink Domecap has a very smooth, domed cap which is pale flesh-coloured to rose-pink. Its white to pale pink gills are broad, crowded, and notched where they join the stem. The slender and smooth stem is fragile and tapers.

FOUND *growing in small troops in lawns, pastures, and meadows, also alongside roads, on rich soils.*

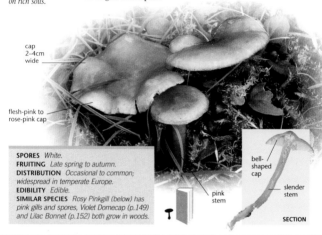

cap 2–4cm wide

flesh-pink to rose-pink cap

bell-shaped cap

slender stem

pink stem

SECTION

SPORES *White.*
FRUITING *Late spring to autumn.*
DISTRIBUTION *Occasional to common; widespread in temperate Europe.*
EDIBILITY *Edible.*
SIMILAR SPECIES *Rosy Pinkgill (below) has pink gills and spores, Violet Domecap (p.149) and Lilac Bonnet (p.152) both grow in woods.*

Rosy Pinkgill

Entoloma roseum (Entolomataceae)

The bright pink-red cap of the Rosy Pinkgill is bell-shaped with a central depression or navel. The surface of the cap is finely scaly. Broad, pale-pink gills are loosely joined to the similarly coloured stem, which is slender, smooth, and rather shiny, as though it has been polished.

GROWS *in unimproved pastures, fields, and meadows, on alkaline soils.*

slender stem

bell-shaped cap

broad gills

cap 1–3cm wide

SPORES *Pink.*
FRUITING *Summer to autumn.*
DISTRIBUTION *Very rare to rare, widespread in temperate Europe.*
EDIBILITY *Inedible.*
SIMILAR SPECIES *Pink Domecap (above), which is a similar colour but lacks the depression in the cap and has white spores.*

Pink Waxcap

Hygrocybe calyptriformis (Hygrophoraceae)

This species never grows in soils that have been treated
with fertilizers. Its presence is therefore a particularly good
indication of the quality of grasslands and meadows. Its
sharply pointed, waxy pink caps often split as they expand.
The broad and almost free, white to very pale pink gills are
fleshy and waxy. The fragile, waxy stem is pale pink above,
whitish below, and extremely smooth. Old,
grassy churchyards are an important preserve
for this beautiful and increasingly rare species.
Pink Waxcap seems to be particularly
widespread in Britain but is absent or very rare
in other parts of northern Europe.

OCCURS *in grasslands
where fertilizers have
not been applied,
meadows, parks, old
churchyards, especially
on alkaline soils.*

thick, waxy
gills

almost free
gills

SECTION

NOTE

*Many waxcaps,
including the Pink
Waxcap, are becoming
endangered through
loss of natural habitat,
as rich, frequently
fertilized meadows
are not suitable for
these fungi.*

sharply
pointed
top

cap 4–7cm
wide

pale to
bright rose-
pink cap

SPORES White.
FRUITING *Late autumn to early winter.*
DISTRIBUTION *Rare to locally frequent, widespread throughout
temperate N. Europe; particularly common in Britain.*
EDIBILITY *Inedible.*
SIMILAR SPECIES *Citrine Waxcap (p.131), which is similar in shape,
but is pale yellow-green; it is difficult to mistake the Pink Waxcap
for any other species.*

Scarlet Bonnet

Mycena adonis (Tricholomataceae)

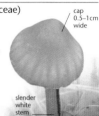

cap 0.5–1cm wide

A tiny but exquisite species, the smooth, domed to conical cap is a rich, deep rose-red to coral-pink, fading to paler pink with age. The narrow gills are broadly attached to the stem or slightly notched, and white to pale pink. Finely dusted with glistening granules, the slender stem is white to almost transparent.

slender white stem

SEEN *singly or in small groups, among mosses and on plant debris, in coniferous woods.*

white to pale pink gills

rose-red to coral-pink cap

SPORES *White.*
FRUITING *Autumn to late autumn.*
DISTRIBUTION *Occasional to frequent, widespread in temperate N. Europe.*
EDIBILITY *Inedible.*
SIMILAR SPECIES M. adonis *var.* coccinea *has a brighter scarlet cap with a red, rather than white, stem.*

The Flirt

Russula vesca (Russulaceae)

This species has two features unique among *Russulas*: its cap is the pinkish brown to flesh-pink colour of old ham, and, as it expands, the skin at the cap margin pulls back to expose the white flesh below. The cap surface is smooth or finely veined. The cream gills are brittle, the stem is white and firm, and the edible flesh tastes mild and nutty.

FOUND *under both broadleaf and coniferous trees on a wide range of soils.*

flesh-pink to reddish brown cap

cap 4–10cm wide

pale cream gills

stocky white stem

SECTION

SPORES *White.*
FRUITING *Summer to late autumn.*
DISTRIBUTION *Common and widespread in temperate N. Europe.*
EDIBILITY *Edible and tasty.*
SIMILAR SPECIES *Greasy Green Brittlegill* (R. heterophylla) *is much tougher, with flexible white gills.*

Dappled Webcap ☠

Cortinarius bolaris (Cortinariaceae)

This striking species has a rounded then flattened cap, covered in flattened red scales on a cream background. The gills are cinnamon- to rust-brown and the cylindrical stem is speckled with red scales and girdles. There is a fine, cobwebby zone at the top of the stem.
This species is poisonous.

GROWS *often in small groups in leaf litter, especially under oaks and birch, on acid soils.*

cap 4–6cm wide

reddish scales on cap

flattened cap

SECTION

cylindrical stem

yellowish orange flesh

SPORES *Brown.*
FRUITING *Summer to late autumn.*
DISTRIBUTION *Locally frequent, widespread in temperate N. Europe.*
EDIBILITY *Poisonous.*
SIMILAR SPECIES *C. rubicundulus has reddish fibres but no scales, and stains slowly red to orange.*

Goblet Waxcap

Hygrocybe cantharellus (Cantharellaceae)

A small, but dramatically coloured species, the rounded to slightly depressed cap is vivid scarlet with a dry, felty or minutely scaly surface. The widely spaced white gills are waxy and curved down the stem. The slender, silky stem is deep scarlet with a paler base. This waxcap may smell of raw potatoes.

OCCURS *in small groups in meadows, unimproved grasslands, sometimes in woods and sphagnum bogs.*

cap 0.5–3cm wide

scarlet cap

rounded then flattened cap

widely spaced white gills

paler flesh at stem base

SECTION

SPORES *White.*
FRUITING *Summer to late autumn.*
DISTRIBUTION *Locally frequent, widespread.*
EDIBILITY *Inedible.*
SIMILAR SPECIES *H. turunda is paler orange, with fine, dark blackish brown scales at the centre of the cap.*

Fly Agaric

Amanita muscaria (Amanitaceae)

The striking red cap with white spots makes this species the classic "toadstool" of children's storybooks. Depending on age and weathering, the colour of the fungus varies, tending to wash out with rain. The cap – domed when young, flattened later – can vary in colour from vivid red to orange or even a very pale orange-yellow. Its margin is grooved and the surface covered in wart-like white veil scales which wash off in the rain. The gills, stem, and drooping stem ring are all white; the stem has a scaly surface and a volval swelling at the base. Extremely toxic, the Fly Agaric can cause severe symptoms if eaten.

red to orange-red cap

cap up to 15cm wide

wart-like cap scales

scaly stem base

crowded gills

white gills free from stem

volval swelling at stem base

SECTION

NOTE

Collect the fungus carefully so that the volval swelling on the stem base is visible. Without it, rain-washed specimens, which do not have any white spots or ring, could be mistaken for red species of Russula.

SPORES Off-white.
FRUITING Summer to late autumn.
DISTRIBUTION Locally very common and widespread.
EDIBILITY Highly poisonous.
SIMILAR SPECIES Caesar's Amanita (p.114), which has a golden-orange cap and is edible; Orange Grisette (p.115), which is more golden orange and without a ring; red species of Russula, which have no ring or volva.

Scurfy Brittlegill

Russula melzeri (Russulaceae)

This is an unusually small species of *Russula*, but with distinctive features. Its rounded, deep scarlet cap is finely cracked and granular. As the common name suggests, its widely spaced, pale cream to ochre gills are brittle. The fungus has a soft, fragile white stem which is cylindrical. The edible flesh is mild to taste and lacks a distinctive smell.

GROWS *in small groups and circles under sweet chestnuts or beech, often close to the trunk in deep shade.*

cap 2–3cm wide

scarlet cap

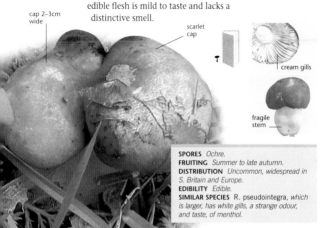

cream gills

fragile stem

SPORES *Ochre.*
FRUITING *Summer to late autumn.*
DISTRIBUTION *Uncommon, widespread in S. Britain and Europe.*
EDIBILITY *Edible.*
SIMILAR SPECIES R. pseudointegra, *which is larger, has white gills, a strange odour, and taste, of menthol.*

Bloody Brittlegill

Russula sanguinea (Russulaceae)

This is perhaps the commonest all-red species of *Russula*. Its cap is rounded at first, then expands and becomes depressed. Initially bright crimson to rose-red, the cap soon becomes paler. This species has a red-flushed stem which stains yellow with age. Its white flesh has a fruity odour.

APPEARS *in groups and circles under pines, occasionally larch, on sandy soils.*

scarlet cap

cap 5–10cm wide

arched cream gills

white flesh

red-flushed stem

SECTION

SPORES *Ochre.*
FRUITING *Summer to late autumn.*
DISTRIBUTION *Common and widespread throughout temperate N. Europe.*
EDIBILITY *Inedible.*
SIMILAR SPECIES Crab Brittlegill (p.163), *which is much darker and more purple-red, with the odour of old shellfish.*

The Sickener

Russula emetica (Russulaceae)

APPEARS usually in wet, mossy, or even boggy areas in conifer woods, singly but often in small troops.

This striking and common species has a bright scarlet-red cap contrasting with pure white stem and pale gills. The stem is often tall and cylindrical while the cap is smooth, domed to flattened, and depressed when old. White to pale cream in colour, the gills are medium-spaced. The mildly poisonous, crumbly white flesh tastes extremely hot but has no particular smell and does not stain. One of a number of bright red species, this poisonous mushroom stands apart by its pure red cap without any trace of purple or black; the skin of the cap also peels off almost completely.

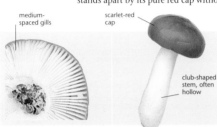

medium-spaced gills

scarlet-red cap

club-shaped stem, often hollow

cap up to 10cm wide

smooth, glossy surface

domed to flattened cap

slightly furrowed margin

SPORES White.
FRUITING Summer to late autumn.
DISTRIBUTION Common throughout, widespread in N. temperate regions.
EDIBILITY Poisonous.
SIMILAR SPECIES R. grisescens, which looks extremely similar but the stem stains strongly greyish; it grows in sphagnum bogs.
R. mairei, which looks and tastes very similar but grows with beech.

NOTE

There are many species with red caps. However, The Sickener is among a few that have unique features, which make them easily identifiable.

Scarlet Waxcap

Hygrocybe coccinea (Hygrophoraceae)

The greasy scarlet cap, stem, and gills of this species make it one of the most brightly coloured grassland fungi. It is distinguished from other red waxcaps by the minute lumps on its umbonate cap. The red gills have a yellowish edge, but may sometimes be entirely yellow. Occasionally paler, the stem is smooth, dry, and compressed with a groove along its length.

FOUND *singly but often in scattered groups in grassland not treated chemically, including pastures, lawns, and churchyards.*

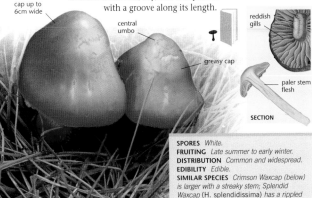

cap up to 6cm wide

central umbo

greasy cap

reddish gills

paler stem flesh

SECTION

SPORES *White.*
FRUITING *Late summer to early winter.*
DISTRIBUTION *Common and widespread.*
EDIBILITY *Edible.*
SIMILAR SPECIES *Crimson Waxcap (below) is larger with a streaky stem; Splendid Waxcap (H. splendidissima) has a rippled stem; H. marchii is more orange.*

Crimson Waxcap

Hygrocybe punicea (Hygrophoraceae)

The spectacular greasy to sticky, blood-red cap of this large waxcap fades with age. It has a central umbo which can be a very dark red and a margin which is often yellow and may split. The gills are dark red with a yellow edge, while the stem is yellow with coarse orange-red fibres.

SEEN *singly or scattered mainly in unimproved pastures; also in mown, mossy lawns and churchyards.*

dark central umbo

paler yellow margin

cap up to 15cm wide

orange-red fibres on yellow stem

SPORES *White.*
FRUITING *Late summer to early winter.*
DISTRIBUTION *Very rare to rare, but widespread.*
EDIBILITY *Edible.*
SIMILAR SPECIES *Scarlet Waxcap (above) and Splendid Waxcap (H. splendidissima); both lack stem fibres and dark red colour.*

red gills

yellow to white base

SECTION

Blackening Waxcap 💀

Hygrocybe conica (Hygrophoraceae)

One of the most common waxcaps, this species occurs in a variable range of colours, combining yellow, orange, tomato-red, and even olive-green tones with grey and black. The one constant feature which enables easy recognition of this poisonous species is the slow blackening of the entire fruitbody with age and after collection. The sticky cap of the fungus is conical and the greasy stem is finely fibrous. Although a similar colour to the cap, the gills tend to be more yellowish. Some of the more distinctive forms have been classified as separate species by certain scientists.

GROWS *singly and in small groups in grasslands, including lawns, parks, and churchyards, and occasionally in woods.*

NOTE

Carefully check waxcap specimens a while after collection, for signs of blackening. This process of dramatic colour change may take several hours, until the entire fungus is pitch black as if burnt.

sticky, fibrous cap

gills narrowly attached to stem

fruitbody turns black

finely fibrous stem

SECTION

conical cap

cap up to 5cm wide

cap colour variable

SPORES White.
FRUITING Late summer to early winter.
DISTRIBUTION Occasional to very common, widespread.
EDIBILITY Poisonous.
SIMILAR SPECIES Date Waxcap (p.84), which is very rare and has a date-brown cap and pure yellow gills; Dune Waxcap (H. conicoides), which occurs in sand dunes; Persistent Waxcap (H. persistens), which is also conical, predominantly yellow, and does not blacken.

NOTE

The Blackening Waxcap is one of a small number of Hygrocybe species which can grow in woodlands as well as open fields and dunes.

Crab Brittlegill

Russula xerampelina (Russulaceae)

FOUND *singly or in groups with conifers, especially pine and fir.*

This is one of several closely related *Russula* species, all smelling of crabmeat, which can only be separated microscopically or by habitat. Slightly sticky and often depressed, the cap of Crab Brittlegill is dark crimson-red, almost black in the centre. The gills are cream and the white stem is flushed rose-red with browning spots. Mild to taste, the white edible flesh gradually becomes brown.

depressed cap centre

cap up to 15cm wide

brown spots on stem

white flesh

SECTION

SPORES *Ochre.*
FRUITING *Summer to autumn.*
DISTRIBUTION *Very common to common, widespread.*
EDIBILITY *Edible and tasty.*
SIMILAR SPECIES *Some other* Russula *species, which have slightly varying colours but can be reliably separated microscopically.*

Blackening Brittlegill

Russula nigricans (Russulaceae)

OCCURS *mainly with broadleaf trees, sometimes with conifers, singly or in troops on the ground.*

When young and undamaged, this species has a mottled off-white to sooty brown cap with a depressed centre. However, the fruitbody gradually turns black with age. If cut or damaged, it slowly becomes a dull cherry-red before turning grey then black. The flesh is mild but very firm. The yellowish gills are widely spaced and unequal in length.

cap up to 20cm wide

depressed centre

brittle gills

off-white flesh

SECTION

incurved cap margin

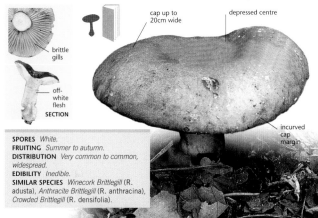

SPORES *White.*
FRUITING *Summer to autumn.*
DISTRIBUTION *Very common to common, widespread.*
EDIBILITY *Inedible.*
SIMILAR SPECIES *Winecork Brittlegill (R. adusta), Anthracite Brittlegill (R. anthracina), Crowded Brittlegill (R. densifolia).*

Grey-veiled Amanita

Amanita porphyria (Amanitaceae)

GROWS *singly or in groups on the ground, in woodland on acid soil, especially with pine, spruce, and birch.*

This innocuous fungus could be mistaken for the poisonous Death Cap (p.133) by the inexperienced but, like the False Death Cap (p.123), it smells of raw potato. It has a convex to flattened, greyish purple cap which is streaky and occasionally covered with greyish veil patches. The gills are white and the stem is greyish or yellowish white. Often missing, the stem ring is also greyish. The volval swelling at the stem base is bulb-like with a rim.

cap up to 9cm wide

streaky, fibrous, purple-grey cap

drooping, greyish stem ring

white gills free from stem

swollen stem base

SECTION

SECTION

SPORES White.
FRUITING Summer to autumn.
DISTRIBUTION Locally common and widespread.
EDIBILITY Inedible.
SIMILAR SPECIES Panthercap (p.71) has white veil patches and no smell; Death Cap (p.133) is greenish and smells sickly sweet.

Beech Milkcap

Lactarius blennius (Russulaceae)

FOUND *singly or in groups on the ground; associated with beech.*

This milkcap has a depressed and very sticky cap which is a combination of greyish brown, olive, and dark reddish brown. It has indistinct darker zones and more conspicuous dark spots at the cap margin. The gills are white becoming pale cream, and the milk is white drying pale olive-grey on the gills. Often hollow, the stem is smooth and sticky.

cap up to 9cm wide

white to cream gills

grey acrid flesh

slightly funnel-shaped cap

SECTION

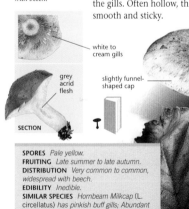

SPORES Pale yellow.
FRUITING Late summer to late autumn.
DISTRIBUTION Very common to common, widespread with beech.
EDIBILITY Inedible.
SIMILAR SPECIES Hornbeam Milkcap (L. circellatus) has pinkish buff gills; Abundant Milkcap (L. fluens) has a white cap margin.

Ashen Chanterelle

Cantharellus cinereus (Cantharellaceae)

This grey-brown to blackish brown fungus is often radially wrinkled or grooved, and has a wavy or lobed margin. Like all chanterelles, it does not have proper gills but blunt, ashen to bluish grey veins or wrinkles on the underside, which are branching and run part-way down the stem. The hollow stem is grey to black; the edible flesh is thin, greyish, and smells fruity.

SEEN *singly or in clustered groups on the ground among moss; mainly with beech, though occasionally with spruce.*

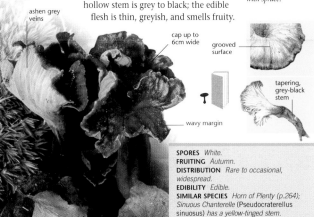

ashen grey veins

cap up to 6cm wide

grooved surface

tapering, grey-black stem

wavy margin

SPORES *White.*
FRUITING *Autumn.*
DISTRIBUTION *Rare to occasional, widespread.*
EDIBILITY *Edible.*
SIMILAR SPECIES *Horn of Plenty (p.264); Sinuous Chanterelle (Pseudocraterellus sinuosus) has a yellow-tinged stem.*

Trumpet Chanterelle

Cantharellus tubaeformis (Cantharellaceae)

Funnel- to trumpet-shaped, this popular edible fungus is greyish ochre to brown-grey with yellow tones. The cap has an irregular margin and becomes more wrinkled with age; its underside has thick, branched veins or wrinkles, which are yellow with greenish or grey tints. The stem is also grey-yellow, hollow, and often compressed, with a groove along its length. The flesh is thin and pale.

OCCURS *most often in clusters, sometimes singly, on the ground among mosses in woods of all kinds.*

deep central dip

cap up to 6cm wide

uneven cap margin

yellow, wrinkled stem

branched, ridge-like veins

SPORES *Cream to pale yellow.*
FRUITING *Autumn to late winter.*
DISTRIBUTION *Widespread; especially common in the north.*
EDIBILITY *Edible.*
SIMILAR SPECIES *False Chanterelle (p.129), and Clitocybe and Cortinarius species, some of which are toxic, but have gills, not veins.*

Club Foot

Clitocybe clavipes (Tricholomataceae)

SEEN *singly or in groups on the ground, in woods; also grassy glades or along paths.*

Grey-brown with a broad central umbo, the cap of the Club Foot has a slightly velvety and greasy texture and is often spongy in the centre. The crowded yellow-cream gills run down the stem. Swelling considerably at the base, the stem has pale flesh and a sweetish smell.

cap up to 8cm wide

gills run down stem

crowded gills

grey-brown stem

SECTION

stem wider at base

SPORES *White.*
FRUITING *Late summer to late autumn.*
DISTRIBUTION *Rare and widespread.*
EDIBILITY *Edible, but best avoided as it can cause stomach upsets.*
SIMILAR SPECIES *Various grey* Clitocybe *species including the edible Clouded Funnel (p.171).*

Crazed Cap ☠

Dermoloma cuneifolium (Tricholomataceae)

APPEARS *singly or in small groups, on unimproved grassland such as meadows, mossy lawns, and cemeteries.*

The domed, light to dark grey cap of this fungus sometimes has an attractive bloom when young, like that on grapes. Later, it becomes "crazed" or cracked and wrinkled. The whitish to pale grey gills are fairly widely spaced and thick and the similarly coloured stem is fibrous, sometimes tapered and hollow with age. It also has a powdery surface bloom. The poisonous flesh has a distinctive smell and taste of flour.

cracked, mature cap

cap up to 5cm wide

pale, fibrous stem

SPORES *White.*
FRUITING *Autumn to early winter.*
DISTRIBUTION *Rare to occasional, widespread throughout.*
EDIBILITY *Poisonous.*
SIMILAR SPECIES Porpoloma metapodium, *which has a mealy smell but with reddening then blackening flesh.*

Tiger Knight ☠

Tricholoma pardinum (Tricholomataceae)

The very poisonous Tiger Knight has a patterned cap with grey-black scales arranged in concentric circles on a white background, with a hint of yellow. The cap is dry and umbonate with an inrolled margin. The white gills have a greenish tinge, and the grainy white flesh has a strong smell of meal and does not stain when cut. Club-shaped towards the base, the white stem sometimes has pale brown fibres. This is not an easy species to identify as it shares several features in common with other *Tricholoma* species, such as its mealy smell and dry, scaly-fibrous grey cap.

FOUND *singly or in small groups, mainly with broadleaf trees especially beech but also conifers, on alkaline soil.*

white gills with green or yellow tinge

NOTE

As this species causes severe poisoning and is frequently eaten in error, extreme caution should be taken when identifying any scaly grey Tricholoma *species. If in doubt, do not eat any similar-looking fungus.*

white flesh

SECTION

grey-black scales

cap up to 12cm wide

inrolled margin

stout, club-shaped stem

SPORES White.
FRUITING Late summer to autumn.
DISTRIBUTION Rare to occasional, widespread.
EDIBILITY Highly poisonous.
SIMILAR SPECIES Edible Tricholoma species with scaly greyish black caps such as Dark Scaled Knight (T. atrosquamosum), which has a peppery to fruity smell like geraniums, and Reddening Knight (T. orirubens), which stains slowly pinkish.

Willow Shield

Pluteus salicinus (Pluteaceae)

The grey cap of this fungus, which is dry and fibrous, has a distinctive willowy green tinge. Its centre may have a few tiny, scattered blackish scales. The gills are flesh-pink, while the stem is white and smooth, tinged with green especially at the base, which can be swollen. The flesh is white and smells slightly of radish.

GROWS *singly or in small groups on decaying, standing or fallen wood of trees and conifers.*

white gills mature to pink

free gills

swollen base

SECTION

dark scales at cap centre

cap up to 8cm wide

SPORES *Reddish ochre.*
FRUITING *Summer to autumn.*
DISTRIBUTION *Occasional to common, widespread.*
EDIBILITY *Inedible.*
SIMILAR SPECIES *Ghost Shield (P. pellitus), which is white, lacking green tones; Volvariella caesiotincta has a basal volva.*

Soapy Knight

Tricholoma saponaceum (Tricholomataceae)

This rather variable species has a wide combination of possible cap colours, including greenish brown to creamy grey, but it always smells strongly of soap. Its widely spaced gills are cream, with yellow to grey tones. The scaly cap is broadly umbonate with an inrolled margin that is sometimes wavy. Paler in colour, the smooth or scaly stem is often pinkish at the base.

FOUND *in small troops or singly on the ground with both broadleaf trees and conifers.*

cap up to 10cm wide

greasy cap

off-white flesh

wavy, inrolled margin

tapering stem

SECTION

SPORES *White.*
FRUITING *Summer to autumn.*
DISTRIBUTION *Common and widespread.*
EDIBILITY *Inedible.*
SIMILAR SPECIES *Deceiving Knight (p.134) and Yellow-grey Knight (T. portentosum) can both be greenish grey or brown but do not have the soapy smell.*

Grisette

Amanita vaginata (Amanitaceae)

This *Amanita* should only be eaten cooked; make absolutely certain it is not one of the deadly species. Sticky when damp, the cap has a distinctly lined margin and hardly any veil patches. It is oval when young, gradually becoming flat, often retaining its central bump. The gills are white with a frosted edge; the stem has no ring but is tinged with pale grey zig-zag markings and has a baggy grey volva.

OCCURS *singly or in small numbers on the ground in woods, especially with broadleaf trees.*

emerging
fruitbody

greyish
brown cap

central
umbo

cap
up to
15cm
wide

thick, cup-like
volva

faint
markings
on stem

SPORES *White.*
FRUITING *Summer to autumn.*
DISTRIBUTION *Common and widespread.*
EDIBILITY *Edible when cooked.*
SIMILAR SPECIES *Tawny Grisette (p.100) is tawny brown; A. mairei, lacks an umbo and is inedible; A. pantherina, is poisonous, has a ring and distinct white veil patches.*

Wood Pinkgill

Entoloma rhodopolium (Entolomataceae)

This poisonous species changes colour on drying. The cap progresses from creamy yellow to grey to greyish brown. It has a broad central umbo and a wavy margin with grooves. Grey at first, the gills later become pink, while the slender stem is silvery grey. The Wood Pinkgill can be odourless or have a bleach-like nitrous smell.

SEEN *singly, or in small numbers, in broadleaf woods, in rich litter; often with beech.*

cap up to
12cm wide

creamy to
greyish brown
cap

notched
gills

lined, wavy
margin

pale grey
to brown
flesh

SECTION

SPORES *Pink.*
FRUITING *Autumn.*
DISTRIBUTION *Common and widespread.*
EDIBILITY *Poisonous.*
SIMILAR SPECIES *Various large autumn-fruiting Entoloma species including Livid Pinkgill (E. sinuatum), which is more robust, paler, with yellow gills, and smells of meal.*

Almond Woodwax

Hygrophorus agathosmus (Hygrophoraceae)

A strong smell of bitter almonds characterizes the Almond Woodwax. Its rounded grey cap has a broad umbo and strongly inrolled edge, and may be sticky when moist. The gills are white, moderately spaced, and run down the stem slightly. The white stem is scurfy and is sometimes swollen at the base.

GROWS *singly and in troops among conifers, especially spruce.*

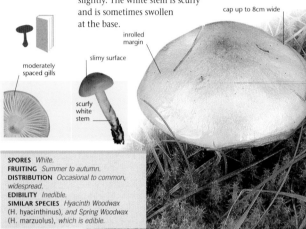

cap up to 8cm wide

inrolled margin

slimy surface

moderately spaced gills

scurfy white stem

SPORES *White.*
FRUITING *Summer to autumn.*
DISTRIBUTION *Occasional to common, widespread.*
EDIBILITY *Inedible.*
SIMILAR SPECIES *Hyacinth Woodwax (H. hyacinthinus), and Spring Woodwax (H. marzuolus), which is edible.*

Ashen Knight

Tricholoma virgatum (Tricholomataceae)

This species tends to remain conical for some time, and even when expanded, is umbonate. The cap has a distinctive silky grey appearance, with a dry, fibrous texture, and often has a splitting margin. The gills are greyish white with a plain edge, and the fibrous stem is white. The flesh is hot and burning to taste.

FOUND *in small numbers or singly usually below broadleaf trees or sometimes conifers, in the mountains.*

dry, silky surface

white fibres on cap

greyish white gills

cap up to 8cm wide

conical cap

white stem

SECTION

SPORES *White.*
FRUITING *Late summer to late autumn.*
DISTRIBUTION *Common and widespread.*
EDIBILITY *Inedible.*
SIMILAR SPECIES *T. sciodes, which has pinkish gills with a dark or flecked edge; Reddening Knight (T. orirubens), the flesh of which turns pinkish with age.*

Clouded Funnel

Clitocybe nebularis (Tricholomataceae)

A rather variable, mid-grey species, the Clouded Funnel has a felty grey cap, domed when young, later becoming largely flattened to deeply funnel-shaped, with a wavy margin. The margin is often paler and inrolled, and the entire cap surface becomes increasingly dusted with a white bloom. The cap is blue-grey to brown-grey or even yellowish, and may be slightly sticky. Creamy yellow to greyish gills run part way down the club-shaped stem, which has a strong, distinctive, and slightly unpleasant smell. The Clouded Funnel causes severe gastric upsets in some people, possibly as an allergic reaction, although many find it a tasty edible species. However, it is best eaten only when young.

APPEARS *in troops and rings – often in large numbers late in the year – or occasionally singly, in leaf litter in woods of all types.*

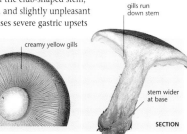

gills run down stem

creamy yellow gills

stem wider at base

SECTION

cap up to 25cm wide

domed blue-grey cap

whitish dust on cap surface

paler margin

NOTE

In older specimens, a whitish bloom may develop on the cap. There is also a tendency for the already pungent smell to become stronger and more unpleasant as the fruitbody ages.

SPORES Cream.
FRUITING Late summer to winter.
DISTRIBUTION Very common and widespread, especially in N. regions.
EDIBILITY Edible when young but may cause gastric upset.
SIMILAR SPECIES Livid Pinkgill (p.22), which is poisonous, has a similar wavy, inrolled grey cap, but the gills become pinkish and the spores are pink.

Fiery Milkcap

Lactarius pyrogalus (Russulaceae)

The ferociously hot tasting milk of this species gives rise to its common name. The milk, which dries to pale green grey, and its association with hazel, make the Fiery Milkcap relatively easy to identify. Its sticky cap is pinkish buff to smoke-grey, with indistinct zones. The widely spaced gills are yellow-buff and its tapering stem is pale grey and often hollow.

GROWS singly or in small numbers on the ground, always associated with hazel.

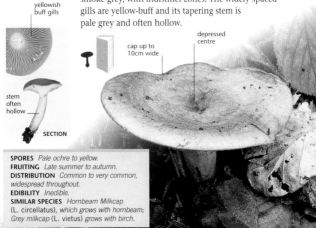

yellowish buff gills

stem often hollow

SECTION

cap up to 10cm wide

depressed centre

SPORES *Pale ochre to yellow.*
FRUITING *Late summer to autumn.*
DISTRIBUTION *Common to very common, widespread throughout.*
EDIBILITY *Inedible.*
SIMILAR SPECIES *Hornbeam Milkcap (L. circellatus), which grows with hornbeam; Grey milkcap (L. vietus) grows with birch.*

Stubble Rosegill

Volvariella gloiocephala (Pluteaceae)

One of the larger Rosegills, this species has a sticky, conical cap that is bluish grey when young but flattened and creamy-brown when old. The gills are free from the stem and the cap can be easily removed. The stem has a white to pale grey volva – apart from *Amanita* this is the only genus to have one. This fungus can smell radishy and tastes of cucumber.

GROWS, in nutrient-rich places such as compost heaps, gardens, and arable fields.

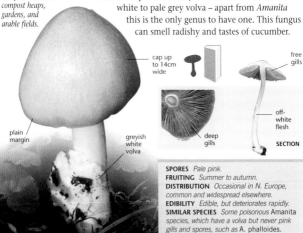

cap up to 14cm wide

free gills

off-white flesh

SECTION

plain margin

greyish white volva

deep gills

SPORES *Pale pink.*
FRUITING *Summer to autumn.*
DISTRIBUTION *Occasional in N. Europe, common and widespread elsewhere.*
EDIBILITY *Edible, but deteriorates rapidly.*
SIMILAR SPECIES *Some poisonous* Amanita *species, which have a volva but never pink gills and spores, such as* A. phalloides.

The Humpback

Cantharellula umbonata (Tricholomataceae)

This is a small, grey, umbonate to funnel-shaped species with a persistent central umbo. Incurved and radially wrinkled, the cap margin sometimes has grey-brown, olive, or violet tones. The white to cream gills are forked and run strongly down the stem; they discolour reddish when bruised. The slender, velvety stem is often paler than the cap. The thin flesh is flushed pink.

FOUND *in small groups in acid soils, usually amongst moss in coniferous woods, gravel, and moorland sites with heather.*

cap up to 5cm wide

raised centre

funnel-shaped cap

slender stem

SPORES *White.*
FRUITING *Autumn.*
DISTRIBUTION *Locally common, widespread throughout.*
EDIBILITY *Inedible.*
SIMILAR SPECIES *The Goblet (Pseudoclitocybe cyathiformis) has grey, unforked gills which do not stain red.*

Aromatic Strangler

Squamanita odorata (Tricholomataceae)

One of an unusual group of fungi that parasitizes others, this species smells like pear drops. The cap has dark grey scales on a light grey base, often with a violet tint. The white gills become dingy grey, and the white stem is covered in grey fibres. At the base is a swollen bulb with a rim, above which are girdles of erect grey scales.

OCCURS *in woods, parks, gardens, and alongside paths, especially on sandy soil; several fruitbodies arise from one base.*

cap up to 3cm wide

white gills

swollen basal bulb

SPORES *White to pink.*
FRUITING *Autumn.*
DISTRIBUTION *Extremely rare but widespread throughout.*
EDIBILITY *Inedible.*
SIMILAR SPECIES *Strathy Strangler (S. pearsonii) and Powdered Strangler (S. paradoxa), which lack any smell.*

Shield Pinkgill

Entoloma clypeatum (Entolomataceae)

This stout, spring species has a sticky grey cap changing to dark brown as it dries, and developing a streaky, fissured, or even scaly texture. Shield Pinkgill has a shield-like cap, wavy at the margin with a central umbo. Its closely notched gills are pale grey, ageing to pink, while the stem is whitish grey and the flesh smells of meal.

FOUND *singly or in small groups in grass or leaf litter, in woods, coppices, and wood edges, with blackthorn and hawthorn.*

greyish to pink gills

shield-shaped cap

grey to dark brown cap

cap up to 10 cm wide

SPORES *Pink.*
FRUITING *Spring.*
DISTRIBUTION *Occasional to common, widespread.*
EDIBILITY *Inedible.*
SIMILAR SPECIES *St. George's Mushroom (p.23), which has white gills; E. aprile which is slender and grows mainly with elm.*

Whitelaced Shank

Megacollybia platyphylla (Tricholomataceae)

This very common grey to brown species has distinctive, white, bootlace-like rhizomorphs emerging from its stem base. The flattened, umbonate cap with radiating fibres, is sometimes wrinkled with a thin, splitting margin. The pale brown stem has longitudinal fibres and often becomes hollow. The white gills are widely spaced.

GROWS *singly or in small groups in broadleaf woods on fallen debris and trunks.*

greyish brown cap

radiating fibres on cap

convex cap

hollow stem

SECTION

cap up to 15cm wide

white fibres on stem

SPORES *Pale cream.*
FRUITING *Summer to autumn.*
DISTRIBUTION *Common to very common, widespread.*
EDIBILITY *Inedible.*
SIMILAR SPECIES *Rooting Shank (p.56), which has a slender, rooting stem; Deer Shield (p.72), which has pink gills.*

Common Inkcap

Coprinus atramentarius (Coprinaceae)

This is a potentially edible species except when mixed with alcohol in any form in the system, including alcohol in cosmetic preparations. This species reacts with alcohol even when it enters the bloodstream days after eating the fungus, to cause palpitations and sickness. The Common Inkcap has an egg-shaped, grey to grey-brown cap, with a red-brown centre and a smooth surface that is ridged. The cap expands slightly and gradually becomes inky black, liquifying from the margin, which can be lobed. Its stem is silvery white with a ring-zone and a hollow centre. At the stem base, there are reddish brown fibres. The free and crowded gills are grey to black and edged with white.

FOUND in clusters in humus-rich places, often on buried wood of broadleaf trees, in woods, parks, and gardens.

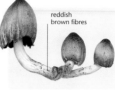

reddish brown fibres

free gills

hollow white stem

SECTION

grey to grey-brown cap

cap up to 7cm wide

SPORES *Black.*
FRUITING *Spring to autumn.*
DISTRIBUTION *Common and widespread in N. temperate regions.*
EDIBILITY *Potentially poisonous; edible with extreme caution.*
SIMILAR SPECIES *C. acuminatus, which has a pointed central umbo on the cap; C. alopecia, which is found in less dense clusters and has warty spores; C. micaceus, which has a granular surface.*

NOTE

If in doubt about the presence of alcohol in the system for up to 48 hours before or after anticipated consumption, it is best to avoid this species, which many fungi guides list as poisonous.

Magpie Inkcap ☠

Coprinus picaceus (Coprinaceae)

GROWS *singly, or in small numbers, in humus-rich sites with leaf litter or chippings, in broadleaf woods, particularly beech.*

This very distinctive inkcap is easy to recognize with its magpie-like black-and-white markings. The long bell-shaped cap is brown-black with an attractive scattering of white veil patches over its surface. These break up, becoming less frequent at the margin, although the centre often remains white. The young gills are white but rapidly become black as the whole cap liquefies into an ink of spores.

white gills turn black

firm white stem

SECTION

black cap with whitish veil patches

cap up to 6cm wide

SPORES *Black.*
FRUITING *Autumn.*
DISTRIBUTION *Occasional to common, widespread.*
EDIBILITY *Poisonous.*
SIMILAR SPECIES *Shaggy Inkcap (p.39), which has a taller cap covered with recurved white scales; superficially like young Amanita.*

Milking Bonnet

Mycena galopus (Tricholomataceae)

The caps of Milking Bonnets occur in a range of colours from white *(M. galopus v. candida)*, to black *(M. galopus v. nigra)*. The grey form has a darker cap centre with a white stem top; the stem of the Black Milking Bonnet is fully black, while the White Milking Bonnet is pale throughout. They all exude a white, milk-like juice when damaged, and smell of radish.

SEEN *singly or in groups in humus-rich sites on litter in broadleaf and conifer woods.*

conical cap with striped edge

cap up to 2cm wide

white liquid from broken stem

thicker, base

fragile dark stem

pale gills

SPORES *Pale cream.*
FRUITING *Late summer to autumn.*
DISTRIBUTION *Common to very common, widespread.*
EDIBILITY *Inedible.*
SIMILAR SPECIES *Saffrondrop Bonnet (p.112) and Bleeding Bonnet (M. sanguinolenta) have dark red or orange latex.*

Clustered Domecap

Lyophyllum decastes (Tricholomataceae)

The Clustered Domecap is probably a group of several closely related species which are difficult to separate. The common feature is its clustering habit, often with fused stem bases. Ochre-beige to grey-brown, the cap has a pale margin and flattens with an umbo. The cuticle is peelable, the flesh elastic, and the gills and stem are pale grey.

FOUND *in clusters on woodland fringes in litter, grass, or bare ground along paths, woodland rides, parks, and gardens.*

pale grey gills

margin often pale

SECTION

domed umbo

cap up to 10cm wide

SPORES *White.*
FRUITING *Autumn to late autumn.*
DISTRIBUTION *Common and widespread.*
EDIBILITY *Edible.*
SIMILAR SPECIES L. fumosum, *which is green-brown;* L. loricatum, *which has a tough, cartilage-like cap cuticle that snaps when broken.*

Grey Knight

Tricholoma terreum (Tricholomataceae)

This conifer-loving species has a dry, grey to dark grey cap with very fibrous texture, giving it an almost silky white sheen. The cap is distinctly conical with a central umbo, and has a smooth margin. The stem is whitish grey; the gills are pale grey and the flesh is pale and mild tasting.

OCCURS *singly but more commonly in small groups among conifers, on rich soils.*

cap up to 7cm wide

silky, fibrous grey cap

notched gills

pale flesh

SECTION

SPORES *White.*
FRUITING *Autumn.*
DISTRIBUTION *Common with conifers and widespread.*
EDIBILITY *Edible.*
SIMILAR SPECIES T. gausapatum, *which has a cobwebby ring-zone;* T. myomyces, *which is paler.*

Ugly Milkcap

Lactarius turpis (Russulaceae)

GROWS *singly, in troops or rings, with birch and spruce in woods, parks, or gardens.*

This poisonous species has a very dirty looking olive-green almost blackish brown cap, with a sticky centre and a slightly hairy margin. The stem is a similar colour, smooth, and sometimes hollow. By contrast, the gills are pale cream, with a white acrid milk which dries greenish brown.

crowded cream to ochre gills

central dip

cap up to 15cm wide

stem paler at top

SPORES Off-white.
FRUITING Summer to late autumn.
DISTRIBUTION Common to very common and widespread.
EDIBILITY Poisonous.
SIMILAR SPECIES Beech Milkcap (p.164) and Abundant Milkcap (L. fluens) have no olive tones, and are paler with distinct cap zones.

Camembert Brittlegill

Russula amoenolens (Russulaceae)

FOUND *singly or in small numbers especially with oak trees.*

Camembert Brittlegill is one of a group of very similar-looking brittlegills, best separated by their chemical and microscopic features. The dark sepia cap usually has a central dip and is sticky. The gills are often rust spotted and the flesh has an acrid taste and sour, slightly fishy smell like ripe camembert cheese. The stem is pale at the top and more russet below.

cap up to 6cm wide

white to cream gills

grooved, slightly warty margin

stem darkest toward base

SPORES Cream to pale ochre.
FRUITING Summer to autumn.
DISTRIBUTION Occasional to common, widespread.
EDIBILITY Inedible.
SIMILAR SPECIES R. pseudoaffinis has minute veil flakes when young; Sepia Brittlegill (R. sororia) has a more spermatic smell.

Frosty Webcap

Cortinarius hemitrichus (Cortinariaceae)

This distinctive *Cortinarius* has a delicate umbonate to sharply pointed grey-brown cap flecked with white veil fragments. The stem, by contrast, is silvery white becoming brownish with zoned banding below an indistinct ring-zone. When young, the upper stem may have faint lilac tints. The gills are violet-grey when young and brown with age. The flesh is thin and odourless.

FOUND *on the ground in leaf litter, either singly or in small groups, especially with birch and sometimes with conifers.*

cap up to 4cm wide

gills brown with age

ochre to dark brown flesh

SECTION

brown stem girdled with white bands

SPORES *Rust brown.*
FRUITING *Summer to autumn.*
DISTRIBUTION *Common and widespread, throughout.*
EDIBILITY *Inedible.*
SIMILAR SPECIES C. paleacus *has a strong smell like geraniums. Other closely related species can only be told apart by their spores.*

Velvet Milkcap

Lactarius lignyotus (Russulaceae)

Distinctive among milkcaps for its dark, sooty-brown almost black, velvety cap and stem. The cap of the Velvet Milkcap has a central dip with a distinct nipple-like bump in the centre, and an inrolled margin. The gills run down the stem and become pinkish with dried milk then blackish where bruised. The mild white milk turns slowly pink.

SEEN *singly and in groups with conifers, especially spruce and fir.*

cap up to 11cm wide

dark, dry velvety cap

white to cream gills

dark, sooty-brown stem

SPORES *Cream.*
FRUITING *Late summer to autumn.*
DISTRIBUTION *Rare to occasional but widespread.*
EDIBILITY *Inedible.*
SIMILAR SPECIES *Sooty Milkcap (p.57) and* L. acris, *both of which are paler and grow with oak or beech.*

Wood Hedgehog

Hydnum repandum (Hydnaceae)

This common, highly prized edible species has soft but brittle ochre spines below the cap, which are easily rubbed off. The cap has a depressed centre, inrolled margins, and is often lobed and irregularly shaped. It is dry to felty in texture, and pale cream to pinkish ochre in colour. The stem, which is paler than the cap and fairly smooth, is sometimes off-centre. It has very solid whitish flesh that usually discolours pinkish. Older specimens of Wood Hedgehog tend to become bitter so if it is to be eaten it is best collected when young. There is no particular smell to this species.

GROWS *in rings, troops, or clusters in conifer as well as broadleaf woodland, especially with spruce, pine, beech, oak, and birch.*

spines 4–6mm long

tapering stem

SECTION

yellow-ochre spines

CAP UNDERSIDE

NOTE

Hydnum species are distinguished from the tooth fungi (Phellodon, Bankera, Sarcodon, and Hydnellum species) by their fleshy fruitbodies and brittle, not tough flesh. Cutting through with a knife will help to confirm this. Also check that the specimen lacks any smell, and for colour changes to the flesh.

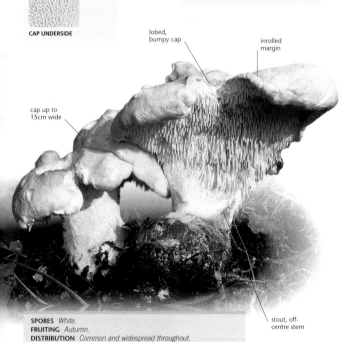

lobed, bumpy cap

inrolled margin

cap up to 15cm wide

stout, off-centre stem

SPORES *White.*
FRUITING *Autumn.*
DISTRIBUTION *Common and widespread throughout.*
EDIBILITY *Edible, especially tasty when young.*
SIMILAR SPECIES *Terracotta Hedgehog (H. rufescens), which is also edible, but is smaller and more orange in colour; Phellodon, Bankera, Sarcodon, and Hydnellum species, which have spines but tough, corky flesh.*

Fused Tooth

Phellodon confluens (Bankeraceae)

The cap of the Fused Tooth is buff to grey-brown with a whitish edge, the colours merging and not distinctly zoned. Very irregular in shape, the cap quickly fuses with the caps of adjacent fruitbodies. The spines on the underside are whitish at first, later becoming greyish brown. Like all *Phellodon* species, the Fused Tooth smells strongly of curry powder when dried.

APPEARS *in groups, often fusing together, in old beech, oak, and chestnut woods.*

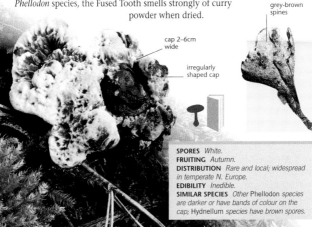

grey-brown spines

cap 2–6cm wide

irregularly shaped cap

SPORES *White.*
FRUITING *Autumn.*
DISTRIBUTION *Rare and local; widespread in temperate N. Europe.*
EDIBILITY *Inedible.*
SIMILAR SPECIES *Other* Phellodon *species are darker or have bands of colour on the cap;* Hydnellum *species have brown spores.*

Earpick Fungus

Auriscalpium vulgare (Auriscalpiaceae)

A species that is distinctive yet difficult to spot, the tiny Earpick Fungus has a kidney shaped, hairy, reddish brown cap with a paler margin. The underside of the cap has pointed greyish spines that are 3mm long. The stem is dark brown and covered in velvety hairs. The texture of the fungus is tough and leathery.

FOUND *mostly growing on fallen or buried pine cones; sometimes spruce cones.*

kidney-shaped cap

cap up to 2cm wide

velvety, dark brown stem

velvety brown cap

pointed spines

SPORES *White.*
FRUITING *Year round.*
DISTRIBUTION *Common and widespread throughout.*
EDIBILITY *Inedible.*
SIMILAR SPECIES Baeospora myosura *and* Strobilurus *species, which also grow on fallen cones, but have gills and not spines.*

Scaly Tooth

Sarcodon imbricatus (Bankeraceae)

GROWS *in small groups in native forests and old plantations of pine and spruce.*

The Scaly Tooth is distinguished by the erect scales on its off-white cap, which are often a contrasting dark brown. There are teeth on the underside, which are pale brown, and the stem is similarly coloured. Unlike *Hydnellum* and *Phellodon* species, *Sarcodon* species have caps which do not fuse with other fruitbodies and are much larger.

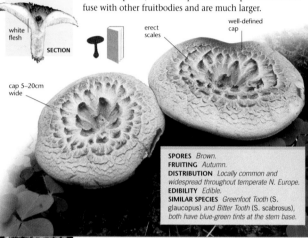

white flesh

SECTION

erect scales

well-defined cap

cap 5–20cm wide

SPORES *Brown.*
FRUITING *Autumn.*
DISTRIBUTION *Locally common and widespread throughout temperate N. Europe.*
EDIBILITY *Edible.*
SIMILAR SPECIES *Greenfoot Tooth (S. glaucopus) and Bitter Tooth (S. scabrosus), both have blue-green tints at the stem base.*

Drab Tooth

Bankera fuligineoalba (Bankeraceae)

APPEARS *on the ground, often in some numbers, in fallen pine litter.*

The cap of the Drab Tooth is irregular with a wavy, lobed edge and often has pine debris embedded in it. It is pale cream when young, later becoming brownish tinged with reddish pink. The white to grey spines below the cap are up to 5mm long. The stem is pale at the top and brown at the base; it may be off-centre and is short and stout. When dry, the flesh smells of fenugreek.

cap up to 10cm wide

cap flushed pink with age

wavy margin

embedded debris

grey-white spines

SECTION

SPORES *White.*
FRUITING *Autumn.*
DISTRIBUTION *Locally common and widespread, especially in N. Europe.*
EDIBILITY *Inedible.*
SIMILAR SPECIES *Wood Hedgehog (p.180), which has a paler, more uniform colour, and softer, edible flesh.*

Zoned Tooth

Hydnellum concrescens (Bankeraceae)

This is probably the commonest *Hydnellum* species, often growing in large clusters that are fused together. Its irregular and frequently ridged cap is zoned in shades of reddish brown and has similarly coloured teeth on the underside. It is whitish at the margin when young. The stem is also reddish brown, and all parts of the fungus develop blackish blotches. Zoned Tooth resembles the Turkeytail (p.222), however, close examination reveals minute teeth and not tubes on the underside.

OCCURS *in clusters, often fusing together, in old broadleaf woodlands and coniferous forests.*

cap 2–8cm wide

bands of reddish brown

SPORES *Brown.*
FRUITING *Autumn.*
DISTRIBUTION *Occasional and local, widespread in temperate N. Europe.*
EDIBILITY *Inedible.*
SIMILAR SPECIES *Turkeytail (p.222); Ridged Tooth (H. scrobiculatum), which has diffused colours on the cap.*

Jelly Tooth

Pseudohydnum gelatinosum (Exidiaceae)

This species has the appearance of a shelf-like bracket with a short, stout, often lateral, stem, and has a firm but jelly-like consistency throughout. The downy to rough cap surface is whitish when young becoming grey-brown with age. The underside is covered in soft gelatinous spines and the whole fruitbody is semi-translucent.

FOUND *on decaying wood and stumps, mainly coniferous.*

wavy, lobed margin

cap up to 8cm wide

translucent appearance

SPORES *White.*
FRUITING *Autumn to winter.*
DISTRIBUTION *Occasional to locally common; widespread especially in N. Europe.*
EDIBILITY *Edible.*
SIMILAR SPECIES *Jelly Ear (p.235), which is ear-like in appearance, has folds instead of spines, and grows mainly on broadleaf trees.*

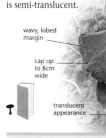

soft spines

short stem

Blue Tooth

Hydnellum caeruleum (Bankeraceae)

GROWS *in small groups in native pine and spruce forests on acid, sandy soil. Occasionally in disturbed areas.*

The Blue Tooth is one of the most striking tooth fungi, easily distinguished – at least when young – by the bright blue or blue-grey tints in the cap and the spore-bearing teeth on the underside. Like all other *Hydnellum* species, the velvety cap grows irregularly after the initial round fruitbody appears. Not only is its surface uneven, but the gradually expanding edge may envelop twigs and vegetation or merge into the caps of adjacent fruitbodies. Older fruitbodies of the Blue Tooth lack the velvety appearance, and have short white spines which turn greyish, then gradually brown with age. The stem is orange-brown from its inception, while the flesh is bluish grey in the cap but orange-brown in the stem. If cut in half, the flesh is zoned and may smell mealy.

NOTE

Look for specimens of tooth fungi in native forests and ancient woodlands. Several species quite often grow together and they have a particular liking for forest banks and pathsides.

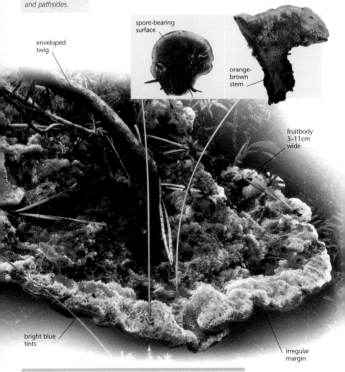

spore-bearing surface

orange-brown stem

enveloped twig

fruitbody 3–11cm wide

bright blue tints

irregular margin

SPORES *Brown.*
FRUITING *Autumn.*
DISTRIBUTION *Rare to locally common, but widespread in native coniferous forest.*
EDIBILITY *Inedible.*
SIMILAR SPECIES *H. suaveolens, which is blue-tinted in the stem and has a distinct aniseed smell; it is not found in Britain. Other Tooth fungi lack bluish tints and many have thinner flesh.*

Sheep Polypore

Albatrellus ovinus (Albatrellaceae)

This fleshy, cream to greyish brown edible fungus, is especially popular in Nordic countries, although it can cause gastric irritation in some cases. The cap has an inrolled, wavy margin giving it a lobed appearance like a sheep's hoof. Often cracked, the surface can become tinged greenish with age. The fairly stout greyish stem may be off centre. Superficially, this species looks like a gilled fungus until the underside is checked revealing minute pores – a feature of all *Albatrellus* species. These pores run down the stem and stain yellow when touched or bruised. The flesh of this fungus is firm and white.

FOUND *in troops on the ground in coniferous woods, often in large numbers, in mossy places associated with spruce.*

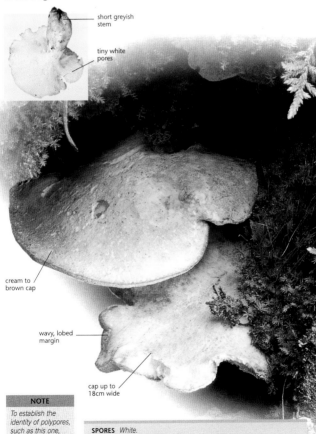

short greyish stem

tiny white pores

cream to brown cap

wavy, lobed margin

cap up to 18cm wide

SPORES *White.*
FRUITING *Summer to autumn.*
DISTRIBUTION *Locally common, widespread in temperate N. Europe.*
EDIBILITY *Edible but may cause gastric upset.*
SIMILAR SPECIES *A. confluens, which grows with pine, has orange tones, and does not stain yellow; A. subrubescens, which also grows with pine, stains orange, and is inedible.*

Ghost Bolete

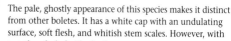

Leccinum holopus (Boletaceae)

GROWS *singly or in small numbers, often in damp, mossy places like moors and heaths; associated with birch.*

The pale, ghostly appearance of this species makes it distinct from other boletes. It has a white cap with an undulating surface, soft flesh, and whitish stem scales. However, with age, the whole fruitbody, the cap and stem base in particular, can take on a distinctly pale greenish tinge. The flesh remains white and unchanging.

cap up to 10cm wide

whitish to light brown stem scales

greenish old cap

white flesh

SECTION

SPORES *Dark reddish brown.*
FRUITING *Late summer to late autumn.*
DISTRIBUTION *Occasional to locally common, widespread but not well known.*
EDIBILITY *Edible.*
SIMILAR SPECIES *L. percandidum is white-capped but has pink instead of green tones and blackening flesh.*

Rooting Bolete

Boletus radicans (Boletaceae)

This species has a large, bun-shaped, pale cream to greyish beige cap with a suede-like texture, sometimes cracking. The yellow pores bruise to blue and become dingy and greenish with age. Stout and yellow, the stem sometimes has a light flush of red in the middle and is covered with a fine yellow network which may be reddish towards the base. The stem base is distinctly tapering, and also bruises to blue, fading after some minutes.

SEEN *singly and in small troops, in broadleaf woods on clay and basic sites.*

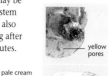

yellow pores

pale cream to grey cap

cap up to 20cm wide

tapering stem base **SECTION**

SPORES *Olive-green.*
FRUITING *Summer to autumn.*
DISTRIBUTION *Common and widespread except in N. regions.*
EDIBILITY *Inedible.*
SIMILAR SPECIES *Devil's Bolete (right) has red pores and stem network; Iodine Bolete (B. impolitus) has no stem network.*

Devil's Bolete ☠

Boletus satanas (Boletaceae)

This spectacular, poisonous bolete can cause severe stomach upsets. It has a large, bun-shaped, suede-like cap that is sometimes sticky; pale cream to grey, this may also have grey-green tones. When very young, the pores start yellow but rapidly become a distinctive blood-red, remaining orange-yellow only at the margin. The stem is usually very stout and swollen, yellow at the top, reddish towards the middle and base, and covered in a fine blood-red network. The thick cream to straw-coloured flesh bruises pale blue, as do the pores. The Devil's Bolete smells spicy when young but develops an unpleasant odour with age, said to be reminiscent of rotting meat. Fruitbodies may persist for some time during dry conditions.

OCCURS *singly or in small numbers in warm, often south-facing, chalky sites with broadleaf trees, especially beech and oak.*

bun-shaped cap

yellow and red stem with blood-red network

domed, cream to grey cap

cap up to 25cm wide

SPORES *Olive-brown.*
FRUITING *Summer to early autumn.*
DISTRIBUTION *Very local, widespread especially in S. regions.*
EDIBILITY *Poisonous.*
SIMILAR SPECIES *Rooting Bolete (left), which has a yellower stem network; B. legaliae, which has a pale, smooth cap flushed with pink-orange. These and other such large, blue-staining boletes are all poisonous and should be avoided.*

NOTE

Check that the network colour on the stem is red by using a hand lens or magnifying glass. Also, cut the fungus in half to observe changes in flesh colour – this may take longer in dry conditions.

Alder Bolete

Gyrodon lividus (Boletaceae)

OCCURS *in broadleaf woodland, associated exclusively with alder.*

This Bolete grows strictly with alder. It can be recognized by its yellowish tubes which unlike other members of its genus, run down the stem. The sticky cap has an inrolled margin. It is pale yellow when young, becoming yellow brown with age. The stem tapers slightly and has reddish brown tones on a yellow base. The pale flesh and tubes turn blue when they are cut.

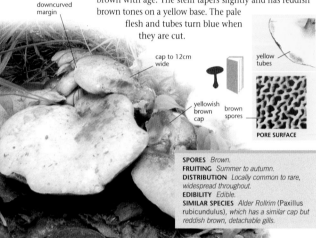

downcurved margin

cap to 12cm wide

yellowish brown cap

brown spores

yellow tubes

PORE SURFACE

SPORES *Brown.*
FRUITING *Summer to autumn.*
DISTRIBUTION *Locally common to rare, widespread throughout.*
EDIBILITY *Edible.*
SIMILAR SPECIES *Alder Rollrim (Paxillus rubicundulus), which has a similar cap but reddish brown, detachable gills.*

Bitter Beech Bolete

Boletus calopus (Boletaceae)

GROWS *singly or in small groups, in acid soil, especially in beech woodland.*

This very large and colourful bolete has a domed cream cap with a felty texture, which may crack in dry weather and can also be tinged with ochre-brown or olive-green. The pores are bright yellow, becoming more olive with age. They bruise blue, as does the bitter, cream-coloured flesh. The bright crimson stem is yellow at the top and covered in a fine, contrasting yellow network of veins that darkens towards the base.

cap up to 14cm wide

pale cream or ochre cap

yellow pores

crimson stem

SECTION

SPORES *Olive-brown.*
FRUITING *Summer to autumn.*
DISTRIBUTION *Occasional but more common in S. Europe; widespread throughout.*
EDIBILITY *Inedible.*
SIMILAR SPECIES *Rooting Bolete (p.186) has a yellow stem and Pale Bolete (B. fechtneri) has mild-tasting flesh.*

Dryad's Saddle

Polyporus squamosus (Polyporaceae)

The change from young to old in the Dryad's Saddle is quite dramatic. When immature, it appears as a large, rounded brown lump with a flattened top. This gradually expands to form a wide, round or kidney-shaped shelf or bracket with a short, stout stem at the inner edge, making the species appear somewhere between a cap and stem and bracket fungus. While the undersurface is formed of big, honeycomb-like pores, the pale brown upper surface has numerous, flattened, dark brown scales. The tough stem is deep brown or black and almost woody, and the white flesh smells strongly of flour when young. This large fungus looks like a seat for a woodland dryad or fairy.

FOUND *usually low down on standing broadleaf trees in woods, parks, and gardens; sometimes on fallen logs.*

large, rounded bracket

cap 10–60cm wide

concentric, flat, dark brown scales

honeycomb-like pores and tubes

woody, dark brown stem

saddle-shaped mature cap

SECTION

PORE SURFACE

SPORES White.
FRUITING Spring to early autumn.
DISTRIBUTION Common, widespread throughout temperate Europe.
EDIBILITY Edible and tasty when young.
SIMILAR SPECIES Chicken of the Woods (p.230), which is bright yellow; Tuberous Polypore (P. tuberaster), which is smaller with a woolly cap margin and hairy cap scales.

Velvet Bolete

Suillus variegatus (Gomphidiaceae)

GROWS *in small troops among needle litter in pine woods, and often in heaths on sandy, acid soil.*

Like all *Suillus* species, the Velvet Bolete is associated with conifers. However, unlike the others, its cap is dry, felty rather than slimy, and is a rich orange-brown. The small tubes and pores are brown to olive-brown and stain blue when touched. Its tall stem is brown with olive and red tints and the flesh is lemon-yellow, turning blue when cut.

cap 5–10cm wide

broadly domed cap

scaly cap surface

brown pores

lemon flesh

SECTION

SPORES *Brown.*
FRUITING *Summer to late autumn.*
DISTRIBUTION *Common in pine forests of temperate N. Europe.*
EDIBILITY *Edible and tasty.*
SIMILAR SPECIES *Weeping Bolete (p.201), which is smaller, and has a smooth, sticky orange-brown cap and yellow-white stem.*

Foxy Bolete

Leccinum vulpinum (Boletaceae)

APPEARS *in small numbers among needle litter of pine woods.*

Members of this genus can sometimes be identified by their host trees and the Foxy Bolete is specific to pines. It has a dark, fox-red to chestnut cap, which is rounded, with a felty texture and a small, overhanging margin. Its pores are dark cream. The stout, cylindrical stem is covered with dark red-brown scales, while the edible whitish flesh slowly stains smoky-purple then blackish.

bun-shaped cap

cap 5–15cm wide

flesh stains smoky-purple

white flesh

SECTION

dark, woolly scales

SPORES *Brown.*
FRUITING *Summer to late autumn.*
DISTRIBUTION *Common in N. temperate pine forests, mainly in Scotland.*
EDIBILITY *Edible and tasty.*
SIMILAR SPECIES *Orange Oak Bolete (p.205), grows with oak; L. piceinum grows with spruce; L. aurantiacum grows with poplar.*

Penny Bun

Boletus edulis (Boletaceae)

Among the most famous edible fungi, the Penny Bun, also known as Cep Steinpilz and Porcini, grows in both deciduous and coniferous woodland. It can be a very large, robust fungus and has a yellow-brown to dark brown cap that appears toasted on the outer surface. The usually swollen, pale brown stem has a fine network of white veins over the upper half, while the pores are white turning yellowish to olive when old. Widely sought-after for its white flesh that does not stain on being cut, the Penny Bun has a pleasant smell and mild taste.

FOUND *in leaf litter or moss of deciduous and coniferous woods, associated with a large variety of different trees.*

cap up to 25cm wide

bun-shaped brown cap

network of veins

pores start white then turn yellowish olive

white flesh

SECTION

swollen, pale brown stem

NOTE

Before cooking, check the flesh for maggot holes, and for yellowish stains, which may be caused by parasites. These affected portions can be cut out but if badly damaged, discard the entire fruitbody.

SPORES *Olive-brown.*
FRUITING *Summer to late autumn.*
DISTRIBUTION *Common to very common; widespread in N. temperate woods down to the Mediterranean.*
EDIBILITY *Edible and tasty.*
SIMILAR SPECIES Boletus aereus *has a darker, black-brown cap and a dark brown network on the stem;* B. aestivalis, *has a pale biscuit-brown cap and stem, and a dry, roughened cap surface. Both are edible.*

Bitter Bolete

Tylopilus felleus (Strobilomycetaceae)

GROWS *in small groups in needle- or leaf litter in both broadleaf and coniferous woods, on acid soils.*

There are a number of boletes that, although not poisonous, are distinctly bitter to taste. The Bitter Bolete is one of those and if picked and eaten carelessly can spoil a meal. It has some distinctive features, however. Both the bun-shaped cap and stem vary from pale tawny-buff to yellow-brown, and the cap is dry and rough to touch. The tubes and pores are initially pale cream but soon become deep pink, bruising slightly darker. The stem has a prominent, dark raised mesh or network over almost the entire surface. The white flesh is unchanging when cut.

NOTE

It is important to check the mature pore colour with boletes since this may change quite dramatically as they age. Also, always cut boletes to assess any colour changes in the flesh.

young, pale cream pores

mature, deep pink pores

tawny-buff to yellow-brown cap

rough, minutely cracked cap

club-shaped tawny stem

cap 5–15cm wide

dark raised net

SPORES *Brown.*
FRUITING *Summer to autumn.*
DISTRIBUTION *Common, widespread from temperate N. Europe to the Mediterranean.*
EDIBILITY *Inedible.*
SIMILAR SPECIES *Penny Bun (p.191) and Summer Bolete (B. reticulatus), which can both look similar to this species but have white to yellow mature gills and a mild, pleasant taste.*

Bay Bolete

Boletus badius (Boletaceae)

A popular edible species, this bolete has a rounded cap which soon expands and flattens, and is deep bay brown to reddish brown, or even light orange-brown in some forms. When dry, the cap is finely felty or velvety to smooth, but when wet it may be quite sticky. The tubes and pores start pale cream and age to greenish yellow. Often cylindrical, the stem is coloured like the cap but slightly paler and is finely streaked with darker brown, with no raised network. The whitish flesh and the tubes and pores bruise blue when cut.

SEEN *in small groups in needle or leaf litter in both broadleaf and coniferous woods, on acid soils.*

cap 5–15cm wide

bay brown cap

slightly streaked stem surface

cylindrical, pale reddish brown stem

pores bruise blue

yellow-olive pores

whitish flesh

SECTION

SPORES *Brown.*
FRUITING *Summer to autumn.*
DISTRIBUTION *Common, widespread throughout temperate N. Europe.*
EDIBILITY *Edible and tasty.*
SIMILAR SPECIES B. ferrugineus, *which is smaller, softer, and more slender and has a brown or greenish brown cap with a velvety-furry surface.*

NOTE

The presence or absence of a network on the stem is a diagnostic feature of species in this genus. Use a magnifying glass and closely examine the top of the stem, where the markings are most prominent.

Slippery Jack

Suillus luteus (Gomphidiaceae)

FOUND *in large groups, in coniferous forests, only under two-needled pine trees.*

Like all *Suillus* species, Slippery Jack is associated with conifers , in this case pines. It has a slimy, convex, purple-brown cap whose skin is easily peeled. The stout off-white stem has a large, floppy ring at the top, which covers the pores when young; it has dark dots above the ring, while the stem below and the underside of the ring are purple. Slippery Jack has pale yellow pores and tubes that are rather short. Its flesh is pale yellowish white and does not stain when cut.

cap 5–10cm wide

large, floppy ring

slimy purple-brown cap

pale yellow pores

pale yellowish white flesh

SECTION

SPORES *Brown.*
FRUITING *Summer to autumn.*
DISTRIBUTION *Common, widespread throughout in temperate N. Europe.*
EDIBILITY *Edible with caution – it is essential to remove the slimy cap skin which may be toxic.*
SIMILAR SPECIES *S. collinitus, which is ochre-brown, lacks a ring, and has bright pink mycelium at the very bottom of the stem.*

Scarletina Bolete

Boletus luridiformis (Boletaceae)

A stout fungus, Scarletina Bolete, like several other *Boletus* species, turns blue rapidly when bruised or cut. The bun-shaped cap is velvety, dark brown when young, becoming paler with age. However, it nearly always has a distinct yellow-orange edge. The stem is yellow but appears orange-red since it is covered with red dots, which can be seen only through a hand lens. Although the flesh and tubes are bright yellow to olive, they turn bright blue within seconds of being cut, then fade to a dull shade. The pores are bright blood-red, becoming orange with age. Its popularity as an edible species varies across Europe as it is poisonous when raw, and may cause gastric upsets if not well cooked.

GROWS *in woods, especially broadleaf, and along woodland edges; mycorrhizal with oak, beech, and sometimes conifers.*

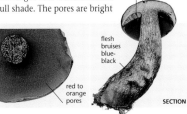

yellow tubes

flesh bruises blue-black

red to orange pores

SECTION

cap 5–20cm across

velvety brown cap

yellow cap edge

reddish tinge on yellow stem

SPORES *Olive-brown.*
FRUITING *Summer to autumn.*
DISTRIBUTION *Common and widespread throughout Europe.*
EDIBILITY *Poisonous raw, edible when cooked.*
SIMILAR SPECIES *Inkstain Bolete (p.196), which has yellow pores and turns inky blue more rapidly; Lurid Bolete (p.196), which has a net pattern on the stem and is orange above the tubes; Deceiving Bolete (p.197), which has dots only at the stem base and more orange pores.*

NOTE

To identify this mushroom, cut it in half to see whether the flesh turns blue; also use a hand lens to check that there is no orange line above the tubes or fine network on the stem.

Inkstain Bolete

Boletus pulverulentus (Boletaceae)

The cap of this bolete is a dark reddish to yellow-brown, with a felty to smooth surface. The pores are pale yellow while the stem is yellow above and reddish brown below. This species is easily identified when bruised or cut, when the entire bolete stains blue-black almost instantly.

FOUND *in open, broadleaf woods, especially with oak, often along pathsides, roads, and woodland edges, on rich soils.*

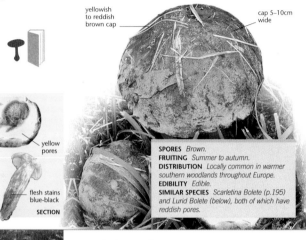

yellowish to reddish brown cap

cap 5–10cm wide

yellow pores

flesh stains blue-black

SECTION

SPORES *Brown.*
FRUITING *Summer to autumn.*
DISTRIBUTION *Locally common in warmer southern woodlands throughout Europe.*
EDIBILITY *Edible.*
SIMILAR SPECIES *Scarletina Bolete (p.195) and Lurid Bolete (below), both of which have reddish pores.*

Lurid Bolete

Boletus luridus (Boletaceae)

This is a beautiful, and very variable, species. The cap can be yellow-orange, olive-yellow, or darker brown, often mixed with pink or apricot. The pores are orange to red and bruise deep blue when touched. The club-shaped stem is yellow to apricot-orange with a fine, raised red network. The flesh is yellowish, except for the purplish stem base, and stains deep blue when cut.

SEEN *in broadleaf woods, especially with oaks and beech, in grassy areas, often on alkaline soils.*

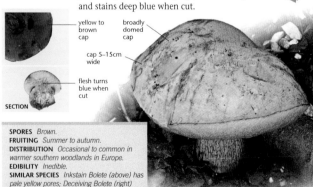

yellow to brown cap

broadly domed cap

cap 5–15cm wide

flesh turns blue when cut

SECTION

SPORES *Brown.*
FRUITING *Summer to autumn.*
DISTRIBUTION *Occasional to common in warmer southern woodlands in Europe.*
EDIBILITY *Inedible.*
SIMILAR SPECIES *Inkstain Bolete (above) has pale yellow pores; Deceiving Bolete (right) has a brighter red cap and orange pores.*

Red Cracking Bolete

Boletus chrysenteron (Boletaceae)

Fine cracks appear on the older, olive-brown caps, revealing the dull reddish flesh beneath, which give this species its name. The angular pores are yellow to dull olive and the flesh is white to pale yellow. Yellowish and streaked red below, the slender stem has fine red dots and fibrous lines. The stem, pores, and flesh stain slightly blue.

OCCURS *in broadleaf and coniferous woods, on a wide range of soil types although prefers acid soils.*

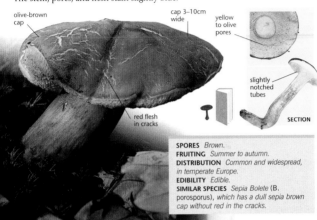

olive-brown cap

cap 3–10cm wide

yellow to olive pores

red flesh in cracks

slightly notched tubes

SECTION

SPORES *Brown.*
FRUITING *Summer to autumn.*
DISTRIBUTION *Common and widespread, in temperate Europe.*
EDIBILITY *Edible.*
SIMILAR SPECIES *Sepia Bolete (B. porosporus), which has a dull sepia brown cap without red in the cracks.*

Deceiving Bolete

Boletus queletii (Boletaceae)

The colour of this felty fungus varies from yellowish brown to yellow-olive with red, to entirely reddish. The pores are a beautiful apricot-orange, bruising blue. Stout and pointed, the stem is yellow to orange covered with fine red dots and has a purple base. The flesh is yellow in the cap and top part of the stem, but deep purple-red lower down, and stains blue when cut.

GROWS *with broadleaf trees, especially oak, beech, and lime, on rich, chalky soils.*

apricot-orange pores

olive-brown to reddish cap

cap 5–15cm wide

SECTION

purple-red flesh at stem base

yellow stem with red dots

SPORES *Brown.*
FRUITING *Summer to autumn.*
DISTRIBUTION *Rare to locally common, especially in warmer, southern woodlands.*
EDIBILITY *Inedible.*
SIMILAR SPECIES *Scarletina Bolete (p.195) has a brown cap, red to orange pores, and lacks the purple-red flesh in the stem base.*

Suede Bolete

Boletus subtomentosus (Boletaceae)

As its common name suggests, the cap of this species is velvety and suede-like in texture, and varies in colour from yellow or yellow-brown to olive or reddish brown. Its tubes and pores are bright yellow. The usually slender stem is yellowish, often with brown dots or ridges at the top. The flesh is pale whitish yellow and does not stain when cut or bruised. Although it is edible, it tastes quite bland.

OCCURS *in broadleaf and coniferous woods, on a wide range of soil types, but prefers acid soils.*

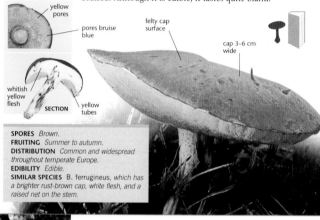

yellow pores

pores bruise blue

felty cap surface

cap 3–6 cm wide

whitish yellow flesh

SECTION

yellow tubes

SPORES *Brown.*
FRUITING *Summer to autumn.*
DISTRIBUTION *Common and widespread throughout temperate Europe.*
EDIBILITY *Edible.*
SIMILAR SPECIES *B. ferrugineus, which has a brighter rust-brown cap, white flesh, and a raised net on the stem.*

Peppery Bolete

Chalciporus piperatus (Boletaceae)

This small species of bolete has a pale yellow-ochre to tan cap that becomes smooth and sticky when wet. Its tubes and pores are a bright rust-red and run down the stem to some extent. The slender stem is pale buff, while the flesh is pale yellow in the cap and chrome yellow at the stem base. This fungus tastes hot and peppery.

OCCURS *with birch and coniferous trees, usually in close proximity with Fly Agaric (p.158).*

cap 3–6cm wide

ochre to tan cap

pale yellow flesh

slender stem

rust-red pores

SECTION

chrome yellow stem base

SPORES *Brown.*
FRUITING *Summer to autumn.*
DISTRIBUTION *Common and widespread throughout temperate Europe.*
EDIBILITY *Edible if well cooked.*
SIMILAR SPECIES *Crimson Bolete (p.209), which has even brighter, carmine-red tubes and pores, and grows with oak.*

Oak Bolete

Boletus appendiculatus (Boletaceae)

The cap of this large species is a rich reddish ochre to red-brown or bay. Smooth and slightly fibrous, it often cracks with age. Its tubes and pores are bright golden yellow, ageing to brownish yellow, and they bruise to a bluish shade. The stout, tapering stem of the Oak Bolete is pale yellow with a fine, raised network of the same colour on its surface. The flesh of this edible fungus is yellow, staining blue when bruised, and it has a pungent odour.

FOUND *growing under oak on warm, rich soils, especially in the south.*

cap 3–15cm wide

yellow pores bruise blue

SECTION

stem pointed at base

stout, pale yellow stem

SPORES *Brown.*
FRUITING *Summer to autumn.*
DISTRIBUTION *Occasional to frequent, widespread throughout temperate Europe.*
EDIBILITY *Edible.*
SIMILAR SPECIES *Rooting Bolete (p.186), has a paler cap; Pale Bolete (B. fechtneri) is pale greyish buff to smoky grey.*

Brown Birch Bolete

Leccinum scabrum (Boletaceae)

Reaching large sizes, this common species has a dark to medium- or buff-brown cap, which is smooth and sticky when wet. The off-white tubes and pores turn pale brown with age. Often tall, the cylindrical or club-shaped stem is cream with tiny blackish brown scales. The cream flesh hardly changes colour when cut or bruised.

ASSOCIATED *with birch, singly or in small clumps, often in damper areas.*

buff to brown cap

cap 5–20cm wide

smooth surface

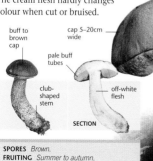
pale buff tubes

club-shaped stem

off-white flesh

blackish scales on stem

SECTION

SPORES *Brown.*
FRUITING *Summer to autumn.*
DISTRIBUTION *Common and widespread throughout temperate N. Europe.*
EDIBILITY *Edible.*
SIMILAR SPECIES *Mottled Bolete (L. variicolor), which has a mottled grey-brown cap.*

Slate Bolete

Leccinum duriusculum (Boletaceae)

This species has a greyish brown to buff cap, which is dry to finely felty, smooth, and cracks with age. The pores and the tubes are cream, bruising brown. The stout stem is cream with woolly brown or blackish scales. Also cream, the flesh stains pinkish violet then smoky-grey or black, sometimes bluish at the base.

SEEN *growing with white poplar and aspen, often in large numbers.*

woolly scales

cap 5–15cm wide

overhanging margin

cream flesh

SECTION

SPORES *Brown.*
FRUITING *Summer to autumn.*
DISTRIBUTION *Rare to occasional, locally common in warmer woodlands of N. Europe.*
EDIBILITY *Edible.*
SIMILAR SPECIES *L. aurantiacu, which has an orange cap and stem scales.*

Hazel Bolete

Leccinum pseudoscabrum (Boletaceae)

One of the earliest species to appear after summer rains, the Hornbeam Bolete has a rather lumpy, irregular brown cap, often finely cracking all over. The tubes and pores are yellowish cream, bruising black. The slender, often curved, cream stem has fine dark brown scales, while the flesh is cream, staining pale violet-grey then black when cut.

GROWS *with hornbeam or hazel, often in groups, at times in deep shade.*

lumpy brown cap

cap 5–10cm wide

off-white flesh

curved stem

SECTION

SPORES *Brown.*
FRUITING *Summer to autumn.*
DISTRIBUTION *Locally common, widespread in temperate N. Europe.*
EDIBILITY *Edible.*
SIMILAR SPECIES *Saffron Bolete (p.205), which grows under oak and starts bright yellow but soons turns dull brown.*

Hollow Bolete

Suillus cavipes (Gomphidiaceae)

Unlike other *Suillus* species which are mostly sticky, this fungus has a dry, fibrous or scaly, rust-brown to orange-russet cap. The dull olive-yellow tubes with large, angular pores run a short way down the stem. With a fleecy, ragged white ring at the top, the short stem is pale orange-brown, becoming hollow, with soft white flesh.

ASSOCIATED *with larch, often in more northerly or mountainous areas.*

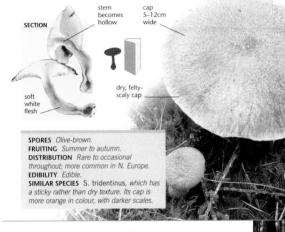

SECTION

stem becomes hollow

cap 5–12cm wide

soft white flesh

dry, felty-scaly cap

SPORES *Olive-brown.*
FRUITING *Summer to autumn.*
DISTRIBUTION *Rare to occasional throughout; more common in N. Europe.*
EDIBILITY *Edible.*
SIMILAR SPECIES S. tridentinus, *which has a sticky rather than dry texture. Its cap is more orange in colour, with darker scales.*

Weeping Bolete

Suillus granulatus (Gomphidiaceae)

This rather small bolete has a smooth, sticky, rounded then flattened, orange-brown cap. The tubes and pores are small, pale yellow, and weep white droplets when young. The short, stout stem also weeps droplets, and is pointed, yellowish, and soon covered with dark rust-brown flecks at the top. The pale yellow flesh is acidic to taste.

ASSOCIATED *with two-needled pines, often on alkaline soils.*

cap 5–8cm wide

felty-scaly cap

pale yellow pores

yellowish flesh

SECTION

rust-brown flecks

SPORES *Olive-brown.*
FRUITING *Summer to autumn.*
DISTRIBUTION *Common throughout temperate N. Europe.*
EDIBILITY *Edible.*
SIMILAR SPECIES S. collinitus, *which has a darker brown cap and is pink at the extreme base of the stem.*

Winter Polypore

Polyporus brumalis (Polyporaceae)

FOUND on fallen branches and logs of a variety of broadleaf trees.

The Winter Polypore superficially resembles a bolete, but grows on wood and has tougher and corky flesh. Its smooth yellow-brown cap is flat to funnel-shaped and very thinly fleshed, with a wavy margin. The shallow tubes and pores are whitish to ochre, with 4–6 pores per millimetre. The thin, off-centre stem is hard and black towards the base.

ochre pores

yellow- to cinnamon-brown cap

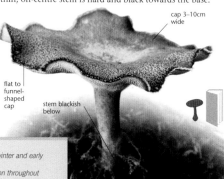

cap 3–10cm wide

flat to funnel-shaped cap

stem blackish below

SPORES White.
FRUITING Autumn to winter and early spring.
DISTRIBUTION Common throughout temperate N. Europe.
EDIBILITY Inedible.
SIMILAR SPECIES P. badius, which is larger, with a dark red-brown and very shiny cap.

Bovine Bolete

Suillus bovinus (Boletaceae)

ASSOCIATED with two-needled pines, often grows along with Rosy Spike (Gomphidius roseus).

This small bolete has a convex to flat, sticky, pale orange-brown to rust-brown cap, often with a whitish inrolled margin, best seen from below. The tubes are greyish olive while the pores are dull orange to olive, wide and angular, with finer pores inside the larger ones. The often short stem is light brownish yellow, smooth, and without a ring.

rust-brown to orange-brown cap

cap 5–8cm wide

olive-grey tubes

large, angular pores

PORE SURFACE

SPORES Olive.
FRUITING Summer to autumn.
DISTRIBUTION Common throughout temperate N. Europe.
EDIBILITY Edible.
SIMILAR SPECIES S. variegatus, which has a felty to finely scaly cap, brown pores, taller stem, and flesh that stains pale blue.

Tiger's Eye

Coltricia perennis (Hymenochaetaceae)

Found growing on soil rather than on wood, this unusual polypore forms a thin-fleshed funnel with an irregular margin. The silky surface is yellow- to golden brown with darker and paler zones. The very thin tubes and pores are greyish brown and run down the felty brown stem. When cut, the tough flesh is dark rust-brown.

GROWS on sandy soils, often in coniferous woods or on heaths, more rarely in broadleaf woods.

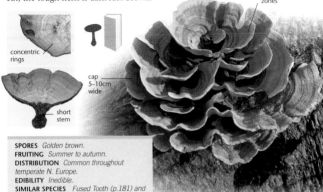

golden brown zones

concentric rings

short stem

cap 5–10cm wide

SPORES *Golden brown.*
FRUITING *Summer to autumn.*
DISTRIBUTION *Common throughout temperate N. Europe.*
EDIBILITY *Inedible.*
SIMILAR SPECIES *Fused Tooth (p.181) and Zoned Tooth (p.183), both tooth-fungi which have spiny undersides.*

funnel-shaped cap with wavy margins

Zoned Rosette

Podoscypha multizonata (Podoscyphaceae)

This is often a large fungus forming dense rosettes of tough, leathery lobes, arranged in overlapping layers rather like a cabbage. It is pale buff- to reddish brown with darker bands and the surface is suede-like. The lobes are joined into a stout base. They are grey-brown and without tubes or spines below.

APPEARS on the ground in deciduous woods, also along roadsides with planted trees.

cap 5–20cm wide

rosette of overlapping lobes

suede-like texture

UPPER SURFACE

smooth surface

LOWER SURFACE

SPORES *White.*
FRUITING *Summer to autumn.*
DISTRIBUTION *Rare to occasional in temperate Europe.*
EDIBILITY *Inedible.*
SIMILAR SPECIES *Wood Cauliflower (p.284), which is larger, softer, cream-coloured, and grows with pines.*

Orange Birch Bolete

Leccinum versipelle (Boletaceae)

ASSOCIATED *with birch in wet woodlands, sometimes found in large numbers.*

A popular edible species, the Orange Birch Bolete often grows to a very large size. Bright yellow-orange to orange, its cap is rounded and felty when young, but later expands broadly. A ragged, overhanging margin is visible on the "buttons" or young fruitbodies. The tubes of the fungus are up to 3cm long and pale buff in colour. Very young pores are almost black, but they soon become pale ochre-buff and bruise to a darker brown. The stout, often quite tall stem is off-white and densely covered in small black scales. When cut, the thick white flesh rapidly turns lavender-grey, and later becomes grey-black.

NOTE

Since young pores may be a different colour from those of mature fruitbodies in the Bolete family, try to collect specimens in a range of different sizes.

bright yellow-orange cap

cap 8–20cm wide

grey scales on stem

pale buff tubes

flesh stains lavender-grey

SECTION

stout stem

SPORES *Brown.*
FRUITING *Summer to autumn.*
DISTRIBUTION *Common throughout temperate N. Europe.*
EDIBILITY *Edible and tasty.*
SIMILAR SPECIES *Orange Oak Bolete (right), which has a dark fox-red cap and stem, and grows with oaks;*
Poplar Bolete (L. aurantiacum), which is reddish orange and grows with aspen rather than birch.

Orange Oak Bolete

Leccinum quercinum (Boletaceae)

This bolete's bun-shaped cap is reddish orange to orange-brown, with a dry, felty texture, and an overhanging margin when young. Its stout stem is pale buff with reddish brown scales. When cut, the white stem flesh turns grey-pink and then violet-black, whereas the pale buff tubes and pores stain deep brown.

GROWS *only under oak trees, usually in warm, southern woodlands.*

deep reddish orange cap

cap 5–15cm wide

buff stem with red-brown scales

fleshy cap

cream-buff tubes

flesh stains grey-pink

SECTION

SPORES *Olive.*
FRUITING *Summer to autumn.*
DISTRIBUTION *Occasional to locally common in warmer temperate Europe.*
EDIBILITY *Edible.*
SIMILAR SPECIES L. aurantiacum, *which has an orange cap and grows under aspen trees.*

Saffron Bolete

Leccinum crocipodium (Boletaceae)

This entire fungus is bright saffron-yellow to ochre-yellow when young, but rapidly becomes dull brown as it ages. The smooth, rounded cap cracks like a mosaic as it expands. Its tubes and pores are yellow, bruising black, while its stout stem is pale yellow with fine, darker yellow scales. The flesh stains pale reddish, then black.

FOUND *only under oak trees, largely in warmer, southerly regions.*

pale yellow flesh

cap cracks with age

cap 5–10cm wide

flesh bruises pale red

SECTION

stout stem

SPORES *Olive.*
FRUITING *Summer to autumn.*
DISTRIBUTION *Rare to locally common in warmer parts of temperate Europe.*
EDIBILITY *Edible.*
SIMILAR SPECIES *Hazel Bolete (p.200), which has a brown cap and is found under hornbeam and hazel.*

Cornflower Bolete

Gyroporus cyanescens (Gyroporaceae)

ASSOCIATED with a wide range of trees, both broadleaf and coniferous, on acid soil.

The cap and stem of this species are both off-white to buff and hard and brittle. The surface of the convex cap is finely felted. The tubes and pores are cream to straw-yellow and the stem soon develops hollow chambers. All parts of this edible fungus turn deep blue when cut or bruised.

cream-buff pores

cap 5–10cm wide

matt cap surface

stout stem

flesh stains blue

SECTION

SPORES *Yellow.*
FRUITING *Summer to autumn.*
DISTRIBUTION *Rare to occasional, and very localized, widespread in N. Europe.*
EDIBILITY *Edible and tasty.*
SIMILAR SPECIES *Ochre Brittlegill* (Russula ochroleuca), *which has gills rather than pores, and does not bruise violet.*

Larch Bolete

Suillus grevillei (Gomphidiaceae)

FOUND in woodland, only under larch, often abundant in plantations.

Very common wherever larch grows, this edible species has a convex, slimy, bright yellow-orange to deep orange-brown cap. The fine tubes and pores are lemon-yellow. The stem is orange-brown with a slimy, yellow-white ring at the top and the firm, thick, deep yellow flesh does not change colour when cut.

broadly rounded cap

cap 5–12cm wide

tiny pores

yellow flesh

yellow ring

SECTION

SPORES *Olive.*
FRUITING *Summer to autumn.*
DISTRIBUTION *Common and widespread in N. Europe.*
EDIBILITY *Edible.*
SIMILAR SPECIES *S. flavidus, which is smaller, pale yellow with darker streaks, and grows under pines.*

Oldrose Bolete

Boletus rhodopurpureus (Boletaceae)

This eye-catching species has a cap that starts pinkish white but soon turns deep purple-pink, mottled with yellow and wine-red; it bruises blue. The tubes are yellow and the pores are golden-yellow then orange- to blood-red. The stout stem is yellow with a fine, raised, bright red network. The bright yellow flesh stains blue-black when cut.

GROWS *under broadleaf trees, especially oaks, mainly in warm, southern woodlands.*

broadly rounded cap

red veins

cap 5–15cm wide

flesh stains blue

SECTION

SPORES *Olive.*
FRUITING *Summer to autumn.*
DISTRIBUTION *Rare to locally common in warmer S. temperate Europe.*
EDIBILITY *Inedible.*
SIMILAR SPECIES *B. legaliae, which has a pinkish purple cap that does not stain, and flesh that stains only weakly.*

Heavy Bolete

Boletus torosus (Boletaceae)

The often mottled cap of this bolete is greyish yellow or greenish grey, sometimes flushed purple. The tubes and pores are yellow to deep reddish orange, while the yellow stem is flushed with a fine red network at the base. The bright yellow flesh is unusually dense and heavy. All parts of this fungus stain blue-black when cut or bruised.

GROWS *under broadleaf trees and conifers, mainly in warm, southern woodlands.*

cap 5–20cm wide

yellow pores

broadly rounded cap

stout yellow stem

SPORES *Olive.*
FRUITING *Summer to autumn.*
DISTRIBUTION *Rare to occasional in warmer temperate S. Europe.*
EDIBILITY *Inedible.*
SIMILAR SPECIES *Oldrose Bolete (above), which has a purplish cap; B. xanthocyaneus, which is lemon yellow bruising instantly blue.*

Ruby Bolete

Boletus rubellus (Boletaceae)

GROWS *under oaks, usually in damp grassy areas along paths and woodland edges.*

The cap of this small bolete is velvety, rounded, and blood-red to scarlet when young. It slowly flattens out, becoming smooth, then cracked, and dull red-brown. The red stem may have darker streaks. The yellow flesh stains deep blue and may be carrot-orange in the stem base.

bright yellow tubes and pores

broadly rounded cap

cap 2–6cm wide

yellow flesh

blood-red stem

SECTION

SPORES *Olive.*
FRUITING *Summer to autumn.*
DISTRIBUTION *Occasional to frequent, warm temperate S. Europe.*
EDIBILITY *Edible.*
SIMILAR SPECIES *Red Cracking Bolete (p.197) and Matt Bolete* (B. pruinatus), *which do not have orange flesh at the stem base.*

Gilded Bolete

Aureoboletus gentilis (Boletaceae)

FOUND *growing under oak, chestnut, and rarely other broadleaf trees, on clay soils.*

The small rounded cap of the Gilded Bolete is pale pinkish brown to dull coral with darker red streaks. It has a smooth surface that becomes sticky when wet. The tubes and pores are bright golden-yellow, and do not change colour when bruised or cut. The slender stem is smooth and sticky, rooting at the base, pale pinkish below and yellow towards the top. The edible white flesh is flushed pink, especially in the cap region.

cap 2–5cm wide

red streaks on cap

golden yellow pores

stem yellow above

stem pinkish below

pinkish white flesh

SECTION

SPORES *Ochre.*
FRUITING *Summer to autumn.*
DISTRIBUTION *Rare to occasional, warmer parts of temperate S. Europe.*
EDIBILITY *Edible.*
SIMILAR SPECIES *None – it is the only bolete in broadleaf woods with bright yellow, unchanging pores and a pinkish, sticky cap.*

Royal Bolete

Boletus regius (Boletaceae)

This imposing bolete has a rose-red to crimson cap, which
is dry and felty to fibrous. The tubes and pores are bright
yellow and do not bruise blue like those of many other
boletes. The pale yellow stem is slightly reddish at the base
and has a fine yellow network especially at the top. The
thick flesh is yellow and more or less unchanging when cut.

ASSOCIATED *with
beech and occasionally
chestnut, on neutral
to alkaline soils.*

broadly
rounded cap

yellow
pores

cap 5–20cm
wide

stout
stem

often curved
stem

SPORES *Olive.*
FRUITING *Summer to autumn.*
DISTRIBUTION *Rare to occasional,
warmer parts of temperate S. Europe.*
EDIBILITY *Edible.*
SIMILAR SPECIES *The Pretender
(B. pseudoregius), which has a paler pinkish
brown cap and stem bruising blue.*

Crimson Bolete

Rubinoboletus rubinus (Boletaceae)

This rare species has a small, rounded, light reddish brown
cap, which is usually dry and felty to touch but becomes
slightly sticky when very wet. The tubes run a short way
down the stem and are bright carmine-red, as are the pores.
The short stem is yellowish brown, flushed carmine above,
and the edible flesh is whitish to slightly coral in
the cap but a bright chrome-yellow
in the stem base.

GROWS *in small
groups, associated with
oak trees, often in
grassy areas.*

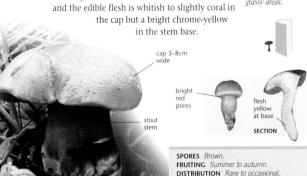

cap 3–8cm
wide

bright
red
pores

stout
stem

flesh
yellow
at base

SECTION

SPORES *Brown.*
FRUITING *Summer to autumn.*
DISTRIBUTION *Rare to occasional,
warmer parts of temperate S. Europe.*
EDIBILITY *Edible.*
SIMILAR SPECIES *B. piperatus, which
has coppery pores and grows with birch
or conifers.*

Boletus dupainii

Boletus dupainii (Boletaceae)

The bright scarlet cap of this species is first rounded then broadly expanded. The tubes are yellow, while the pores are bright orange-red to scarlet, bruising blue when touched. The stout, cylindrical stem is yellow at the top, reddish below, and is covered in fine red dots. The yellow flesh turns blue when cut, especially above the tubes.

FOUND *in small groups with various oak species, often in grassy areas.*

glossy, sticky cap

cap 5–8cm wide

scarlet pores

stem reddish at base

SPORES *Brown.*
FRUITING *Summer to autumn.*
DISTRIBUTION *Rare to occasional in warmer, S. temperate Europe.*
EDIBILITY *Inedible.*
SIMILAR SPECIES *Deceiving Bolete (p.197), which also has a reddish cap, but a pointed stem and deep purple-red flesh at the base.*

Sticky Bolete

Suillus viscidus (Boletaceae)

The very sticky cap of this species ranges from grey-brown or olive-grey to ochre, mottled with darker patches. The pores are whitish to dirty olive-grey, bruising darker. Coloured like the cap, the stem has a thin, glutinous ring at the top. The soft flesh is white to dull green-blue with some purplish areas.

GROWS *exclusively with larch, on rich soils, rarely in any numbers.*

cap 5–10cm wide

broadly rounded cap

grey-buff stem

large, angular pores

PORE SURFACE

SPORES *Brown.*
FRUITING *Summer to autumn.*
DISTRIBUTION *Rare to occasional, widespread in N. Europe.*
EDIBILITY *Edible but not tasty.*
SIMILAR SPECIES *None – no other Suillus species has such a dull, dirty looking, and slimy cap.*

Black Falsebolete

Boletopsis leucomelaena (Thelephoraceae)

Although this fungus looks like a bolete at first sight it is related to some of the toothed fungi such as those belonging to the genus *Sarcodon*. The tough, leathery fruitbodies have a rounded, dark grey-brown to blackish grey cap. Smooth at first, this develops radial cracks and becomes scaly with age. The underside has a thin layer of tough white tubes with fine cream-grey pores. The short, stout, blackish-grey stem may be central or off-centre and is sometimes covered with fine, woolly orange fibres. This species is a good example of how different families have evolved very similar shapes.

GROWS *in small troops on bare soil or in needle litter, under conifers, especially spruce trees, in mountainous regions.*

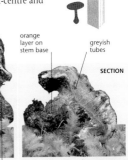

orange layer on stem base

greyish tubes

SECTION

leathery fruitbody

radially cracked cap

short grey-black stem

tough, blackish grey cap

fruitbody 4–10cm wide

rounded cap

SPORES White.
FRUITING *Summer to autumn.*
DISTRIBUTION *Very rare to occasional, widespread in temperate N. Europe.*
EDIBILITY *Inedible.*
SIMILAR SPECIES *B. grisea, which lacks the orange woolly coating Black Falsebolete has on the stem base, and is more frequently found growing with pine.*

NOTE

In the true boletes the pores are soft and easily removed from the cap; in the false boletes they are fixed firmly to the tougher flesh.

Dusky Bolete

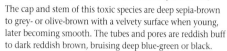

Porphyrellus porphyrosporus (Strobilomycetaceae)

GROWS *with both broadleaf and coniferous trees, usually on acid soils.*

The cap and stem of this toxic species are deep sepia-brown to grey- or olive-brown with a velvety surface when young, later becoming smooth. The tubes and pores are reddish buff to dark reddish brown, bruising deep blue-green or black. When cut, the pale buff flesh, which has an unpleasant smell, turns blue, green, or black, with red patches.

cap 5–10cm wide

dark sepia-brown stem

pale flesh

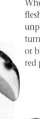

SECTION

SPORES *Purple-brown.*
FRUITING *Summer to autumn.*
DISTRIBUTION *Rare to occasional, widespread in N. Europe.*
EDIBILITY *Poisonous.*
SIMILAR SPECIES *None – no other bolete in Europe has its dull sepia colours and reddish buff pores.*

Old Man of the Woods

Strobilomyces strobilaceus (Strobilomycetaceae)

FOUND *growing with both broadleaf and coniferous trees, usually on rich soils.*

The blackish grey cap of this unmistakable species is densely shaggy with thick scales, often with paler flesh showing between them. The tubes and pores are greyish white, bruising red, then black. The cylindrical blackish stem has a shaggy covering and a ragged ring at the top. The tough flesh stains slowly dull red then black.

cap 5–15cm wide

greyish pores

blunt, woolly scales

flesh stains black

SECTION

blackish brown stem

SPORES *Purple-black.*
FRUITING *Summer to autumn.*
DISTRIBUTION *Rare to occasional and very localized, widespread throughout Europe.*
EDIBILITY *Edible.*
SIMILAR SPECIES *None – its shaggy, scaly dark cap and reddening then blackening flesh make it unique.*

Shelf & Bracket Fungi

Shelf and bracket fungi grow on dead or living woody material, some high up on the trunks of standing trees, others at ground level. There are about 300 fungi that fit into this group. Some have a rudimentary stem, but all are attached to the wood from one side of the fruitbody and may grow singly or in tiers. Shelf fungi are very thin, while brackets are thicker. Ear-shaped species tend to be soft and have gills or folds underneath. Other species may have pores; most of these, such as the Hoof Fungus (pictured), are woody and inedible.

TURKEYTAIL

CHICKEN OF THE WOODS

HAIRY CURTAIN CRUST

BIRCH POLYPORE

Coral Tooth

Hericium coralloides (Hericiaceae)

GROWS *high up on standing broadleaf trees, but also on fallen logs, especially beech and birch.*

An important and rare species of conservation interest, this fungus forms a large shelf-like clump of numerous branching stems emerging from a fleshy base. Each branch has several pendent white spines on the underside, often with a longer group of spines hanging down at the end. The white flesh is soft and brittle and tastes of radish when raw. Although edible, Coral Tooth should be conserved because of its rarity. One of the most beautiful of the larger fungi, it looks very much like an exotic undersea coral.

drooping white spines

fruitbody 10–20cm wide

yellow mature fungus

SPORES *White.*
FRUITING *Summer to autumn.*
DISTRIBUTION *Rare to occasional and very localized, throughout N. Europe.*
EDIBILITY *Edible, but too rare to eat.*
SIMILAR SPECIES *Bearded Tooth (H. erinaceum), which forms a single, rounded ball or mass of long, pendent white spines; H. alpestre, which looks identical but grows on fir trees.*

NOTE

This, and similar species, are now being cultivated on a wide scale for food, reducing the pressure on wild fungi.

Tiered Tooth

Hericium cirrhatum (Hericiaceae)

This uncommon but spectacular species forms large tiers of overlapping shelves or brackets. Each white shelf is thick and fleshy, covered with felty hairs on the upper surface and with short, densely packed white teeth on the underside. The thick white flesh smells and tastes quite pleasant but because of its rarity should not be eaten.

FOUND *usually on fallen logs and trees, especially beech.*

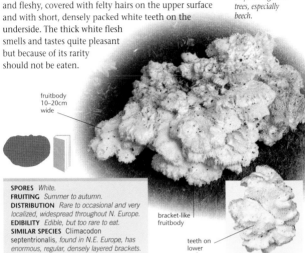

fruitbody 10–20cm wide

SPORES *White.*
FRUITING *Summer to autumn.*
DISTRIBUTION *Rare to occasional and very localized, widespread throughout N. Europe.*
EDIBILITY *Edible, but too rare to eat.*
SIMILAR SPECIES Climacodon septentrionalis, *found in N.E. Europe, has enormous, regular, densely layered brackets.*

bracket-like fruitbody

teeth on lower surface

Bitter Bracket

Postia stiptica (Fomitopsidaceae)

A small, bitter, pure white to cream species, its semicircular fruitbody is soft and fleshy with small pores on the underside. The edge of the bracket is very narrow and triangular when viewed from the side. When squeezed, the flesh exudes copious amounts of water.

FOUND *on fallen logs, stumps and branches of broadleaf trees, but sometimes on conifers.*

fruitbody 5–10cm wide

white to cream pores

PORE SURFACE

broad attached area

SPORES *White.*
FRUITING *Summer to autumn.*
DISTRIBUTION *Common and widespread throughout N. Europe.*
EDIBILITY *Inedible.*
SIMILAR SPECIES Conifer Blueing Bracket (P. caesia), *which begins white but soon ages pale bluish and has a felty-hairy surface.*

Lumpy Bracket

Trametes gibbosa (Coriolaceae)

This species is unusual in that it associates with a particular alga that stains the centre of the cream-yellow brackets green. The upper surface is lumpy while the rounded to slightly irregular and maze-like pores are pale cream to buff. The flesh is tough and inedible.

FOUND *on old stumps and logs of broadleaf trees, especially beech, causing a white rot.*

fruitbody 10–30cm wide

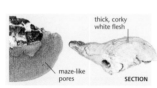

thick, corky white flesh

maze-like pores

SECTION

brackets with irregular surface

SPORES *White.*
FRUITING *Summer to autumn.*
DISTRIBUTION *Locally common, widespread throughout temperate N. Europe.*
EDIBILITY *Inedible.*
SIMILAR SPECIES *Hairy Bracket (T. hirsuta), which is thinner, has a hairier surface, and rounder, greyer pores.*

Birch Mazegill

Lenzites betulinus (Coriolaceae)

This bracket fungus is distinctive in having elongated pores that look like thin, tough gills. These are pale cream to greyish in colour. The rounded brackets of Birch Mazegill have a fine hairy surface, zoned in shades of brown. Corky in texture, the flesh is tough, white, and inedible. Often growing in large clusters of brackets this fungus causes a soft white rot in the host timber that it infects.

GROWS *on fallen logs and stumps, mainly on broadleaved trees, but sometimes on conifers.*

fruitbody 5–10cm wide

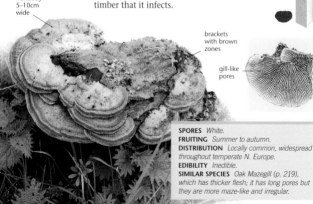

brackets with brown zones

gill-like pores

SPORES *White.*
FRUITING *Summer to autumn.*
DISTRIBUTION *Locally common, widespread throughout temperate N. Europe.*
EDIBILITY *Inedible.*
SIMILAR SPECIES *Oak Mazegill (p. 219), which has thicker flesh; it has long pores but they are more maze-like and irregular.*

Root Rot

Heterobasidion annosum (Perenniporiaceae)

This serious parasite of conifer trees can spread underground from tree to tree. When attacked by this fungus, the trees often produce secretions of resin and thicken at the base of the trunk. Root Rot is very uneven in shape with a lumpy, irregular surface, often flattened against the woody substrate and hardly forming a bracket. The bracket is dark reddish brown with a paler cream margin, often with a brighter orange zone immediately behind it. The cream pores are rather small. The pale yellowish cream flesh is thick and cork-like to spongy, and has a sweet, strong fungal smell.

PROLIFERATES, *often on standing conifers trees, especially spruce, but also on old stumps.*

2–4 pores per mm

PORE SURFACE

white to cream pores

SECTION

thick, yellowish cream flesh

fruitbody 5–20cm wide

reddish brown surface darkens with age

pale cream margin

NOTE

Root Rot is known to attack even relatively young saplings and may often cause serious loss of timber in forestry plantations. Its spores are quite unusual for a bracket fungus in being minutely spiny.

SPORES *White.*
FRUITING *Summer to autumn.*
DISTRIBUTION *Common, widespread throughout temperate N. Europe.*
EDIBILITY *Inedible.*
SIMILAR SPECIES *Anise Mazegill (Gloeophyllum odoratum), which also grows on conifers, has golden orange pores and an orange margin with blackish central area.*

Birch Polypore

Piptoporus betulinus (Fomitopsidaceae)

The most common and widespread species of bracket fungi to be found in birch woods, the Birch Polypore is the cause of death of a great many trees. The fungus starts as a round, brownish ball emerging from the trunk. It then expands to form a kidney-shaped bracket. The smooth, leathery upper surface is pale brown, while the blunt, rounded margin and lower surface with minute pores, are white. The white flesh is soft, corky, and fragrant. Despite its pleasant smell, it tastes bitter and is inedible. This is one of the few bracket fungi that is extremely host specific and is hardly ever absent in any birch woodland.

ASSOCIATED *only with birch, on living and dead standing trees, also on fallen logs.*

fruitbody 10–25cm wide

kidney-shaped bracket

smooth upper surface

rounded margin

minute white pores

swollen attachment point

soft, spongy flesh

SECTION

NOTE

In the past, the Birch Polypore has been put to various unusual uses. To name just a few, as a strap for sharpening razors, to stop bleeding, as a tinder to light fires, and, when cut into thin strips, for mounting insect collections in museums.

SPORES *White.*
FRUITING *Summer to autumn.*
DISTRIBUTION *Common, widespread throughout temperate N. Europe.*
EDIBILITY *Inedible.*
SIMILAR SPECIES *Oak Polypore (p.231), which is more yellow and grows on ancient oak trees. No other polypore on birch looks like this species.*

Oak Mazegill

Daedalea quercina (Fomitopsidaceae)

The pores of this species, which grows year round, are so elongated and irregular that they appear like thick, tough gills. The elongated tubes are dull ochre and often maze-like. Often in tiers, the brackets are fairly thick-fleshed and irregular in shape. The dull ochre-brown to pale greyish yellow upper surface is lumpy and uneven, while the brownish flesh is very tough, drying woody.

FOUND *on old stumps and logs of broadleaf trees, especially oak and sweet chestnut, causing a brown rot.*

long pores

lumpy, tiered surface

fruitbody 10–30cm wide

SPORES *White.*
FRUITING *Summer to autumn.*
DISTRIBUTION *Locally common, widespread throughout temperate N. Europe.*
EDIBILITY *Inedible.*
SIMILAR SPECIES *Blushing Bracket (p.220), which is thinner with round or slightly elongated pores and bruises pinkish.*

Aniseed Bracket

Hapalopilus odorus (Hapalopilaceae)

This very rare bracket can be identified by its strong, often penetrating smell of aniseed and by its restricted habitat. When young, it is rounded and entirely white, later becoming greyish brown, hoof-shaped, and woody. It has a matted upper surface and creamy white lower pore surface, which bruises brownish. The whitish flesh is corky with a bitter taste.

RESTRICTED *to willow in Scandinavia, along streams in ancient woodlands.*

bracket up to 15cm wide

young white bracket

hoof-shaped with age

SECTION

SPORES *White.*
FRUITING *All year round.*
DISTRIBUTION *Rare to very rare, restricted to Scandinavia.*
EDIBILITY *Inedible.*
SIMILAR SPECIES *Anise Mazegill (Gloeophyllum odoratum), which has hairy, cinnamon-brown brackets with angular pores.*

Blushing Bracket

Daedaleopsis confragosa (Coriolaceae)

FOUND *on old stumps, logs, and branches of broadleaf trees, especially willow, causing a white rot; common in damp areas, along streams and near bogs.*

This is an unusual species for its pores, which vary in shape from small and round to elongated and maze or gill-like. The species forms annual brackets, which are semicircular, with an uneven upper surface, often zoned in shades of reddish brown or yellow-brown. When old and wet, the entire bracket becomes dark red then blackish brown. The tough flesh is white and corky. The pores are pale cream to greyish and bruise to a dull reddish pink, especially when young. It can be hard to accept that specimens with gill-like pores are the same species as those with small round pores but this can be confirmed by bruising.

bracket
5–15cm
wide

round to irregular
pores

thick, corky
white flesh

red
bruise

reddish brown
tube layer **SECTION**

lumpy, irregular,
zoned surface

NOTE

A variety of this species, D. c. tricolor, has a deep red-black bracket with extremely thin gill-like tubes. It grows on beech or cherry trees.

SPORES *White.*
FRUITING *Summer to winter.*
DISTRIBUTION *Common and widespread throughout temperate N. Europe.*
EDIBILITY *Inedible.*
SIMILAR SPECIES *Oak Mazegill (p.219) is more robust and grows on oak or chestnut; Cinnabar Bracket (right); Hairy Bracket (Trametes hirsuta) is thinner with a hairier surface and rounder, greyer pores.*

Hairy Curtain Crust

Stereum hirsutum (Stereaceae)

Although it looks like other thin brackets, this species does not have tubes or pores but a smooth, spore-bearing underside, which is yellow-ochre to orange-tan. The thin, tough flesh is similarly coloured. The upper surface of the elongated, irregular brackets is pale greyish yellow to ochre-brown, zoned with darker bands, and finely hairy.

GROWS *on old stumps and logs of broadleaf trees, especially oak, birch, and beech.*

fruitbody 3–7cm wide

irregular, lobed brackets in long strips

smooth underside

concentric zones from tan to yellow

SPORES White.
FRUITING Summer to autumn.
DISTRIBUTION Common and widespread throughout temperate N. Europe.
EDIBILITY Inedible.
SIMILAR SPECIES Bleeding Broadleaf Crust (S. rugosum) usually grows more flattened against the wood and bruises red.

Cinnabar Bracket

Pycnoporus cinnabarinus (Coriolaceae)

This intensely cinnabar-red species is easy to identify. The bracket is semicircular and rather fleshy, with an uneven, slightly lumpy and vaguely-zoned upper surface. There are fine hairs on the surface, which can be seen with a hand lens. The tubes are short, about 4–6mm thick, and the pores are rounded. The flesh is also cinnabar-red.

SEEN *on old stumps and logs of broadleaf trees, more rarely on conifer wood, causing a soft white rot.*

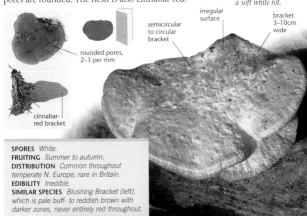

irregular surface

semicircular to circular bracket

bracket 3–10cm wide

rounded pores, 2–3 per mm

cinnabar-red bracket

SPORES White.
FRUITING Summer to autumn.
DISTRIBUTION Common throughout temperate N. Europe; rare in Britain.
EDIBILITY Inedible.
SIMILAR SPECIES Blushing Bracket (left), which is pale buff- to reddish brown with darker zones, never entirely red throughout.

Turkeytail

Trametes versicolor (Coriolaceae)

FOUND *on old stumps and logs of a wide range of broadleaf trees; much rarer on conifers.*

One of the commonest wood-rotting fungi, this species occurs in a wide range of colours. In all forms, fan-shaped, semicircular brackets are fused with their neighbours to form long strips or shelves. The upper surface is concentrically zoned in shades of black, brown, grey, blue-grey, purplish, or yellow, and is finely silky. The very shallow, fine tubes are pale cream. When fresh, the pallid flesh is tough and leathery. Tiers of Turkeytail brackets are one of the most striking and beautiful sights of broadleaf woodlands.

tiny, white to cream pores

PORE SURFACE

concentric, multicoloured zones

bracket 3–7cm wide

irregular, lobed brackets in tiers

SPORES *White.*
FRUITING *Year round.*
DISTRIBUTION *Common, widespread in temperate N. Europe.*
EDIBILITY *Inedible.*
SIMILAR SPECIES T. multicolor, *which is noticeably thicker where it joins the wood;* T. pubescens *is a rare species with paler, unzoned caps growing on dead broadleaf wood.*

NOTE

Check the underside of small, thin brackets with a hand lens. This species has tubes and pores, whereas curtain crust fungi (see p.221) do not.

Hoof Fungus

Fomes fomentarius (Fomitaceae)

This fungus has very broad, deep brackets which are hoof-shaped, hence the common name. The hard, woody perennial brackets are zoned with pale brown to dark grey-brown, and are smooth to slightly downy at the pale margin. A new tube layer is added each year with each layer about 5–6mm deep. The pores are greyish to grey-brown, 2–3 per mm. The very thick, wood-brown flesh is tough, fibrous, and has a pleasant, fruity smell. Depending on its host, the fungus exists in different forms. Once used to help start fires, the species is also known as Tinder Fungus.

GROWS *on standing trees and stumps of broadleaf trees, especially beech and birch, causing a white rot.*

bracket 8–30cm wide

smooth and hard upper surface

SECTION

tough, fibrous brown flesh

concentric zones in tones of grey and brown

small, grey to grey-brown pores

SPORES *White.*
FRUITING *Year round.*
DISTRIBUTION *Common, widespread in temperate N. Europe; uncommon and local in S. Britain.*
EDIBILITY *Inedible.*
SIMILAR SPECIES *Red-belted Bracket (p.233), which has a grey-brown to black surface with a reddish brown marginal zone.*

NOTE

Fomes species can look similar to some Ganoderma species but the latter have red-brown spores very often dusting the upper surface of the bracket.

Lacquered Bracket

Ganoderma lucidum (Ganodermataceae)

Unusual and attractive in appearance, the Lacquered Bracket is highly regarded in Asia for medicinal purposes, the dry cap being ground up to make a tea. The kidney-shaped bracket usually has a distinct lateral stem on the trailing edge, which can be quite long. The upper surface of the bracket is reddish brown to purplish or blackish red and has a highly polished surface, as if lacquered. On the underside, the tiny pores are pale cream. The flesh is whitish, later turning brown. The Lacquered Bracket is an annual species, producing a new bracket each year.

FOUND *on old stumps and standing broadleaf trees, especially oaks and chestnut, rarely on conifers.*

NOTE

Many Ganoderma species have a varnished look with a lumpy, uneven crust; they often develop a shiny stem that is variable in length.

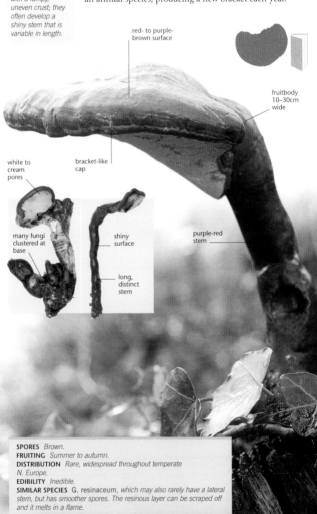

red- to purple-brown surface

fruitbody 10–30cm wide

white to cream pores

bracket-like cap

many fungi clustered at base

shiny surface

purple-red stem

long, distinct stem

SPORES *Brown.*
FRUITING *Summer to autumn.*
DISTRIBUTION *Rare, widespread throughout temperate N. Europe.*
EDIBILITY *Inedible.*
SIMILAR SPECIES G. resinaceum, *which may also rarely have a lateral stem, but has smoother spores. The resinous layer can be scraped off and it melts in a flame.*

Southern Bracket

Ganoderma australe (Ganodermataceae)

A sometimes massive bracket, this perennial species forms broad, semi-circular shelves, building up a new layer of tubes each year; the flesh is very thick where it joins the tree. Its rich reddish brown upper surface lacks granules but is irregular and lumpy. The tubes and pores are pale cream and bruise reddish brown, while the tough flesh is a dark red-brown.

GROWS *on old stumps and standing broadleaf trees, such as beech, oak, and lime, rarely on conifers.*

fibrous, dark brown flesh

SECTION

powdery layer of spores

fruitbody 10–60cm wide

SPORES *Brown.*	

FRUITING *All year round.*
DISTRIBUTION *Common, widespread in warmer parts of temperate N. Europe.*
EDIBILITY *Inedible.*
SIMILAR SPECIES *Artist's Bracket (G. applanatum), which is thinner, with paler flesh, often with pockets of whitish tissue.*

Shaggy Bracket

Inonotus hispidus (Hymenochaetaceae)

Unusual because of its densely furred surface, the large bracket of this fungus is thick-fleshed and broadly rounded with a blunt margin. The upper surface is bright reddish brown when young, turning black when very old. The tubes and pores are pale greenish yellow then greyish brown, while the rather soft, yellowish flesh bruises brown.

OCCURS *on trees such as ash, walnut, pear, and apple, often high up on the trunk.*

reddish brown upper surface

greenish yellow pores

fruitbody 10–40cm wide

blunt margin

thick, semicircular bracket

SPORES *Yellow.*
FRUITING *Summer to autumn.*
DISTRIBUTION *Locally common, widespread in temperate N. Europe.*
EDIBILITY *Inedible.*
SIMILAR SPECIES *Dyer's Mazegill (p.227); Alder Bracket (I. radiatus), which only grows on alder.*

Oak Bracket

Inonotus dryadeus (Hymenochaetaceae)

This species forms very thick brackets once a year, with a velvety or furry, pitted upper surface that is ochre to reddish brown. Large droplets of red-brown liquid ooze out when it is fresh and young. The tubes and pores are grey-white to yellowish when old, and the thick, red-brown flesh is soft and slightly zoned, with an unpleasant odour.

APPEARS *on wounds on broadleaf trees, mainly oak, as well as maple, elm, and chestnut.*

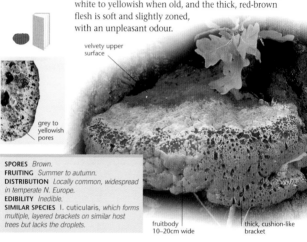

velvety upper surface

grey to yellowish pores

fruitbody 10–20cm wide

thick, cushion-like bracket

SPORES *Brown.*
FRUITING *Summer to autumn.*
DISTRIBUTION *Locally common, widespread in temperate N. Europe.*
EDIBILITY *Inedible.*
SIMILAR SPECIES I. cuticularis, *which forms multiple, layered brackets on similar host trees but lacks the droplets.*

Smoky Bracket

Bjerkandera adusta (Bjerkanderaceae)

This distinctive fungus is easy to identify. It often spreads over logs on which it produces small, irregular brackets with blunt, rounded margins, the upper surfaces being pale grey-brown with concentric zones. The lower tube layer is dark smoky grey. In cross-section, the flesh is white, contrasting sharply with the grey tubes.

GROWS *on fallen logs and stumps of broadleaf trees, especially beech.*

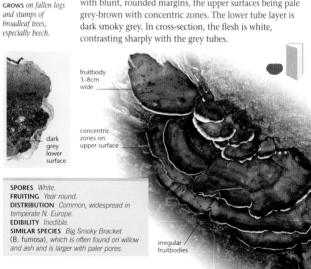

fruitbody 3–8cm wide

concentric zones on upper surface

dark grey lower surface

irregular fruitbodies

SPORES *White.*
FRUITING *Year round.*
DISTRIBUTION *Common, widespread in temperate N. Europe.*
EDIBILITY *Inedible.*
SIMILAR SPECIES *Big Smoky Bracket* (B. fumosa), *which is often found on willow and ash and is larger with paler pores.*

Dyer's Mazegill

Phaeolus schweinitzii (Polyporaceae)

A parasite of conifers, this species is a favourite with dyers, who extract a yellow-brown pigment from it to dye wool and cloth. The spongy bracket emerges from conifer roots as a rather shapeless ball or lump that is very furry-velvety and bright yellow. As the bracket develops, it forms a broad, irregular, rounded cap with a thick, short, central trunk or stem. The mature surface is a dark reddish brown, while the tubes and pores are sulphur-yellow, turning brown with age, and bruising a darker shade. Its thick, spongy flesh is brown and rather sour tasting.

PARASITIC *on conifers, especially pines, emerging from the ground near the roots of the tree.*

velvety yellow to red-brown upper surface

thick, plate-like brackets

young yellow specimen

yellow pores

PORE SURFACE

fruitbody 10–30cm wide

SPORES *White.*
FRUITING *Summer to autumn.*
DISTRIBUTION *Common to very common, widespread in temperate N. Europe.*
EDIBILITY *Inedible.*
SIMILAR SPECIES *Shaggy Bracket (p.225), which is also velvety-hairy but grows high up on the trunk of broadleaf trees.*

NOTE

When identifying bracket fungi, it is important to try and find specimens at different stages of growth, as many species change shape dramatically as they mature.

Hen of the Woods

Grifola frondosa (Bjerkanderaceae)

FOUND *in large compound clusters at the base of living broadleaf trees, particularly oak.*

This species produces large compound clusters of fruitbodies. The fleshy, individual brackets arise from a common stem and are pale grey on top becoming brown when old. Each is tongue-shaped, with radial fibres or furrows forming darker streaks on a pale background. Hen of the Woods smells pleasant when young but becomes increasingly sour, like old cheese, with age. The pores are white at first, gradually becoming light ochre-brown. This fungus prefers oak, but can be found with a wide range of broadleaf trees including sweet chestnut and beech. It is edible when young, and in the early nineteenth century used to be gathered and sold in local East Anglian markets. Now available worldwide, it is grown commercially principally in Japan where it is known as 'Maitake' and is claimed to have a wide range of medicinal benefits. Specially prepared logs can be bought for growing at home.

bracket 2–8cm wide

brown mature fungus

common stem

fruitbody up to 50cm wide

pale grey upper surface

large, compound fruitbody

SPORES *White.*
FRUITING *Summer to autumn.*
DISTRIBUTION *Occasional, widespread throughout temperate N. Europe.*
EDIBILITY *Edible when young.*
SIMILAR SPECIES *Giant Polypore (right), which produces larger, fan-like brackets; Umbrella Polypore (Polyporus umbellatus), which produces down-curving, umbrella-shaped brackets.*

NOTE

This fungus always grows at the base of trees but the similar Chicken of the Woods (Laetiporus sulphureus) grows higher up.

Giant Polypore

Meripilus giganteus (Bjerkanderaceae)

The Giant Polypore lives up to its name and typically produces massive tiers or rosettes of soft, fleshy, fan-like brackets arising from a common basal stem. The brackets are ochre-brown, the pores whitish, and all parts of the fungus bruise grey to blackish. It always grows on or close to the ground, at the base of trees, around stumps, or on buried roots.

GROWS *at the base of trees and around stumps, with oak and beech, but also with a variety of other species.*

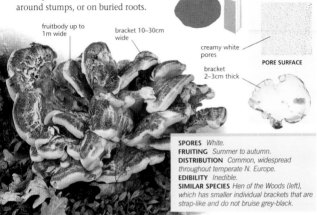

fruitbody up to 1m wide

bracket 10–30cm wide

creamy white pores

PORE SURFACE

bracket 2–3cm thick

SPORES White.	

FRUITING Summer to autumn.
DISTRIBUTION Common, widespread throughout temperate N. Europe.
EDIBILITY Inedible.
SIMILAR SPECIES Hen of the Woods (left), which has smaller individual brackets that are strap-like and do not bruise grey-black.

Willow Bracket

Phellinus igniarius (Hymenochaetaceae)

The hard, woody fruitbodies of Willow Bracket can last for years, gradually increasing in size and often becoming overgrown with moss and algae. The surface is blackish grey and smooth, cracking with age. The pores are brown, as is the flesh. Despite its common name, it is found on a wide range of trees, particularly birch, willow, and alder.

GROWS *on old living trunks, dead trunks, and fallen limbs of broadleaf trees.*

cracked blackish grey surface

woody flesh

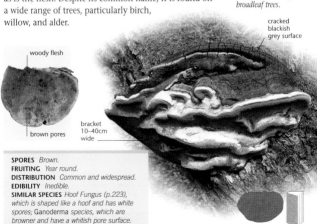

brown pores

bracket 10–40cm wide

SPORES Brown.
FRUITING Year round.
DISTRIBUTION Common and widespread.
EDIBILITY Inedible.
SIMILAR SPECIES Hoof Fungus (p.223), which is shaped like a hoof and has white spores; Ganoderma species, which are browner and have a whitish pore surface.

Chicken of the Woods

Laetiporus sulphureus (Polyporaceae)

Bright yellow when fresh and forming large, tiered clusters of fan-shaped fruitbodies, Chicken of the Woods is one of the most spectacular and easily identifiable bracket fungi. When very young, the fruitbodies are almost orange with a meat-like texture. However, they decay quite rapidly: the colour fades to pale buff and the soft flesh becomes cheesy and crumbles easily. This fungus is often considered edible when young, but can cause stomach upsets for some so should be treated with caution. This is thought to be an allergic reaction with rapid onset and affects about one in ten people.

GROWS *on living trees, rarely on dead trunks. Commonest on broadleaf trees such as oak; also on yew.*

bright yellow bracket

SECTION

soft flesh

NOTE
Do not forget to look upwards at tree trunks when foraging for fungi. Despite their size, tree fungi, such as this one, are often missed by gatherers who have their gaze fixed firmly on the ground.

fan-shaped fruitbody

bracket 10–50cm wide

fruitbody in tiered clusters

SPORES *White.*
FRUITING *Late spring to early autumn.*
DISTRIBUTION *Very common, widespread throughout temperate N. Europe.*
EDIBILITY *Edible when young, but can cause stomach upsets.*
SIMILAR SPECIES *Giant Polypore (p. 229), which is never bright yellow, and always grows at the base of trees; Oak Polypore (right), which is rare and has a leathery texture.*

Oak Polypore

Piptoporus quercinus (Fomitopsidaceae)

This fungus is fleshy but leathery, streaked with chestnut brown on a bright yellow background when fresh, the whitish pores bruising brown. Young fruitbodies are soft and rounded while older specimens are more triangular in section with faded colours. Restricted to ancient oak trees, which are becoming rare, this fungus is legally protected in Britain and should only be collected with a special permit.

FOUND *on the heartwood of ancient oaks, in old deer parks and pasture woodland.*

yellow and brown tones

whitish pores

bracket 5–15cm wide

SPORES *White.*
FRUITING *Mid- to late summer.*
DISTRIBUTION *Rare to locally occasional, widespread with oak.*
EDIBILITY *Inedible.*
SIMILAR SPECIES *Chicken of the Woods (left), which is yellow; Beefsteak Fungus (p.232), which is a blood-red.*

Olive Oysterling

Panellus serotinus (Tricholomataceae)

Appearing late in the year, the edible Olive Oysterling is easily distinguished by its yellow-brown and olive cap, which is sticky when damp, and its yellowish orange gills. The cap is ear-shaped and the stem grows from one side of the fruitbody. The cap cuticle can be very sticky and shiny. The short and stumpy stem is often inconspicuous.

GROWS *in small clusters on broadleaf trees, on dead and living trunks and dead, attached or fallen, branches.*

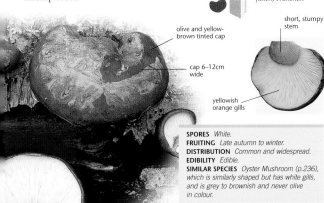

olive and yellow-brown tinted cap

cap 6–12cm wide

short, stumpy stem

yellowish orange gills

SPORES *White.*
FRUITING *Late autumn to winter.*
DISTRIBUTION *Common and widespread.*
EDIBILITY *Edible.*
SIMILAR SPECIES *Oyster Mushroom (p.236), which is similarly shaped but has white gills, and is grey to brownish and never olive in colour.*

Beefsteak Fungus

Fistulina hepatica (Fistulinaceae)

FOUND *singly or scattered on host trees, especially oak but also sweet chestnut. Most often found on living trees but also occurs on dead, fallen, or cut wood.*

This edible, soft-fleshed bracket looks like a bright red clown's nose when it first emerges from its host tree. It rapidly expands to a tongue shape, becoming a darker blood-red, sometimes oozing red droplets when fresh. On the underside, the pale yellow pores become reddish with age and bruising, and are easily separated. The red flesh is soft and thick, exuding a red juice which, together with its distinctive marbled, meat-like appearance, gives the species its common name. Acid- to sour-tasting when old, the Beefsteak Fungus is best consumed when young and fresh.

It is much prized by the furniture industry for the attractive brown rot it causes on host oak trees.

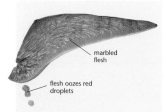

marbled flesh

flesh oozes red droplets

NOTE

Cut in half to observe the soft, marbled, red interior with its red juice reminiscent of rare beefsteak. It used to be called 'Poorman's Beefsteak', which indicates that its slightly sharp taste is not as good as a real beef.

kidney-shaped, blood red bracket

sticky upper surface

bracket up to 25cm wide

SPORES *White.*
FRUITING *Summer to autumn.*
DISTRIBUTION *Occasional to common, widespread with host trees.*
EDIBILITY *Edible.*
SIMILAR SPECIES *Cinnabar Bracket (p.221), Resin Bracket (Ganoderma resinaceum), and Cinnamon Bracket (Hapalopilus nidulans) all have hard, woody flesh and are inedible. Beefsteak Fungus is the only red bracket fungus with a soft, fleshy fruitbody.*

Red-belted Bracket

Fomitopsis pinicola (Fomitopsidaceae)

This is a very hard, perennial, hoof-shaped bracket fungus, distinguished by its smooth, grey-brown to blackish surface (which will melt in a flame) with a sticky reddish brown marginal zone. The pores are cream, bruising yellow when fresh, and the whole fruitbody often has a slightly sour smell. The species occurs on a wide range of hosts, broadleaf as well as conifer.

GROWS on dead and standing trees, fallen trunks, and stumps.

bracket 10–40cm wide

cream pores, bruising yellow

smooth, lacquered, grey-black surface

sticky, reddish brown margin

PORE SECTION

pale growing edge

SPORES White.
FRUITING Year round.
DISTRIBUTION Very common in native Scandinavian and continental conifer forests, less common elsewhere, and rare in Britain.
EDIBILITY Inedible.
SIMILAR SPECIES Hoof Fungus (p.223), which has greyish to grey-brown pores.

Peeling Oysterling

Crepidotus mollis (Cortinariaceae)

This ear-shaped fungus often grows in tiers on broadleaf trunks or branches. Like a miniature oyster fungus in shape, its colour can be quite variable, from grey-brown when wet to nearly white when dry. Its key features are its gelatinous texture and a cap cuticle which can be easily separated from the fruitbody. The cap may be streaked at the margin and the gills are grey-brown. It has a rudimentary stem attached to one side.

GROWS singly or in tiered groups on dead broadleaf wood, especially fallen trunks or branches of elm, ash, poplar, and beech.

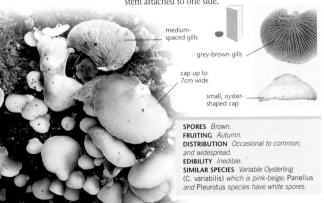

medium-spaced gills

grey-brown gills

cap up to 7cm wide

small, oyster-shaped cap

SPORES Brown.
FRUITING Autumn.
DISTRIBUTION Occasional to common, and widespread.
EDIBILITY Inedible.
SIMILAR SPECIES Variable Oysterling (C. variabilis) which is pink-beige; Panellus and Pleurotus species have white spores.

Splitgill

Schizophyllum commune (Schizophyllaceae)

GROWS *in small groups on exposed fallen wood of all kinds, especially beech. Also found densely clustered on straw bales.*

Forming small, leathery, lobed or fan-like brackets, the edible Splitgill has a nondescript felty beige-grey surface but reveals unusual pinkish grey gills underneath. Each gill is split lengthways, the two sides curling inwards in dry weather; they can be seen clearly with a hand lens. The Splitgill can grow at high temperatures and in very dry conditions, so it thrives on exposed, sun-bleached logs in the tropics. It also grows in similar conditions in northern Europe, where it is much less common. However, it has developed an affinity for polythene-wrapped straw bales left out in fields, on which it frequently forms dense clusters.

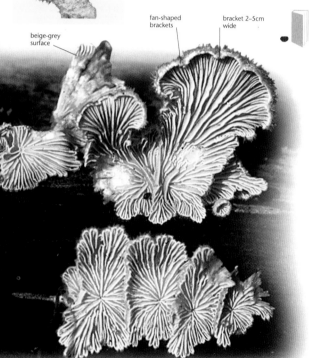

fleecy upper surface

lobed cap margin

beige-grey surface

fan-shaped brackets

bracket 2–5cm wide

SPORES *White.*
FRUITING *Year round.*
DISTRIBUTION *Occasional but widespread in temperate N. Europe.*
EDIBILITY *Edible, but tough.*
SIMILAR SPECIES *Old, weathered fruitbodies of* Stereum *species look similar from above, but are smooth not gilled below. Various other gilled species such as Oysterlings (*Crepidotus*) have plain brown gills, which are not split. The split gills are unique to* Schizophyllum *species.*

NOTE

Look out for the Splitgill while on holiday in tropical or subtropical areas, where it may even be found on driftwood washed up on beaches.

Jelly Ear

Auricularia auricula-judae (Auriculariaceae)

A distinctly ear-shaped fungus, Jelly Ear sometimes has a lobed surface. Velvety brown on the upper side, the inside of the "ear" is greyish and often deeply veined. When fresh, it has a firm feel, like cartilage. However, it shrivels to a crisp texture in dry weather, swelling up again after rain. Jelly Ear is often found in clusters or tiers, rather than singly, and can get quite large and floppy in wet weather when it is sometimes tinged greenish by algae. A very similar tropical species, *A. polytricha*, is extremely popular in Chinese cookery and medicine.

GROWS *on standing trees and fallen wood; prefers elder, but can be found on most broadleaf trees such as beech, ash, and willow; occasionally also on conifers.*

finely velvety upper surface

bracket 4–15cm wide

veined lower surface

velvety brown outside

greyish inside

SPORES *White.*
FRUITING *Year round.*
DISTRIBUTION *Common and widespread.*
EDIBILITY *Edible, but dried out fruitbodies should not be eaten.*
SIMILAR SPECIES *Tripe Fungus (p.285), which grows in bracket-like tiers, and is noticeably zoned greyish brown on the upper surface; brown Exidia and Tremella species, which are also gelatinous but lobed and brain-like, and are inedible.*

NOTE

If you find what you think is Jelly Ear on elm, check whether the upper surface is zoned grey-brown. In this case, it is likely to be the inedible Tripe Fungus (p.285).

Oyster Mushroom

Pleurotus ostreatus (Polyporaceae)

GROWS *on dead or dying hardwood trees, rarely on conifers, often found on the side of standing trees at a great height.*

The rounded, oyster-shaped caps of this species grow in large clumps, often with several fruitbodies overlapping each other. The caps vary from pale brown to deep blue-grey, and may often have a whitish woolly coating at the centre in wet and cold weather. Crowded and narrow, the white gills run down the very short, or almost absent stem, and are often home to small insects. The white flesh of this fungus has a pleasant smell and taste, and a firm, meaty texture. Very easy to cultivate, the edible Oyster Mushroom is now grown around the world for sale as a popular food item. It is available in most supermarkets and even in kits for growing at home.

very crowded gills

many overlapping fruitbodies

smooth cap surface

NOTE

Since small beetles are often found in the gills of Oyster Mushroom, gently shake the caps to make them drop out; wash and dry the fungi before cooking them.

SPORES *Pale lavender.*
FRUITING *Autumn to early winter.*
DISTRIBUTION *Common to very common, widespread throughout N. temperate Europe.*
EDIBILITY *Edible.*
SIMILAR SPECIES *Branching Oyster (p.41), which forms dense trumpet-shaped clusters with distinct stems; P. pulmonarius, which is paler and appears in early summer and autumn.*

Wrinkled Peach

Rhodotus palmatus (Tricholomataceae)

The wrinkled, peachy pink cap of this fungus has a
gelatinous cuticle. The cap, which is often ear-shaped,
has an inrolled margin and in moist weather it sometimes
exudes red droplets on the surface. Paler peach in colour,
the gills are fairly widely spaced and often interconnected
near the stem. The fungus has a stem that is often curved
and off-centre, and it grows in clusters on rotten wood.
The Wrinkled Peach smells delicately fruity, likened by
some to peach or apricot, and the flesh is pinkish with
a slightly bitter taste.

GROWS *in clusters or
in small groups, on
decaying broadleaf
wood, especially, but
not exclusively, elm.*

NOTE

*A good identification
test for Wrinkled
Peach is to try
peeling the cap
cuticle, which is
stretchy and
gelatinous; it should
peel off with
comparative ease.*

widely
spaced gills

off-centre
stem

SECTION

pinkish gills

salmon pink
to peach cap

cap up to
10cm wide

stem up to
7cm long

SPORES Pink.
FRUITING Early autumn to winter.
DISTRIBUTION Occasional to rare and fairly local; widespread
throughout.
EDIBILITY Inedible.
SIMILAR SPECIES Oyster fungi (Pleurotus species), which are grey to
white; Orange Shield (Pluteus aurantiorugosus), which is more upright
and has an orange, wrinkled cap.

Ball, Club, & other Fungi

These fungi include a huge range of fruitbody shapes, but nearly all lack gills, pores, or spines. Very much a simplified grouping, it includes an enormous variety of unrelated fungi, accounting for around 6,500 species in temperate northern Europe. Their sizes, colours, and methods for survival and spore dispersal are correspondingly varied. Among the huge variety of shapes are cups (such as Bay Cup, pictured), fingers, cages, and clubs, as well as the more bizarre brain-shaped fungi.

SMALL STAGSHORN

RED CAGE

SCARLET CATERPILLARCLUB

HORN OF PLENTY

Dusky Puffball

Lycoperdon nigrescens (Lycoperdaceae)

Similar to the Common Puffball (p.240), the Dusky Puffball is equally frequent but has a distinct preference for acidic woodlands, heaths, and moors. As the name suggests, it is darker than the Common Puffball with small, blackish brown, converging spines that fall off to leave a net-like pattern of circular scars.

GROWS *singly or in small groups on the ground in acidic woodlands, heaths, moors, and also sand dunes.*

blackish brown spine tips

fruitbody 2–4cm wide

SPORES *Brown.*
FRUITING *Summer to late autumn.*
DISTRIBUTION *Very common, widespread throughout temperate N. Europe.*
EDIBILITY *Probably edible when young.*
SIMILAR SPECIES *Common Puffball (p. 240); Spiny Puffball (p.241); other* Lycoperdon *species, which may lack the spines.*

pale brown when young

Soft Puffball

Lycoperdon molle (Lycoperdaceae)

This is the commonest of several woodland puffballs and is covered in tiny, soft granules or spicules, which do not fall off. The Soft Puffball is generally a light coffee colour when fresh, becoming more yellow-brown with age. Its sterile stem is often quite short and inconspicuous.

GROWS *singly or in small groups in deciduous and mixed woodlands, on neutral to chalky soils.*

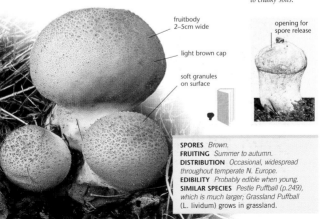

fruitbody 2–5cm wide

light brown cap

soft granules on surface

opening for spore release

SPORES *Brown.*
FRUITING *Summer to autumn.*
DISTRIBUTION *Occasional, widespread throughout temperate N. Europe.*
EDIBILITY *Probably edible when young.*
SIMILAR SPECIES *Pestle Puffball (p.249), which is much larger; Grassland Puffball (L. lividum) grows in grassland.*

Common Puffball

Lycoperdon perlatum (Lycoperdaceae)

ABUNDANT *in small clusters or scattered troops on the ground, occasionally on rotten wood, in broadleaf and conifer woods.*

Like all *Lycoperdon* species, the Common Puffball produces its spores inside the upper part of the fruitbody and, when mature, releases them through an opening which develops at the top. To do this, the fungus relies on rain drops. When a drop falls on the upper part of the fruitbody, spores puff out of the opening, rather like working a miniature bellows. The species is edible when young and still white inside. It can be distinguished from similar species by its covering of tiny, whitish spines which fall off with age, leaving behind a net-like pattern of circular scars.

tiny, conical spines

fruitbody 2–4cm wide

stout, dense stem

firm flesh

SECTION

brown spore mass

fruitbody browns with age

SPORES *Brown.*
FRUITING *Summer to late autumn.*
DISTRIBUTION *Very common and widespread throughout temperate N. Europe.*
EDIBILITY *Edible when young and white throughout.*
SIMILAR SPECIES *Dusky Puffball (p.239), Soft Puffball (p.239), Spiny Puffball (right), Stump Puffball (right), and Flaky Puffball (p.242) – all lack the Common Puffball's distinctive conical spines.*

NOTE

Edible Puffballs should not be confused with poisonous earthballs (p.247), which have heavier, denser, often yellowish fruitbodies.

Spiny Puffball

Lycoperdon echinatum (Lycoperdaceae)

With spines up to half a centimetre long, this is a distinctive but generally uncommon fungus, sometimes also known as the Hedgehog Puffball. The long spines fall off as the puffball matures, leaving a net-like pattern of scars. When young, the flesh is firm and white, becoming yellow then brown as the spores mature.

GROWS *singly or in small groups in deciduous woodland, particulary native beechwoods, on neutral to chalky soils.*

spines up to 5mm long

fruitbody 2–6cm wide

opening for spore-release

net-like pattern where spines fall off

SPORES *Brown.*
FRUITING *Summer to autumn.*
DISTRIBUTION *Rare and local, but widespread throughout temperate N. Europe.*
EDIBILITY *Inedible.*
SIMILAR SPECIES *Dusky Puffball (p.239) has shorter spines and prefers acidic woodlands.*

Stump Puffball

Lycoperdon pyriforme (Lycoperdaceae)

The very young fruitbodies of the Stump Puffball are covered in granular spines, but these are quickly shed to leave a soft, smooth surface. At the base of each fruitbody is a white, root-like strand. Unlike other puffballs, this species always grows on rotten wood, usually in very large clusters.

FOUND *in large, dense clusters on rotten wood such as stumps, buried wood, or fallen trunks.*

cream to buff when young

fruitbody 2–3cm wide

opening for spore-release

smooth surface

root-like strand

SECTION

SPORES *Brown.*
FRUITING *Summer to winter.*
DISTRIBUTION *Very common and widespread throughout temperate N. Europe.*
EDIBILITY *Edible when young and white.*
SIMILAR SPECIES *None – although other Puffballs may grow on rotten wood, none has the distinct, root-like strand at the stem base.*

Flaky Puffball

Lycoperdon mammiforme (Lycoperdaceae)

This rare species is distinctive when young as, unlike any other puffball found in Europe, the entire fruitbody is covered in a thin whitish veil. This quickly breaks up, leaving flaky remnants behind. However, these flakes are lost as the fruitbody matures, making it difficult to distinguish from other similar puffballs.

FOUND *singly or in small groups in deciduous woodlands, on chalky soils.*

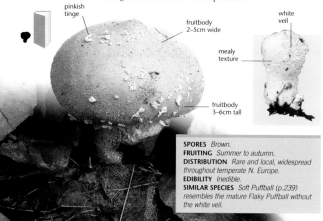

pinkish tinge

fruitbody 2–5cm wide

white veil

mealy texture

fruitbody 3–6cm tall

SPORES *Brown.*
FRUITING *Summer to autumn.*
DISTRIBUTION *Rare and local, widespread throughout temperate N. Europe.*
EDIBILITY *Inedible.*
SIMILAR SPECIES *Soft Puffball (p.239) resembles the mature Flaky Puffball without the white veil.*

Meadow Puffball

Vascellum pratense (Lycoperdaceae)

The Meadow Puffball is cream in colour with scurfy spines when young, with a typical spinning top-like shape. It grows papery and brown with age and splits open to release the spores. When cut in half, the older fruitbodies reveal a distinct diaphragm separating the spore mass from the sterile base – this feature is not present in *Lycoperdon* species.

GROWS *singly or in small groups in short grass, especially nitrogen-rich pastures, lawns, and parks.*

mature cap turns brown

top-like shape

fruitbody 2–5cm wide

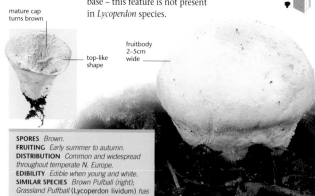

SPORES *Brown.*
FRUITING *Early summer to autumn.*
DISTRIBUTION *Common and widespread throughout temperate N. Europe.*
EDIBILITY *Edible when young and white.*
SIMILAR SPECIES *Brown Puffball (right); Grassland Puffball (Lycoperdon lividum) has a stem and releases spores through a hole.*

Brown Puffball

Bovista nigrescens (Lycoperdaceae)

This fungus is easily recognized by its spherical shape and fairly large size. When immature, it is white and smooth with a sterile basal pad attached to the ground by a cord. As it matures, it becomes shiny brown-black with a ragged slit or pore through which the purple-brown spores are dispersed. At this stage it is light, like polystyrene, and is often found detached from the ground.

SEEN *on the ground in a wide variety of habitats, favouring nitrogen-rich grassland, meadows, and heaths.*

fruitbody up to 9cm wide

spherical fruitbody

papery brown-black skin

SPORES *Purple-brown.*
FRUITING *Summer to late autumn.*
DISTRIBUTION *Common and widespread.*
EDIBILITY *Edible when young and white.*
SIMILAR SPECIES *Meadow Puffball (left) has scurfy spines with a short stem; Grey Puffball (B. plumbea) is white and peeling when young becoming lead-grey when old.*

Mosaic Puffball

Handkea utriformis (Lycoperdaceae)

The Mosaic Puffball can be distinguished when young by its broad, pear-shaped white fruitbody, the surface of which tends to split up into small, many-sided plates. Older specimens are brown and papery, the top gradually distintegrating to release the spores, leaving a cup-shaped sterile base.

APPEARS *singly or in small groups in short grass, especially acidic pastures and dune grassland.*

fruitbody 5–15cm wide

pear-shaped fruitbody

brown or olive-tinged spore mass

SPORES *Brown.*
FRUITING *Summer to autumn.*
DISTRIBUTION *Occasional, widespread throughout temperate N. Europe.*
EDIBILITY *Edible when young and white.*
SIMILAR SPECIES *Giant Puffball (p.244), which is spherical and lacks a stem; Calvatia fragilis has a purplish brown spore mass.*

narrow base

SECTION

Giant Puffball

Calvatia gigantea (Lycoperdaceae)

This impressive fungus is easily recognized by its sheer size, ranging from that of a small football to the size of a sheep – for which it has reportedly been mistaken. It is generally round but with irregular lobes and occasional fissures. When immature and edible, it is creamy white, with firm white flesh throughout and a thick leathery skin that can be easily peeled away. It may have white cords where it is attached to the ground. As it matures, the Giant Puffball becomes yellowish inside, eventually becoming dark olive brown and drying out to become very light and polystyrene-like.

PREFERS nutrient-rich sites in fields and hedgerows, and often near manure heaps, amongst nettles or other nutrient-loving plants.

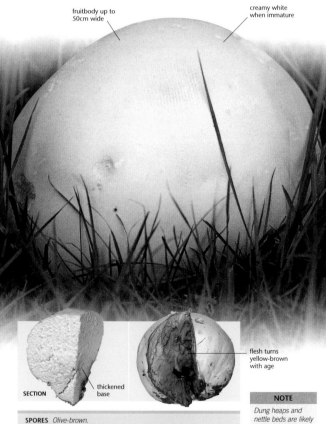

fruitbody up to 50cm wide

creamy white when immature

flesh turns yellow-brown with age

SECTION

thickened base

SPORES *Olive-brown.*
FRUITING *Summer to autumn.*
DISTRIBUTION *Occasional and widespread throughout.*
EDIBILITY *Edible only when young and white.*
SIMILAR SPECIES *Mosaic Puffball (p.243), which is smaller, pear-shaped, with a granular to scurfy appearance. It also has a much more obvious broad stem at the base.*

NOTE

Dung heaps and nettle beds are likely spots to find this fairly uncommon species. The Giant Puffball should not be eaten unless the flesh is firm and white throughout.

Arched Earthstar

Geastrum fornicatum (Geastraceae)

Finding this most spectacular earthstar is a rare pleasure.
The woody outer layer splits into two sets of arms, one set
forming a cup-like base half-buried in the soil, the other set

GROWS *typically in groups of two or three, in rich soil in broadleaf woods and hedgerows.*

arching upwards from the tips to
raise the spore-containing
inner ball high off the
ground. Raindrops hitting
the inner ball help to puff
out the spores.

papery inner ball containing spores

fibrous hole for spore release

fruitbody 4–8cm wide

arms arching upwards

SPORES *Brown.*
FRUITING *Summer to late autumn.*
DISTRIBUTION *Rare to occasional, widespread in temperate N. Europe.*
EDIBILITY *Inedible.*
SIMILAR SPECIES *Rayed Earthstar (G. quadrifidum), which is smaller, more rare, and grows in beech or conifer woods.*

Collared Earthstar

Geastrum triplex (Geastraceae)

This is one of the largest and most common earthstars.
Young fruitbodies are onion-shaped with a distinct point
on top. When mature, the woody outer
surface splits and opens out into a star,
revealing the puffball-like inner ball
which contains the spores. It has a
distinctive collar around the ball,
hence the common name.

fibrous hole

FOUND *in small troops in broadleaved woods, along roadside hedgerows, in scrub, and on sand dunes.*

puffball-like inner ball

thick, raised collar around inner ball

fruitbody 4–12cm wide

5–7 arms, curve back under fruitbody

SPORES *Brown.*
FRUITING *Summer to late autumn.*
DISTRIBUTION *Frequent, widespread in temperate N. Europe.*
EDIBILITY *Inedible.*
SIMILAR SPECIES *Barometer Earthstar (p.246) and Sessile Earthstar (G. fimbriatum) lack raised collar.*

outer surface forms star

onion shaped when young

Barometer Earthstar

Astraeus hygrometricus (Sclerodermataceae)

The young fruitbody of this earthstar forms a rounded tan-brown ball which, as it matures, splits open into a star shape with 6–15 rays. The rays are paler with whitish scales, and the central spore ball is reddish brown with a roughened surface and central pore. Its common name derives from the fact that the rays close into a hard, leathery ball in dry weather and open up again in moist conditions.

FOUND in small numbers in warm, southerly areas in woodlands, especially on sandy soils.

reddish brown spore ball

star-like rays with whitish scales

fruitbody up to 9cm wide

SPORES Brown.
FRUITING Year round.
DISTRIBUTION Rare to occasional, mainly warm southern areas.
EDIBILITY Inedible.
SIMILAR SPECIES Geastrum species have rays and a central spore ball, but none opens and closes according to the weather.

Pepper Pot

Myriostoma coliforme (Geastraceae)

The aptly named Pepper Pot resembles an earthstar, but has multiple holes for spore release instead of a single central hole. The central ball is also supported by multiple stems, making the species unique and easy to identify. Although first described as from East Anglia, it is feared extinct in Britain, but is still found in the Channel Islands and continental Europe.

GROWS in small groups in dry sandy soil, especially near the sea.

multiple stems supporting ball

fruitbody 7–15cm wide

multiple holes for spore release

outer surface opens into 10 or more arms

SPORES Brown.
FRUITING Summer to late autumn.
DISTRIBUTION Very rare, but widespread in temperate N. Europe.
EDIBILITY Inedible.
SIMILAR SPECIES Earthstar (Geastrum) species also have arms or rays but never have multiple holes for spore release.

Scaly Earthball ☠

Scleroderma verrucosum (Sclerodermataceae)

Preferring richer, less acid ground than the Common Earthball (below), this species has a distinct but irregularly ridged and furrowed stem with root-like, whitish strands at the base which may be partly buried. The outer surface is buff-brown, finely scaly, and comparatively thin, containing a black spore mass inside.

SEEN *singly or in small groups with broadleaf trees, alongside paths in gardens, parks, and woodlands.*

dark spore mass

fruitbody 2–8cm wide

scaly, buff-brown surface

ridged, furrowed stem, partly buried

SPORES *Dark brown.*
FRUITING *Summer to late autumn.*
DISTRIBUTION *Common and widespread throughout temperate N. Europe.*
EDIBILITY *Poisonous.*
SIMILAR SPECIES *Leopard Earthball (S. areolatum), which is smaller and lacks a prominent stem.*

Common Earthball ☠

Scleroderma citrinum (Sclerodermataceae)

At first glance this might be confused with a large puffball, but the scaly yellow surface is distinctive. The fruitbody is much heavier and, if cut in two, reveals a thick, fleshy layer containing a dense black mass of spores, which are released when the fruitbody falls apart. It also has a characteristic smell of old rubber.

GROWS *singly or in small groups with broadleaf trees on pathsides and banks, in acid woodland and heaths.*

scaly, yellowish surface

fruitbody 5–15cm wide

dense black spore mass

SECTION

SPORES *Dark brown.*
FRUITING *Summer to late autumn.*
DISTRIBUTION *Very common and widespread in temperate N. Europe.*
EDIBILITY *Poisonous.*
SIMILAR SPECIES *Potato Earthball (S. bovista) prefers less acid ground and has a smoother, greyer surface with a thin skin.*

Dyeball

Pisolithus arrhizus (Sclerodermataceae)

Though large, the lumpy brown Dyeball is not always conspicuous since it can be easily mistaken for old horse dung. The thick stem, when present, is often wholly or partly buried. Cutting through young fruitbodies reveals a characteristic honeycomb of pea-size, spore-containing compartments. When mature, these disintegrate into a mass of powdery brown spores. The species is locally common in southern Europe, rarer in the north, and very rare (probably introduced) in Britain and Ireland. It was formerly used to dye cloth, and produces a variety of yellow to brownish purple tints.

GROWS *with pines (in young plantations in Britain), often in dry, sandy soils, on paths and disturbed ground.*

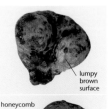

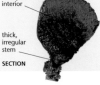

lumpy brown surface

honeycomb interior

thick, irregular stem

SECTION

NOTE

The Dyeball helps to enrich poor soil with vital nutrients. It is one of several fungi that have been deliberately introduced into coniferous plantations in order to help the young trees establish themselves on reclaimed wasteland and spoil heaps.

fruitbody 5–12cm wide

spherical to irregularly rounded fruitbody

SPORES *Brown.*
FRUITING *Summer to autumn.*
DISTRIBUTION *Locally common and widespread in S.Europe; rare and probably introduced in Britain.*
EDIBILITY *Inedible.*
SIMILAR SPECIES *Giant Puffball (p.244), Pestle Puffball (right), and Mosaic Puffball (p.243) may look similar if old and decayed, but lack the honeycombed interior.*

Pestle Puffball

Handkea excipuliformis (Lycoperdaceae)

The Pestle Puffball resembles an oversize Common Puffball (p.240), but disintegrates when mature instead of releasing its spores through a hole in the top. It is rather variable in shape, but typically has a large and prominent stem (with polystyrene-like interior) which is often left behind in winter after the spore-containing head has blown away. It is only edible when white throughout.

OCCURS *singly or in small groups in broadleaf and coniferous woods, also on grassland.*

flesh darkens with age

large, prominent stem

SECTION

fruitbody 5–10cm wide

SPORES *Brown.*
FRUITING *Late summer to autumn.*
DISTRIBUTION *Common and widespread in temperate N. region.*
EDIBILITY *Edible when white throughout.*
SIMILAR SPECIES *Dyeball (left) has a honeycombed interior; Grassland Puffball (L. lividum) is much smaller.*

Winter Stalkball

Tulostoma brumale (Tulostomataceae)

Stalkballs look like miniature puffballs or even rabbit dung on the top of stalks. Their woody stems, however, are often buried in sand, making them hard to spot. The ball itself contains the spores and has a small central opening on top for spore release. The ball and the stalk are fairly uniform pale brown to milky coffee colour.

FOUND *in small groups in dry, open areas, particularly dunes, but also on heaths, dry banks, and even old sandy mortar in walls.*

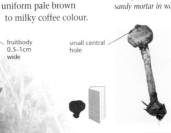

fruitbody 0.5–1cm wide

hard woody stalk

small central hole

SPORES *Brown.*
FRUITING *Late autumn to winter.*
DISTRIBUTION *Occasional to locally common, widespread in temperate N. Europe.*
EDIBILITY *Inedible.*
SIMILAR SPECIES *Scaly Stalkball (T. melanocyclum), which is rarer, and has a darker brown area around the pore mouth.*

Cramp Balls

Daldinia concentrica (Xylariaceae)

These uneven, ball-shaped black fruitbodies, attached to dead standing trees and fallen wood, are hard but relatively light. When young, they are a dark rusty brown colour, blackening with age. When the spores are mature they are spread across the surface, forming a copious black powder that coats everything nearby. The fungi may be single or merged, and when cut in half reveal concentric dark and white bands. Traditionally used as a preventive for cramp, they are also known as King Alfred's Cakes for their resemblance to the cakes the Saxon king supposedly burnt.

GROWS *on dead, standing, and fallen broadleaf wood, especially ash and birch.*

silver-grey and black bands

SECTION

black spores

NOTE

Many bracket fungi develop from a ball-shaped initial stage. The identity of this species may be confirmed by cutting specimens in half to reveal the light and dark banding within.

dark brown to black fruitbodies

stemless balls

SPORES *Black.*
FRUITING *All year round.*
DISTRIBUTION *Common in Britain, occasional elsewhere; widespread, especially in the north.*
EDIBILITY *Inedible.*
SIMILAR SPECIES *Enteridium lycoperdon, which is a slime mould with silver-grey skin that breaks down to reveal a black interior; it is never hard.*

Red Cage

Clathrus ruber (Clathraceae)

When mature, this species can be detected even from a distance by its foetid smell. The cage-like, spongy, vivid pink-red fruitbody has a slimy, dark brown spore mass on the inside, which is dispersed by insects. The cage itself emerges from a golfball-like egg and grows rapidly when conditions are suitable.

SEEN *singly but more often in small numbers, in humus-rich sites, with leaf and wood litter, in warmer regions.*

fruitbody 5–12cm wide

dark spore mass

buff egg

basal cords

SPORES *Olive-brown.*
FRUITING *All year round.*
DISTRIBUTION *Rare; mainly in south.*
EDIBILITY *Inedible.*
SIMILAR SPECIES *Dog Stinkhorn (p.265), Devil's Fingers (p.252), and* Aseroe rubra *all emerge from eggs but have no cage structure.*

Beech Woodwart

Hypoxylon fragiforme (Xylariaceae)

This very common species persists all year round. The hard, crusty fruitbodies are pinkish red when fresh and look densely warted under a lens. As they grow older, they darken to brick-red and finally turn completely black. There are a number of hard, blackish, cinder-like species like Beech Woodwort, which break down dead wood, most of which form flat or cushion crusts.

GROWS *in dense swarms on dead and fallen branches and trunks of beech.*

brownish black mature fruitbodies

fruitbody 1–10mm wide

finely warted surface

SPORES *Brown.*
FRUITING *All year round.*
DISTRIBUTION *Very common and widespread throughout.*
EDIBILITY *Inedible.*
SIMILAR SPECIES *Hazel Woodwart (H. fuscum), which is purplish brown and grows on hazel and alder.*

Devil's Fingers

Clathrus archeri (Clathraceae)

FOUND *singly, but often in groups, in woodland litter; particularly favours man-made habitats.*

Introduced from Australia, Devil's Fingers is becoming established across Europe. It emerges from an oval, gelatinous, buff-pink egg attached to the ground by a mycelial cord. The egg opens and a spongy red column rapidly grows upwards, then splits and peels back into a star shape of four to eight arms. The arms are bright crimson-pink with an unpleasant-smelling black spore mass on their inner surface.

vivid red arms

oval buff egg

honeycomb structure

fruitbody up to 1cm wide

arms joined at base

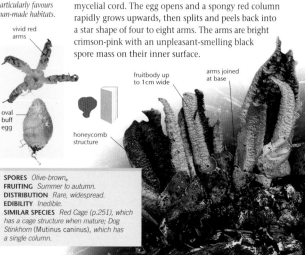

SPORES *Olive-brown.*
FRUITING *Summer to autumn.*
DISTRIBUTION *Rare, widespread.*
EDIBILITY *Inedible.*
SIMILAR SPECIES *Red Cage (p.251), which has a cage structure when mature; Dog Stinkhorn (Mutinus caninus), which has a single column.*

Nail Fungus

Poronia punctata (Xylariaceae)

GROWS *singly or in troops on old horse dung, particularly from ponies and horses grazing on unimproved grasslands.*

The Nail Fungus is a relative of *Xylaria* species (p.280) and produces quite hard fruitbodies which are the size and shape of drawing pins. The flat, spore-producing disc is whitish with black dots and is supported by a slender blackish stem. The species was common a century ago, but has now become rare and local.

disc 0.5–1.5cm wide

flat whitish disc dotted black

drawing pin-like shape

SPORES *Brown.*
FRUITING *Autumn.*
DISTRIBUTION *Rare to very rare and local, though widespread.*
EDIBILITY *Inedible.*
SIMILAR SPECIES *P. erici, which is even rarer and occasionally found on rabbit dung, particularly in dunes.*

Cedar Cup

Geopora sumneriana (Pyronemataceae)

This cup fungus appears in the spring. The fruitbody develops just under the soil and, when mature, breaks through the soil surface and splits apart to reveal the spore-bearing cup. The outside of the fruitbody is brown and slightly velvety, contrasting with the smooth, greyish or yellowish white inner cup.

GROWS in troops in bare earth and grass, always under cedar, in parks, churchyards, and gardens.

whitish inner surface

brown outer surface

fruitbody half-buried in soil

fruitbody 2–7cm wide

SPORES *White.*
FRUITING *Spring.*
DISTRIBUTION *Occasional and local, widespread in N. Europe.*
EDIBILITY *Inedible.*
SIMILAR SPECIES *Other Geopora species, which may be found in dunes and sandy ground but not under cedar.*

Blistered Cup

Peziza vesiculosa (Pezizaceae)

The large fruitbodies of this cup fungus are bladder-like in shape, only a few opening out fully to become saucer-shaped. The inner, spore-bearing surface is smooth and pale yellow-brown, while the outer surface is finely granular and pale buff to brown. The pale yellow flesh is thick but fragile and breaks easily.

FORMS dense clusters on manure and manure-rich ground, stable waste, compost heaps, and flowerbeds.

curved cup margin

pale buff fruitbodies

fruitbody 3–15cm wide

SPORES *White.*
FRUITING *All year, particularly autumn.*
DISTRIBUTION *Common, widespread in temperate N. Europe.*
EDIBILITY *Inedible.*
SIMILAR SPECIES *Cellar Cup (p.254) grows on man-made habitats; Bay Cup (p 258) found on bare soil is a darker brown.*

Cellar Cup

Peziza cerea (Pezizaceae)

GROWS *in the wild on soil and wood, but most commonly found in man-made habitats such as old mortar, plaster, carpets, and other items.*

Due to its particular fondness for damp man-made habitats, the Cellar Cup can be encountered in unexpected places. It is quite a large species with pale yellowish buff fruitbodies, smooth inside the spore-producing cup, and finely scurfy on the outside. Favouring damp spots inside buildings and on external walls, a common place for it to grow is cellars. It has also been reported from a range of domestic habitats including bathrooms, cardboard storage boxes, garages, paving stones, and even car upholstery. Like all cup fungi, the spores are shot out from the fruitbody rather than dropped by gravity as with the gilled and pore fungi. As a result tiny "puffs" of spores can ocassionly be seen emitting from the Cellar Cup.

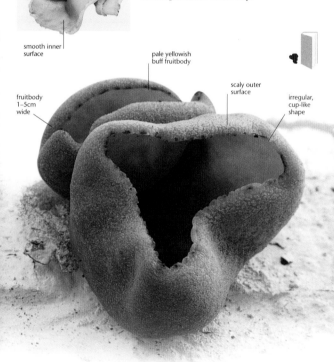

inrolled margin

smooth inner surface

pale yellowish buff fruitbody

scaly outer surface

irregular, cup-like shape

fruitbody 1–5cm wide

NOTE

If you find the Cellar Cup in your home, it is always a sign of extreme dampness and may mean a hidden leak. If you cure the damp problem, the fungus will disappear.

SPORES *White.*
FRUITING *Year round.*
DISTRIBUTION *Very common, widespread throughout.*
EDIBILITY *Inedible.*
SIMILAR SPECIES *Blistered Cup (p.253) is similarly coloured, but grows in straw containing dung and on manured ground. Most other Peziza species are differently coloured or smaller, and grow on rotten wood, bonfire sites, or woodland soil.*

White Saddle ☠

Helvella crispa (Helvellaceae)

White Saddle is probably the commonest and most
conspicuous of the saddle fungi. Although it varies in size,
it is usually large. The stem is white with deep, irregular
ridges and furrows, somewhat like a celery stalk, while its
spore-bearing cap is cream to pale buff, with irregular
lobes. White Saddle is a relative of the morels (pp.283, 288)
but, unlike them, it is an autumn-fruiting fungus. This
species is said to be eaten in some parts of Europe after
drying or repeated boiling.
However, it is actually
poisonous and
best avoided.

GROWS *singly or in
troops among leaf litter
in broadleaf woods,
often on disturbed
ground along
roadsides or tracks.*

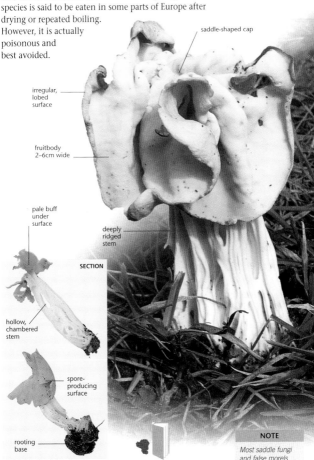

saddle-shaped cap

irregular,
lobed
surface

fruitbody
2–6cm wide

pale buff
under
surface

deeply
ridged
stem

SECTION

hollow,
chambered
stem

spore-
producing
surface

rooting
base

NOTE

*Most saddle fungi
and false morels
fruit in autumn,
whilst the true
morels fruit in
spring. The true
morels also have
caps which are
honeycomb-like,
not merely lobed
and irregular.*

SPORES White.
FRUITING *Late summer to autumn.*
DISTRIBUTION Common, widespread throughout.
EDIBILITY Poisonous.
SIMILAR SPECIES Elfin Saddle (H. lacunosa), which is similar
in shape and size, but has a grey-black cap; Pouched False Morel
(Gyromitra infula), which has a smoother stalk and brown cap.

Common Bird's Nest

Crucibulum laeve (Nidulariaceae)

Resembling miniature bird's nests, these strange-looking fungi hold up to 20 lentil-shaped whitish "eggs" that contain the spores. The vase-shaped or cylindrical, yellow to buff "nests" are velvety when young, becoming smooth with age. Initially, they are covered by a yellowish skin to protect the eggs, which are attached to the nest by short threads. When mature, the skin breaks, allowing the eggs to be dispersed some distance by falling raindrops.

OCCURS *singly or in troops on humus-rich sites, such as leaf litter, bark mulch, or sawdust in woodlands, parks, and gardens.*

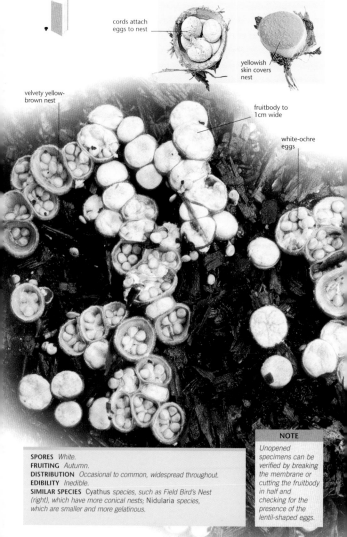

cords attach eggs to nest

yellowish skin covers nest

velvety yellow-brown nest

fruitbody to 1cm wide

white-ochre eggs

SPORES *White.*
FRUITING *Autumn.*
DISTRIBUTION *Occasional to common, widespread throughout.*
EDIBILITY *Inedible.*
SIMILAR SPECIES *Cyathus species, such as Field Bird's Nest (right), which have more conical nests; Nidularia species, which are smaller and more gelatinous.*

NOTE

Unopened specimens can be verified by breaking the membrane or cutting the fruitbody in half and checking for the presence of the lentil-shaped eggs.

Field Bird's Nest

Cyathus olla (Nidulariaceae)

Each cone-shaped "nest" produced by this species is felted and brown to almost black with a flared rim. The inside of the nest is lead-grey, smooth, and shiny. The spore-bearing lentil-shaped "eggs" are grey to blackish in colour and attached to the nest by threads. A pale skin protects the rim of the nest until the eggs are mature and dispersed by raindrops.

SEEN *usually in troops in humus-rich places, in leaf litter, plant debris, and dung, in open sites, woodland margins, gardens, and parks.*

flared rim

lentil-shaped eggs

fruitbody to 1cm wide

hairy nest surface

shiny grey inside

SPORES *White.*
FRUITING *Autumn.*
DISTRIBUTION *Occasional to common, widespread.*
EDIBILITY *Inedible.*
SIMILAR SPECIES *Fluted Bird's Nest (C. striatus), which has a hairier outer nest and obvious grooves on the inside of the rim.*

Bleach Cup

Disciotis venosa (Morchellaceae)

This deep brown, cup-shaped fungus with a bleach-like smell flattens out as it matures, developing a wrinkled and veined upper surface like a morel (see p.283). The underside, by contrast, is pale cream coloured, often powdery to scurfy in texture, and may show on the surface where slug damaged. The stem is thick but rudimentary.

GROWS *singly and in groups in woods, coppices, and gardens, and alongside tracks often in base-rich sites.*

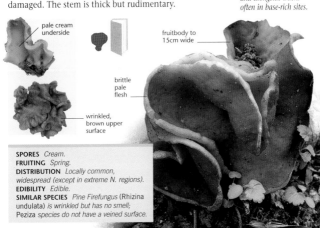

pale cream underside

fruitbody to 15cm wide

brittle pale flesh

wrinkled, brown upper surface

SPORES *Cream.*
FRUITING *Spring.*
DISTRIBUTION *Locally common, widespread (except in extreme N. regions).*
EDIBILITY *Edible.*
SIMILAR SPECIES *Pine Firefungus (Rhizina undulata) is wrinkled but has no smell; Peziza species do not have a veined surface.*

Bay Cup

Peziza badia (Pezizaceae)

FOUND *singly, or in small clusters, on bare soil, pathsides, and acid woodlands.*

This dark brown fungus is one of the commonest of the larger *Peziza* species. The smooth inner surface, which produces the spores, is very dark reddish brown but develops olive-green tints when old. The outer surface is similarly coloured and finely granular. It is edible but is not recommended as there are a number of similar-looking inedible species.

fruitbody
3–8cm wide

smooth, reddish brown inner surface

granular outer surface

irregular, olive-tinted, older fruitbody

young fruitbody

SPORES *White.*
FRUITING *Late summer to autumn.*
DISTRIBUTION *Common and widespread.*
EDIBILITY *Edible when well-cooked.*
SIMILAR SPECIES *Yellowing Cup (P. succosa), which exudes a thin latex when broken. Several other brown Peziza species can only be distinguished microscopically.*

Thimble Morel

Verpa conica (Morchellaceae)

APPEARS *singly or in large troops with hawthorn in chalky scrub and woodlands.*

This morel has an irregular but smooth cap that is both thimble-shaped and thimble-sized, hence the common name. The cap is attached at the tip of the stem, which varies in length. The Thimble Morel has a peculiar fruiting pattern, appearing in thousands in the spring following a very hot summer, but hard to find in more normal years.

cap 2–4cm wide

cap attached at top

smooth, thimble-shaped cap

hollow stem

cylindrical stem

SECTION

SPORES *White.*
FRUITING *Spring.*
DISTRIBUTION *Local and occasional, widespread in temperate N. Europe.*
EDIBILITY *Edible when cooked.*
SIMILAR SPECIES *V. bohemica and Semifree Morel (Mitrophora semilibera), which both have honeycomb-like caps*

Hare's Ear

Otidea onotica (Otideaceae)

Members of this genus are cup fungi, but their cups are split, inrolled, and look somewhat like rabbits' ears. Most are brown, but the large, edible Hare's Ear is a striking, bright ochre-yellow. The spore-bearing inner surface sometimes develops orange or pinkish tints. Like all cup fungi, the spores are shot from special cells triggered by local atmospheric changes.

GROWS *in clusters in leaf litter and soil of broadleaf woods.*

inrolled, ear-like cups

fruitbody 3–5cm wide

clustered fruitbodies

pink-tinted inner surface

SPORES White.
FRUITING Autumn.
DISTRIBUTION Local and occasional, but widespread throughout temperate N. Europe.
EDIBILITY Edible.
SIMILAR SPECIES Salmon Salad (p.262); Tan Ear (*O. alutacea*) is brown; yellowish Otidea species distinguishable only microscopically.

Violet Crowncup ☠

Sarcosphaera coronaria (Pezizaceae)

This toxic species develops from partly buried fruitbodies which break the soil surface when mature, split apart (often in a star shape), and expand to form irregular cups. The outer surface is whitish; the inner spore-bearing surface is violet-tinted.

SEEN *singly or in small clusters in broadleaf woodlands on alkaline soil.*

greyish then violet inner surface

fruitbody 5–15cm wide

whitish, fleshy, brittle outer surface

SPORES White.
FRUITING Spring to early summer.
DISTRIBUTION Rare and local, but widespread.
EDIBILITY Poisonous.
SIMILAR SPECIES No other large cup fungus has this distinctive combination of violet and white, and splits in this way.

Orange Peel Fungus

Aleuria aurantia (Otideaceae)

This striking, usually bright orange cup fungus resembles a piece of discarded orange peel, hence its common name. The underside of the cup is much paler and covered in short, downy white hairs. On young specimens, the margin is inrolled, becoming more flattened and wavy with lobes at the edge with age. The vivid colour may fade in older specimens, whose flesh is thin, brittle, and pale. A short, stem-like base, which may be off-centre, attaches the cup to the ground.

GROWS *in groups, often in large numbers, on bare ground or grass; particularly favours disturbed man-made sites such as dirt or gravel tracks.*

down-like, whitish upperside

inrolled, wavy margin

short, stem-like base

cap to 12cm wide

vivid orange upper surface

NOTE

A very attractive Cup fungus, the Orange Peel Fungus is used more for decoration than as a dish itself. However, it is used in cooking as a garnish, and is also occasionally eaten in salads.

SPORES *White.*
FRUITING *Summer to early winter.*
DISTRIBUTION *Common and widespread.*
EDIBILITY *Edible.*
SIMILAR SPECIES *Scarlet Elfcup (p.263) is scarlet and grows on wood; Orange Cup (Melastiza chateri) is smaller; Scutellinia species have a fringe of hairs at the edge. None are known to be poisonous, and the Scarlet Elfcup is edible.*

Green Elfcup

Chlorociboria aeruginascens (Leotiaceae)

Although tiny, these miniature cup fungi are easy to spot because of their bright blue-green colour. They are clustered or spread out on pieces of dead wood. The inner cup surface, which produces the spores, is smooth and verdigris green with a wavy margin. The underside is paler blue-green, and the short, tough, tapering stem is greenish brown. Because of its tendency to stain green the wood on which it grows, the presence of the fungus can be detected even when the cups are absent.

OCCURS *in groups on dead, usually fallen, wood of all sizes but especially branches. It prefers oak but may be found on a range of broadleaf wood.*

wavy cup margin

darker tapering stem

tiny, smooth cups

cup to 1cm wide

paler green underside

blue-green cups

NOTE

The Green Elfcup grows on fallen branches from broadleaf trees, staining the wood green. Stained oak is particularly prized in marquetry for coloured inlay work known as Tunbridgeware.

SPORES *White.*
FRUITING *All year round.*
DISTRIBUTION *Common and widespread.*
EDIBILITY *Inedible.*
SIMILAR SPECIES *Lemongreen Elfcup* (C. aeruginosa) *also stains wood green but has more yellow-green cups (and larger spores);* Claussenomyces *species are tiny and green, but spherical rather than cup-shaped.*

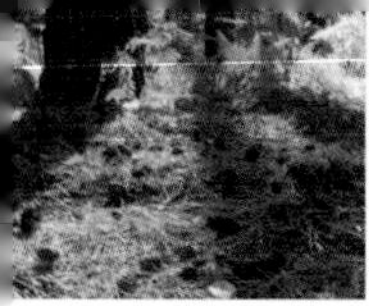

Salmon Salad

Tremiscus helvelloides (Tremellaceae)

It would be hard to mistake this bright coral pink fungus for any other. In many regions it is a rare and significant find. The unusual, petal-like or lobed fruitbodies grow in clusters. Each lobe is trumpet-shaped with a long split down one side. The outer surface of each lobe has fine wrinkles and a rough texture, and it is here that the spores are produced. The flesh has a gelatinous and elastic texture and although edible does not have any distinctive odour or taste.

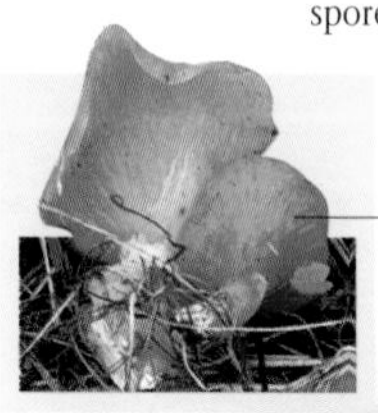

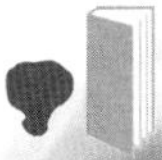

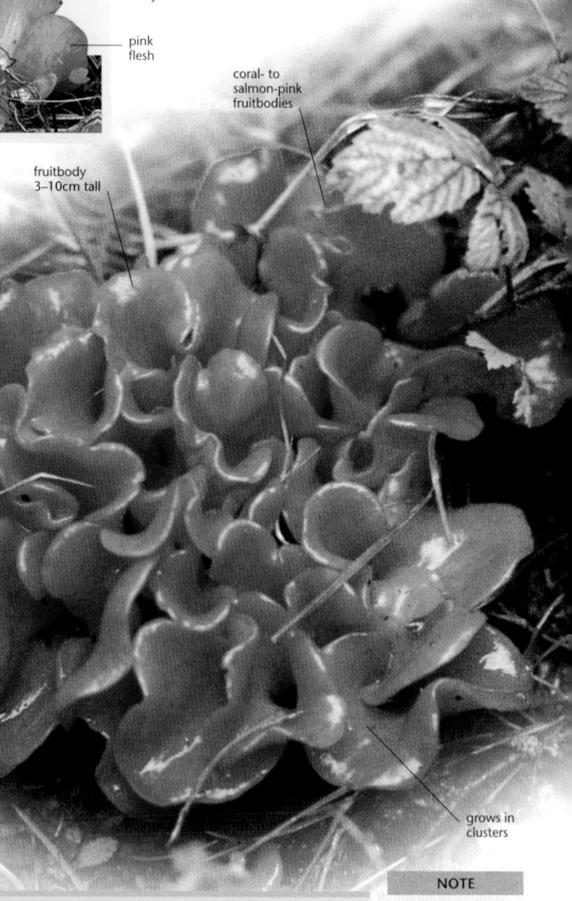

FOUND in clumps on soil in shady, humid woods, mainly conifers usually associated with rotting wood fragments in the soil.

pink flesh

coral- to salmon-pink fruitbodies

fruitbody 3–10cm tall

grows in clusters

NOTE

The elastic, rubbery texture is the first clue in identifying a member of the jelly fungi – a very diverse group, to which the Salmon Salad belongs.

Scarlet Elfcup

Sarcoscypha austriaca (Sarcoscyphaceae)

The Scarlet Elfcup is a fungus with startling colours. The cup-shaped fruitbodies are whitish on the outside due to a coating of numerous, minute, curly white hairs. The smooth, inner spore-producing surface is a bright, uniform scarlet. The cup has a short central stem and the pale red flesh is firm but brittle.

GROWS *on fallen wood, twigs, and branches in broadleaf woods, particularly in more humid habitats.*

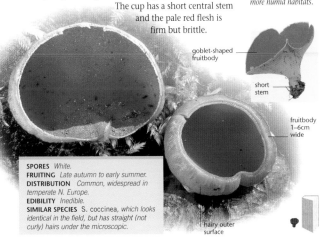

goblet-shaped fruitbody

short stem

fruitbody 1–6cm wide

SPORES *White.*
FRUITING *Late autumn to early summer.*
DISTRIBUTION *Common, widespread in temperate N. Europe.*
EDIBILITY *Inedible.*
SIMILAR SPECIES *S. coccinea, which looks identical in the field, but has straight (not curly) hairs under the microscopic.*

hairy outer surface

Black Bulgar

Bulgaria inquinans (Leotiaceae)

This fungus is also called Rubber Buttons, which is a good description for a species that starts as a small brown ball with a roughened skin and rubbery texture. Over time, the apex of the ball opens and expands, to expose a depressed black inner surface, eventually forming a flat, rubbery disc or button. The disc produces black spores, which stain the fingers when handled.

FOUND *pushing out of the bark of recently fallen trees, usually beech and oak, mostly on the upper surface of the tree.*

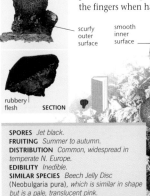

scurfy outer surface

smooth inner surface

rubbery flesh **SECTION**

fruitbody 1–4cm tall

SPORES *Jet black.*
FRUITING *Summer to autumn.*
DISTRIBUTION *Common, widespread in temperate N. Europe.*
EDIBILITY *Inedible.*
SIMILAR SPECIES *Beech Jelly Disc (Neobulgaria pura), which is similar in shape but is a pale, translucent pink.*

Horn of Plenty

Craterellus cornucopioides (Cantharellaceae)

FOUND, *often in large troops, in leaf litter of broadleaf woods, on rich, alkaline soils. Frequently on slopes in deep leaf litter.*

A widely valued edible species, the distinctive Horn of Plenty is difficult to mistake for any other species. Its tall, trumpet-shaped fruitbodies are completely hollow. The inner surface is dark grey-brown to almost black, while the pale whitish grey outer surface is finely wrinkled and has a frosty white bloom. The thin flesh has a peppery, spicy flavour and a sweet aromatic odour. The fungus can be difficult to spot amongst leaf litter but when it is found, it will usually be in large numbers. It dries well and can be ground to use as a spice or flavouring.

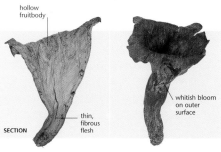

hollow fruitbody

thin, fibrous flesh

SECTION

whitish bloom on outer surface

trumpet-shaped fruitbody

grey-brown to black inner surface

fruitbody 3–10cm tall

SPORES *White.*
FRUITING *Summer to autumn.*
DISTRIBUTION *Often abundant and widespread, but almost absent in some areas of temperate N. Europe.*
EDIBILITY *Edible.*
SIMILAR SPECIES *C. cinereus, which has more distinct gill-like ridges, or wrinkles, on the outer surface.*

Elfin Saddle

Helvella lacunosa (Helvellaceae)

An unusual member of the cup fungi group, the Elfin
Saddle has a folded-back, lobed, thin black cap, which
produces spores on the outer surface. The undersides of
the lobes are paler, with ridges where they join the grey
stem, which is tall and chambered with a fluted structure.
This fungus is very brittle.

GROWS *in leaf litter
and soil in broadleaf
woods, especially along
pathsides, road edges,
and gravelly areas.*

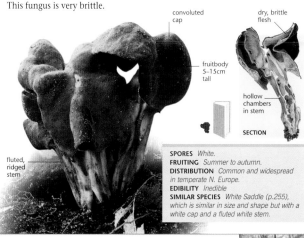

convoluted cap

fruitbody
5–15cm
tall

fluted,
ridged
stem

dry, brittle
flesh

hollow
chambers
in stem

SECTION

SPORES White.
FRUITING Summer to autumn.
DISTRIBUTION Common and widespread
in temperate N. Europe.
EDIBILITY Inedible
SIMILAR SPECIES White Saddle (p.255),
which is similar in size and shape but with a
white cap and a fluted white stem.

Dog Stinkhorn

Mutinus caninus (Phallaceae)

The Dog Stinkhorn has a slender, spongy,
white to orange stem with a pointed red tip
on which blackish olive spores are spread.
The spores liquefy and smell unpleasant,
thus attracting insects which eat and
disperse them in their excreta. The stem
emerges from a white "egg" in the space
of an hour or two.

dark
spores

APPEARS *in leaf litter
and soil, usually close
to dead wood, in
broadleaf woods.*

fruitbody
5–12cm
tall

small,
papery
egg

pointed
stem tip

stem
forming
in egg

white
cords

SECTION

spongy
stem

SPORES Olive-black.
FRUITING Summer to autumn.
DISTRIBUTION Common and widespread
throughout Europe.
EDIBILITY Inedible.
SIMILAR SPECIES M. ravenelii, which is a
N. American species with brighter, carmine-
red colours, and is now spreading in Europe.

Stinkhorn

Phallus impudicus (Phallaceae)

The best-known member of the Phallaceae family, the Stinkhorn is also one of the smelliest, often smelt before it is seen. The odour can carry over many metres and it may be difficult to track the fungus down. The smell, when very diluted, is reminiscent of hyacinths but is more unpleasant as one nears the fungus. Hatching from a large white egg, lined by a gelatinous substance, the stout white stem is spongy and hollow. It is topped by a thimble-shaped, honeycomb-like cap, covered with the greenish spore mass. Unhatched eggs placed on damp tissue, under a jar, will often hatch in a day or two.

FOUND, *usually close to old stumps and dead wood, in both broadleaf and conifer woods, also in sand dunes.*

large white egg

papery skin

SECTION

stem inside egg

thimble-shaped cap

fruitbody 15–20cm tall

cylindrical stem

SPORES *Olive-brown.*
FRUITING *Summer to autumn.*
DISTRIBUTION *Very common, widespread in temperate N. Europe.*
EDIBILITY *Edible in egg stage.*
SIMILAR SPECIES *Sand Stinkhorn (P. hadriani), which is usually found on sand dunes, has a pinkish lilac egg and its cap is larger in proportion to the stem.*

NOTE

In temperate zones, there are rare cases where this fungus has a short, lacy veil hanging from below the cap. In the tropics, there are species where this veil is greatly expanded.

Clavariadelphus ligula

Clavariadelphus ligula (Clavariadelphaceae)

This club fungus belongs to a group that has one of the simplest of all fruitbody structures: an unmodified, smooth, and slender club. Compared to other species of the family, the club of *Clavariadelphus ligula* is quite small. It has a cylindrical shape and a blunt tip. The overall colour is pale ochre, while the flesh is white and spongy.

FOUND *in needle litter of coniferous woods, particularly at higher altitudes.*

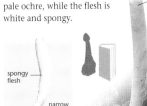

blunt tip

fruitbody 4–8cm tall

ochre to yellow-brown fruitbody

spongy flesh

narrow base

SPORES *White.*
FRUITING *Summer to autumn.*
DISTRIBUTION *Rare, widespread; very rare in Britain.*
EDIBILITY *Inedible.*
SIMILAR SPECIES *Pipe Club* (Macrotyphula fistulosa), *which is taller and more slender with reddish brown colours.*

Giant Club

Clavariadelphus pistillaris (Clavariadelphaceae)

One of the largest of the club fungi, this species has a swollen, club-shaped fruitbody. Its surface varies from smooth to slightly wrinkled, or fissured. The colour is yellow-ochre to pinkish ochre or lilac, staining darker red-brown when bruised.

GROWS *in small troops in leaf litter of beech woods, mainly on alkaline soils.*

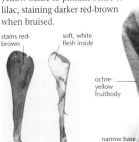

stains red-brown

soft, white flesh inside

fruitbody 10–20cm tall

ochre-yellow fruitbody

stout, cylindrical club

narrow base

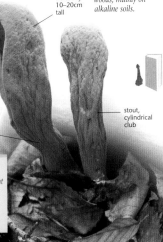

SPORES *Pale yellow.*
FRUITING *Summer to autumn.*
DISTRIBUTION *Rare, widespread throughout temperate N. Europe.*
EDIBILITY *Inedible.*
SIMILAR SPECIES *C. truncatus, which has a broad, flattened apex to the club and grows in chalky conifer or mixed woods.*

Crested Coral

Clavulina coralloides (Clavulinaceae)

This eye-catching coral fungus forms small clumps rather like a miniature marine coral. It is pure white to pale cream, and the branches have pointed, highly-divided tips. The white flesh is brittle. Crested Coral is frequently parasitized by a mould-like fungus and its branches can be blunted in the process.

FOUND *in small troops and clusters in mixed woods, usually along banks, ditches, and other wet areas.*

fruitbody
2–6cm tall

brittle white
flesh

pointed
tips

branches
fused at
base

divided branches

SPORES *White.*
FRUITING *Summer to autumn.*
DISTRIBUTION *Very common and widespread throughout temperate N. Europe.*
EDIBILITY *Inedible.*
SIMILAR SPECIES *Grey Coral (C. cinerea), which is taller, with thicker, blunter branches in shades of greyish lilac.*

Upright Coral

Ramaria stricta (Ramariaceae)

This large coral fungus is usually associated with dead wood. When young, the Upright Coral is bright yellow all over. However, as it ages, its branches become dull ochre-yellow to brownish with pale yellow tips. The usually upright branches have blunt, divided tips, and are fused together at the base into a common trunk. The flesh is firm and yellow with a bitter taste. This species stains wine-red when bruised.

GROWS *in broadleaf woods, on or close to dead, usually half-buried wood, sometimes on sawdust.*

yellow to
ochre
branches

upright
branches

short tips

fruitbody
5–15cm tall

stout
trunk

SPORES *Ochre.*
FRUITING *Summer to autumn.*
DISTRIBUTION *Frequent and widespread throughout temperate N. Europe.*
EDIBILITY *Inedible.*
SIMILAR SPECIES *R. gracilis, which is similar but paler, with an aniseed smell; it grows in coniferous woods.*

Rosso Coral

Ramaria botrytis (Ramariaceae)

Among the most beautiful of the larger coral fungi, the Rosso Coral has a very stout, sometimes massive central base with thick, short branches subdivided into shorter, very small tips. The central trunk and branches are whitish cream to pale brown becoming cream-ochre with age, while the tips are a contrasting deep purple-red. The large fruitbody looks like a brightly coloured cauliflower. The thick white flesh has a sweet, fruity fragrance. Rosso Coral is a rather rare and endangered species, and should therefore not be picked for food. Even though it is edible, it is known to cause stomach upsets in some cases. Although some *Ramaria* species can be eaten, their edibility is often doubtful and many of them are poisonous. Therefore they are all best avoided.

APPEARS *in leaf litter in mature broadleaf woods, especially beech. Where conditions are favourable, coral fungi can grow in large numbers.*

purple-red tips

whitish central stem

NOTE

Coral fungi are some of the most difficult to identify accurately and many can only be distinguished microscopically. There are a vast number of species in this family and most are rare and little known.

---

cauliflower-like appearance

cream to pale brown branches

fruitbody 5–15cm tall

SPORES *Ochre.*
FRUITING *Summer to autumn.*
DISTRIBUTION *Rare, widespread throughout temperate and warm-temperate Europe.*
EDIBILITY *Edible.*
SIMILAR SPECIES *R. formosa, which is a brighter orange-pink without contrasting tips, and is poisonous.*

Sandy Stiltball

Battarrea phalloides (Tulostomataceae)

OCCURS *in small troops on dry sandy soils, often mixed with woody debris, on hedgerows, and on roadside embankments, and gardens.*

The Sandy Stiltball has adapted to dry, sandy or poor soils. It starts life as a tough, brownish egg, the inside of which is gelatinous at first and later turns dry. The leathery egg splits open and from it emerges a tall, dry, shaggy stem. On top of the stem is a rich red-brown, rounded or domed spore-mass, which looks deceptively like a mushroom cap. In Britain and northern Europe, the desert-loving Sandy Stiltball is at the northernmost edge of its range, making it a rare and valued species in this region.

domed spore-mass

leathery egg

NOTE
In parts of Greece and Cyprus the dry spores are used, rather like talcum powder, to dust animals to stop chafing around collars. The leathery eggs are also eaten as a delicacy.

fruitbody 5–20cm tall

reddish brown "cap"

tall, brown stem

SPORES *Brown.*
FRUITING *Summer to autumn.*
DISTRIBUTION *Rare but widespread in N. Europe (more common in the Mediterranean).*
EDIBILITY *Inedible.*
SIMILAR SPECIES *None – this is an unmistakable and unique species. No other puffball-like fungus has a tall, shaggy, tough stem with a thick, leathery volva at the base.*

Small Stagshorn

Calocera cornea (Dacrymycetaceae)

The bright yellow to saffron-orange Small Staghorn appears as gelatinous, rubbery fingers on old wood. These are occasionally branched but usually single. Slightly sticky when wet, they dry to a deeper orange with a very hard and brittle texture.

SEEN *singly or in clusters on broadleaf or conifer wood, such as trunks, fallen branches, cut wood, fences, and steps.*

fruitbody up to 1cm tall

bright yellow or orange fingers

branched clubs

deeply embedded in wood

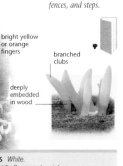

SPORES *White.*
FRUITING *Summer to winter.*
DISTRIBUTION *Common and widespread.*
EDIBILITY *Inedible.*
SIMILAR SPECIES C. glossoides, *has a distinct head; Pale Stagshorn (C. pallidospathulata) is flat with a pale tip; Clavaria species, which grow on the ground.*

Yellow Stagshorn

Calocera viscosa (Dacrymycetaceae)

This clustered, club-like, yellow-orange species is tough, rubbery, and quite sticky when damp. However, it dries out to a much deeper orange, becoming very hard and leathery. The branches are fused at the whitish base and often deeply attached to the wood on which it grows.

GROWS *singly or in small groups, attached strongly to dead and decaying conifer wood, especially old stumps.*

yellow-orange clubs

fruitbody up to 10cm tall

attached to wood substrate

clubs fused at base

branched clubs

SPORES *White.*
FRUITING *Autumn to winter.*
DISTRIBUTION *Common and widespread.*
EDIBILITY *Inedible.*
SIMILAR SPECIES *Other* Calocera *species, which are smaller and less branched; Clavaria species, which grow on the ground.*

Bog Beacon

Mitrula paludosa (Helotiaceae)

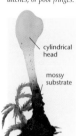

OCCURS *in boggy woods on plant debris or leaflitter, especially in water in track ruts, ditches, or pool fringes.*

cylindrical head

mossy substrate

This small species has a cylindrical, furrowed, bright orange-yellow head and a white stalk, which together give it the appearance of a beacon. The head size can vary between a third and two thirds of the fungus's height. Bog Beacon usually looks moist but dries rapidly. It is found commonly on leaf, needle, and plant debris, mainly in spring and early summer, in very wet, boggy woods or plantations.

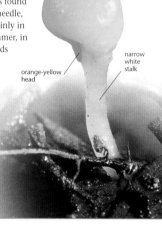

head to 10mm wide

narrow white stalk

orange-yellow head

SPORES *White.*
FRUITING *Spring to summer.*
DISTRIBUTION *Occasional to uncommon, temperate S. Europe.*
EDIBILITY *Inedible.*
SIMILAR SPECIES *M. Gracilis grows on wet moss; Vibrissea truncorum has a lens-shaped head and grows on woody remains.*

Yellow Fan

Spathularia flavida (Cudoniaceae)

FOUND *among needle litter, in rings or large troops, almost exclusively with conifers.*

The Yellow Fan is a distinctive species of needle litter in conifer woods. It has a dry, fan-shaped, yellow, spatula head, which is usually furrowed or lobed. The narrow stem is whitish, often scurfy looking, and is sharply demarcated from the head. It tapers towards the base, and is flattened or laterally compressed.

fruitbody up to 8cm tall

flattened stem

fan-shaped head

tapering base

SPORES *White.*
FRUITING *Summer to autumn.*
DISTRIBUTION *Occasional to locally common, widespread throughout.*
EDIBILITY *Inedible.*
SIMILAR SPECIES *S. rufa, which has a dull ochre head; Jellybaby (Leotia lubrica), which has a greenish head and yellow stem.*

Meadow Coral

Clavulinopsis corniculata (Clavariaceae)

A coral-like species, Meadow Coral has a variable appearance depending on the local conditions, especially grass length. It can be tall and loosely branched, or very compact and tightly divided, and varies from egg-yolk yellow to tan-brown. The incurved tips are

evenly branched in two, and the base is whitish and felted. The thin flesh has a mealy smell.

APPEARS *singly or in groups on the ground in grasslands of all types; prefers unimproved, moss-rich places.*

blunt, incurved tips

antler-like branches

yellow to tan fruitbody

fruitbody up to 8cm tall

SPORES *White.*
FRUITING *Summer to early winter.*
DISTRIBUTION *Occasional to common, widespread throughout.*
EDIBILITY *Edible.*
SIMILAR SPECIES *Ramariopsis crocea, which is smaller and more golden yellow, without a mealy smell.*

Golden Spindles

Clavulinopsis fusiformis (Clavariaceae)

A club-shaped species of grassland, Golden Spindles grow in clusters or dense tufts. The mature fungus is bright golden yellow, gradually becoming brown from the tapered tips as it ages. The smooth surface is often laterally compressed, sometimes with a groove along the length. Slightly tapering bases fuse together, often below the surface. This species is dry to the touch.

CLUSTERS *on the ground especially on unimproved grassland in meadows, parks, lawns, and cemeteries.*

fruitbody up to 10cm tall

club-like golden yellow spindles

fused in tufts at base

SPORES *White.*
FRUITING *Late summer to late autumn.*
DISTRIBUTION *Occasional to common in S. Europe; rare in N. Europe.*
EDIBILITY *Inedible.*
SIMILAR SPECIES *Other yellow Clavulinopsis are not generally clustered, but difficult to tell apart without a microscope.*

Golden Coral

Ramaria aurea (Ramariaceae)

This bright golden-yellow coral fungus is one of a group of similar-looking species which may grow in differing habitats, but can only be accurately distinguished by examination under a microscope. Golden Coral has a short, stout yellow trunk with a white base, and golden-yellow branches with short tips dividing into two. The white flesh lacks a definite smell and does not discolour.

GROWS *singly but more usually in a partial ring or line in broadleaf woods, almost exclusively with beech.*

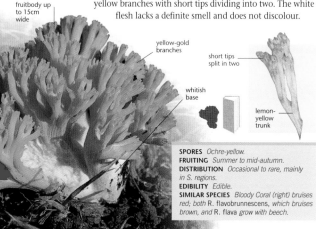

fruitbody up to 15cm wide

yellow-gold branches

short tips split in two

whitish base

lemon-yellow trunk

> **SPORES** *Ochre-yellow.*
> **FRUITING** *Summer to mid-autumn.*
> **DISTRIBUTION** *Occasional to rare, mainly in S. regions.*
> **EDIBILITY** *Edible.*
> **SIMILAR SPECIES** *Bloody Coral (right) bruises red; both R. flavobrunnescens, which bruises brown, and R. flava grow with beech.*

Ochre Coral

Ramaria decurrens (Ramariaceae)

This species is one of a group of ochre-brown to olive-brown coral fungi, made distinctive by its large size and hint of orange in the branches. The thin trunk is pale yellow at the base and darker above. Like the branches, the trunk discolours brownish purple. Ochre Coral may have white rhizomorphs or "bootlaces" at the base. When fresh, it is odourless but smells of fenugreek or curry as it dries.

OCCURS *on the ground in litter-rich sites with broadleaf and conifer trees, especially cedar.*

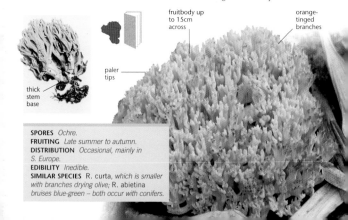

fruitbody up to 15cm across

orange-tinged branches

paler tips

thick stem base

> **SPORES** *Ochre.*
> **FRUITING** *Late summer to autumn.*
> **DISTRIBUTION** *Occasional, mainly in S. Europe.*
> **EDIBILITY** *Inedible.*
> **SIMILAR SPECIES** *R. curta, which is smaller with branches drying olive; R. abietina bruises blue-green – both occur with conifers.*

Scarlet Caterpillarclub

Cordyceps militaris (Clavicipitaceae)

With its bright scarlet colour, this species is fairly easy to spot in short grass, despite its small size. Like many other *Cordyceps* species, it grows parasitically on buried insects, in this case, buried butterfly or moth pupae and larvae.

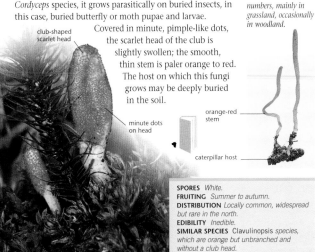

FOUND *singly or scattered in small numbers, mainly in grassland, occasionally in woodland.*

Covered in minute, pimple-like dots, the scarlet head of the club is slightly swollen; the smooth, thin stem is paler orange to red. The host on which this fungi grows may be deeply buried in the soil.

club-shaped scarlet head

minute dots on head

orange-red stem

caterpillar host

SPORES *White.*
FRUITING *Summer to autumn.*
DISTRIBUTION *Locally common, widespread but rare in the north.*
EDIBILITY *Inedible.*
SIMILAR SPECIES Clavulinopsis *species, which are orange but unbranched and without a club head.*

Bloody Coral

Ramaria sanguinea (Ramariaceae)

When it is bruised, this primrose-yellow coral fungus becomes pinkish red, blood-red, or purplish red from the base upwards. While the entire fruitbody colours in this way, the trunk turns the darkest red. On maturing, the pale cream branches become increasingly yellow to intense primrose towards the blunt tips. The thick and sturdy trunk has a paler whitish base.

GROWS *singly or in small groups in leaf litter with beech, especially in warm locations.*

paler trunk

tips brighter yellow than branches

fruitbody up to 10cm wide

thick, sturdy trunk

SPORES *Yellow.*
FRUITING *Summer to autumn.*
DISTRIBUTION *Occasional to locally common, mainly southern distribution; rare in UK.*
EDIBILITY *Inedible.*
SIMILAR SPECIES *Golden Coral (left),* R. flava *and* R. flavobunnescens, *none of which bruise blood-red.*

Violet Coral

Clavaria zollingeri (Clavariaceae)

FOUND *singly or in groups, sometimes in a line or circle, in unimproved grassland including meadows, parks, and cemeteries.*

This is a spectacular and unmistakably violet, coral-shaped species with many branches. The branches can be rounded or pointed at the tips and are joined together at the base. Older specimens can appear faded and even yellowish, often with a whitish base. This species is rarely recorded throughout the area and its whereabouts is a definite indication of the presence of high-quality unimproved grassland. Violet Coral will often be found with *Hygrocybe*, *Entoloma*, *Clavaria*, and *Geoglossum* species, which are all groups that indicate a grassland site of high conservation value. Ocassionally, Violet Coral also occurs with dwarf willow in upland heaths. Older, faded yellowish specimens may be mistaken for other branched species like Ivory Coral (*Ramariopsis kunzei*), which is white.

pointed or blunt tips

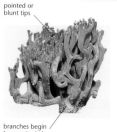

branches begin from a single base

multiple branches

fruitbody up to 10cm wide

violet, coral-like structure

SPORES *White.*
FRUITING *Summer to autumn.*
DISTRIBUTION *Rare to occasional, mainly southern.*
EDIBILITY *Inedible.*
SIMILAR SPECIES *Meadow Coral (p.273), which is yellow; Rose Spindles (right); Ergot (p.278), and C. incarnata, which are smaller with single spindles not joined at the base.*

NOTE

Although the majority of fungi occur in woodland habitats, it is well worth remembering to look for coral fungi in grasslands. Many are brightly coloured and attractive.

Rose Spindles

Clavaria rosea (Clavariaceae)

Not always easy to spot because of its small size, this spindle-shaped fungus is a very attractive rose to lilac-pink colour with a tendency to fade with age. The tips are usually rounded and the texture can be smooth or slightly wrinkled. Although there is no distinct stem there is a slight tapering at the base, which is sometimes whitish. The flesh is thin, often hollow, fragile, and falls apart easily on collection.

OCCURS *singly, but usually in small numbers, on unimproved grassland, especially at basic sites with short turf.*

lilac-pink spindles

fruitbody up to 5cm high

rounded tips

indistinct stem base

SPORES White.
FRUITING Summer to autumn.
DISTRIBUTION Occasional and local widespread in S. regions.
EDIBILITY Inedible.
SIMILAR SPECIES Violet Coral (left) is joined at the base; Purple Spindles (C. purpurea) is more purple-lilac, it may be grey or brown.

Smoky Spindles

Clavaria fumosa (Clavariaceae)

This is an unbranched, club-shaped, greyish ochre fungus. If unbroken, the narrow fingers taper to a point. The flesh is thin and fragile, crumbling easily on collection, and older specimens have hollow fruitbodies. Occasionally growing singly, the species is usually clustered tightly from a central base.

GROWS *on the ground in unimproved grassland, fields, and meadows.*

fruitbody up to 14cm high

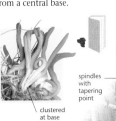

spindles with tapering point

clustered at base

SPORES White.
FRUITING Summer to autumn.
DISTRIBUTION Rare, widespread throughout.
EDIBILITY Inedible.
SIMILAR SPECIES Moor Club (C. argillacea) is creamy yellow and found on heaths; White Spindles (C. fragilis) is white.

Ergot

☠

Claviceps purpurea (Clavicipitaceae)

Small but easy to spot if looked for, Ergot proliferates among roadside grasses and cereal escapes. It forms purple-black, banana-shaped structures called "sclerotia" in the flower-heads of grasses in summer and autumn. These fall to the ground in winter to give rise to small, drumstick-like fruitbodies the following year, re-infecting the next crop of plants. Ergot can be fatal, causing painful burning sensations, hallucinations, and gangrene if eaten. Yet its derivative, ergotamine, is used to aid childbirth.

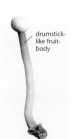

FOUND *in a wide range of grass and cereal species, especially in untreated fields.*

drumstick-like fruit-body

furrowed purple surface

fruitbody up to 2cm long

host grass

SPORES *Black.*
FRUITING *Summer to autumn.*
DISTRIBUTION *Locally common and widespread throughout.*
EDIBILITY *Highly poisonous.*
SIMILAR SPECIES Acrospermum compressum, *which looks very similar but grows on dead stems of nettles.*

Wrinkled Club

Clavulina rugosa (Clavulinaceae)

This usually simple, club-shaped, white to cream species occasionally develops antler-like branches. Visibly wrinkled and uneven, the fruitbody may taper slightly towards the base. However, there is no differentiation between a head or stem. The solid flesh is soft but not brittle, and is the same colour throughout. Though edible it is not considered worthwhile.

GROWS *in groups, rarely singly, in leaf litter in woods, especially among conifers.*

fuitbody up to 8cm tall

sometimes branched fruitbody

wrinkled surface

single white to cream club

solid flesh

SPORES *White.*
FRUITING *Autumn.*
DISTRIBUTION *Common and widespread.*
EDIBILITY *Edible.*
SIMILAR SPECIES C. argillacea, *which grows on heaths and is never branched;* C. cinerea, *which is grey and* C. cristata, *which is white – both are smooth.*

Green Earthtongue

Microglossum viride (Geoglossaceae)

Coloured unusually green, this small fungus can be difficult to spot, especially as it often grows among moss in woods. Its tongue-like fruitbodies have a club-shaped, blue-green to greenish head, which is usually compressed and furrowed. The stem is a similar colour but covered in tiny, flaky scales.

furrowed greenish head

head up to 7mm wide

fruitbody up to 6cm tall

APPEARS *singly or in small numbers in plant litter and among remains in broadleaf woods, often with moss.*

SPORES *White.*
FRUITING *Late summer to autumn.*
DISTRIBUTION *Occasional to rare, widespread throughout.*
EDIBILITY *Inedible.*
SIMILAR SPECIES Olive Earthtongue (M. olivaceum) *is found in grassland and has olive, brown, or pink-green fruitbodies.*

Hairy Earthtongue

Trichoglossum hirsutum (Geoglossaceae)

There are numerous black earthtongues which can only be separated with certainty on the basis of their microscopic characters. However, this species can be identified in the field by viewing the velvety black hairs that cover its stem, using a magnifying glass or hand lens. The smooth, club- or spade-shaped black head is well differentiated from the rest of the body, and is often compressed and furrowed.

OCCURS *singly or in large numbers in grassland, especially unimproved pasture, lawns, and parks.*

fruitbody up to 8cm tall

velvety black head

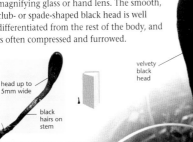

head up to 5mm wide

black hairs on stem

SPORES *Brown.*
FRUITING *Autumn to early winter.*
DISTRIBUTION *Occasional to locally common; widespread throughout.*
EDIBILITY *Inedible.*
SIMILAR SPECIES *Other earthtongues (Geoglossaceae), which may occur in similar habitats but do not have stem hairs.*

Candlesnuff Fungus

Xylaria hypoxylon (Xylariaceae)

This species has two distinct states in its lifecycle. At first, it resembles a snuffed out candle-wick with a slender black base and pointed, powdery, white tips (from asexual spores) that are branched like antlers. When older, it is like a pointed club with a rough, pimply surface in which mature spores are formed.

white tips

fruitbody 1–6cm tall

FOUND *in large numbers on dead wood of logs, stumps, and branches in broadleaf woods.*

antler-like branches

protruding flasks in white flesh

SECTION

SPORES *Black.*
FRUITING *All year round.*
DISTRIBUTION *Common and widespread throughout Europe.*
EDIBILITY *Inedible.*
SIMILAR SPECIES *Other Xylaria species are larger and more club-like. Coral fungi are usually found on the ground and are brittle.*

Dead Man's Fingers

Xylaria polymorpha (Xylariaceae)

This well-known *Xylaria* species has a large, black, club-shaped, composite fruitbody called a stroma. Its hard black surface consists of hundreds of tiny, black, spore-producing flasks embedded in the white underlying flesh. The spores are forcibly ejected from these flasks. The club has a short, cylindrical and brittle stem.

OCCURS *in small clumps like fingers, on dead wood of broadleaf trees such as beech and birch.*

club-shaped stroma

rounded tip

fruitbody 3–10cm tall

rough black surface

flasks embedded in flesh

thick white flesh

SPORES *Black.*
FRUITING *All year round.*
DISTRIBUTION *Commmon and widespread throughout Europe.*
EDIBILITY *Inedible.*
SIMILAR SPECIES *Dead Moll's Fingers (X. longipes), which is slimmer with a flexible stem.*

Toughshank Jellygall

Syzygospora tumefaciens (Syzygosporaceae)

This unusual jelly fungus forms gelatinous, brain-like galls or growths on the stems and caps of the Russet Toughshank (*Collybia dryophila*) and the Butter Cap (p.73). It was originally thought to be nothing more than an outgrowth of the host, but microscopic examination shows the parasitic jelly fungus producing its own spores on the gall surface. In most cases the host fungus is clearly visible, with galls of this jelly fungus scattered or fused mainly on the surface of the cap.

FOUND *only on the Russet Toughshank and Butter Cap (p.73), both very common species in broadleaf and conifer woods.*

gelatinous galls on cap of host

gall mass 0.5–3cm wide

stem of host fungus

SPORES *White.*
FRUITING *Summer to autumn.*
DISTRIBUTION *Rare (probably overlooked), but widespread.*
EDIBILITY *Inedible.*
SIMILAR SPECIES *Several other Syzygospora species form galls on the same hosts, but can only be distinguished microscopically.*

Wrinkled Crust

Phlebia radiata (Meruliaceae)

Beginning as small, rounded spots on the wood surface, this fungus spreads to cover entire logs without forming brackets. Minutely wrinkled to radially furrowed, its surface is bright orange to pinkish orange, or even violet-grey, usually paler at the margin which is woolly and finely fringed. The spores are produced over the entire surface.

APPEARS *on dead wood of broadleaf trees, more rarely on conifers, usually on fallen logs but also standing trees.*

soft, wrinkled surface

fruitbody 1–10cm wide

SPORES *White.*
FRUITING *Autumn to early spring.*
DISTRIBUTION *Common and widespread throughout Europe.*
EDIBILITY *Inedible.*
SIMILAR SPECIES *P. rufa, which is pale ochre to red-brown with a white margin, and is never radially furrowed.*

paler at margin

False Morel

Gyromitra esculenta (Helvellaceae)

GROWS *in conifer woods in sandy soils or in wood chippings in spring and early summer.*

Although it is widely eaten, the False Morel can be dangerously poisonous, even deadly. It has a distinctive wrinkled, almost brain-like red-brown cap folded back over a short, strongly furrowed whitish stem. The chambers of the hollow stem can be seen in cross-section. The very thin cap is fused to the stem at irregular intervals. False Morel can be purchased in Europe preserved in cans and is known to contain a poison destroyed by cooking. If undercooked or if the steam of cooking is inhaled it can be very toxic and is therefore best avoided.

cap 5–15cm wide

wrinkled, brain-like cap

hollow stem

SECTION

furrowed, white stem

SPORES *White*
FRUITING *Spring to early summer.*
DISTRIBUTION *Locally common, widespread throughout Europe.*
EDIBILITY *Poisonous, although edible if expertly cooked – best avoided.*
SIMILAR SPECIES *G. infula, which has a simpler, saddle-shaped cap, slender whitish lavender stem, and grows in autumn.*

NOTE

A number of species are only edible when cooked and toxic when raw. Particular care should be taken not only in identification but also in the correct preparation of these fungi.

Morel

Morchella esculenta (Morchellaceae)

One of the most well-known edible species, the Morel is collected in large numbers in Europe, Asia, and America. Many of the morels for sale in markets are imported from India and Pakistan. The large, sponge or honeycomb-like cap is a bright ochre-yellow to reddish brown, very crisp, and brittle. The cap is fused at the base to the club-shaped, and white or pale brown stem. When cut in half, one can see that the cap and stem are completely hollow. When young, the cap is darker brown with white wrinkles and takes two weeks or more to mature.

FOUND *among herbaceous plants in open woods, especially near dying elms, ash, and old apple trees.*

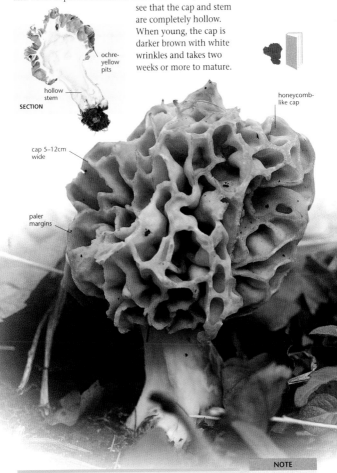

ochre-yellow pits

hollow stem

SECTION

honeycomb-like cap

cap 5–12cm wide

paler margins

SPORES *Ochre.*
FRUITING *Early summer to late autumn.*
DISTRIBUTION *Locally common and widespread.*
EDIBILITY *Edible and tasty when cooked.*
SIMILAR SPECIES *Numerous Morel species have been described by taxonomists. However, most seem to be forms of this very variable species.*

NOTE

Compare the depressed pits and ridges of this edible species with the wrinkles of the potentially poisonous False Morel (left).

Wood Cauliflower

Sparassis crispa (Sparassidaceae)

FOUND *in conifer woods, usually singly, next to or on the roots of pine trees.*

Large, dramatic, and delicious, the Wood Cauliflower looks very much like its namesake. It forms a large rounded ball composed of numerous densely packed, flattened lobes. These lobes are fused together into thicker, root-like stems, and if the Wood Cauliflower is cut in half you can see just how complex the structure is with many chambers and lobes. Like all *Sparassis* species, the spore-producing surface is on the underside only. The fungus varies from pale cream when young to dull ochre with age and it has a rather cheesy odour and nutty flavour. It can be very difficult to clean for cooking because of all the lobes and chambers, but is worth the effort. Each fruitbody usually weighs between 1–9kg, sometimes going up to 14kg.

densely packed lobes

fruitbody 10–40cm wide

complex chambers

SECTION

flattened lobes

cauliflower-like fruitbody

SPORES *White.*
FRUITING *Summer to autumn.*
DISTRIBUTION *Rare, widespread throughout temperate N. Europe.*
EDIBILITY *Edible and tasty.*
SIMILAR SPECIES *Zoned Rosette (p.203), which grows in deciduous woods and resembles a cabbage; S. brevipes, which has a more open, looser texture and grows with oak and beech.*

NOTE

The dense structure combined with brittle flesh is characteristic of this fungus compared to similar but smaller, tougher fungi such as the Zoned Rosette (p.203).

Tripe Fungus

Auricularia mesenterica (Auriculariaceae)

Though initially bracket-like in appearance, this species is a rubbery jelly fungus, which dries out to become leathery, hard, and brittle. When fresh, the upper surface is zoned grey brown due to the short hairs covering it, and is often tinged green by algae. The flesh of the reddish brown lower surface is smooth but deeply wrinkled and veined like tripe, sometimes with a whitish bloom.

GROWS *in tiers on old and decaying deciduous wood, especially elm trunks and branches.*

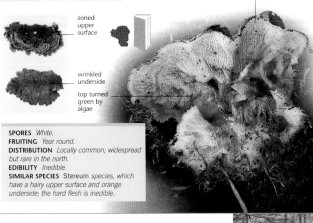

shelf up to 15cm wide

zoned upper surface

wrinkled underside

top turned green by algae

SPORES *White.*
FRUITING *Year round.*
DISTRIBUTION *Locally common; widespread but rare in the north.*
EDIBILITY *Inedible.*
SIMILAR SPECIES *Stereum species, which have a hairy upper surface and orange underside; the hard flesh is inedible.*

Leafy Brain

Tremella foliacea (Tremellaceae)

This unusual-looking jelly fungus has a gelatinous, soft fruitbody made up of wrinkled, shiny, deep brown lobes. As with many jelly fungi, if the Leafy Brain dries, it shrivels, becoming hard and crisp but, when moistened, it rapidly revives and swells to resume its growth and spore production.

PARASITIC *on species of crust fungi, usually on fallen wood of broadleaf trees, rarely on conifers.*

gelatinous brown lobes

fruitbody 3–12cm wide

black when dry

SECTION

SPORES *White.*
FRUITING *Autumn to winter.*
DISTRIBUTION *Common, widespread throughout temperate N. Europe.*
EDIBILITY *Edible.*
SIMILAR SPECIES *Witch's Butter (Exidia glandulosa), which is less leafy and has small warts (visible with a magnifying glass).*

Yellow Brain

Tremella mesenterica (Tremellaceae)

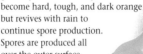

FOUND *usually on fallen wood of broadleaf trees and piles of brushwood; parasitic on crust fungi species.*

Like a soft, gelatinous flower, this edible species forms irregular, wrinkled, and folded flabby fruitbodies. The colour varies from almost white or translucent to bright golden-yellow. When dry, it shrivels to become hard, tough, and dark orange but revives with rain to continue spore production. Spores are produced all over the outer surface.

white specimen

wrinkled lobes

fruitbody 3–8cm wide

SPORES *White.*
FRUITING *Autumn to winter.*
DISTRIBUTION *Frequent, widespread throughout temperate N. Europe.*
EDIBILITY *Edible.*
SIMILAR SPECIES *T. aurantia is a similar colour, but larger, more leafy, and parasitizes Hairy Stereum (Stereum hirsutum).*

Scarlet Splash

Cytidia salicina (Corticiaceae)

APPEARS *on attached but dead willow branches, in cooler upland areas.*

As its common name suggests, this scarlet crust fungus is very noticeable. It forms uneven, circular, and coalescing patches on attached willow twigs. The surface is smooth to bumpy, with a loosening margin. When fresh, the fruitbody is slightly gelatinous, but becomes hard as it dries out.

patches up to 1.5cm wide

SPORES *White.*
FRUITING *Autumn.*
DISTRIBUTION *Very rare in N. Britain, occasional to common elsewhere in Europe.*
EDIBILITY *Inedible.*
SIMILAR SPECIES *Rosy Crust (Peniophora incarnata) forms pink patches; Stereum species form orange patches.*

circular, amalgamating scarlet patches

Cobalt Crust

Pulcherricium caeruleum (Corticiaceae)

Many crust fungi are white and lack distinctive features. The Cobalt Crust, however, is a spectacular exception with its vivid violet-blue colours when fresh. The surface is waxy and soft with a bumpy texture and a growing margin bounded by a white edge. With age the fungus becomes bluish grey to blue-brown.

SEEN *encrusting the underside of fallen branches and logs of broadleaf trees, especially ash and hazel.*

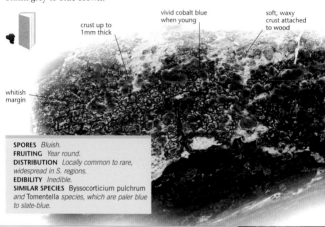

crust up to 1mm thick

vivid cobalt blue when young

soft, waxy crust attached to wood

whitish margin

SPORES *Bluish.*
FRUITING *Year round.*
DISTRIBUTION *Locally common to rare, widespread in S. regions.*
EDIBILITY *Inedible.*
SIMILAR SPECIES *Byssocorticium pulchrum and Tomentella species, which are paler blue to slate-blue.*

Silverleaf Fungus

Chondrostereum purpureum (Meruliaceae)

A common parasite on fruit trees, this species forms flattened leathery patches of deep purple or lilac with a whiter margin. These patches often expand and produce small, overhanging, wrinkled brackets. The upper surface is hairy-velvety while the lower spore-producing surface is smooth. Its flesh is sticky and waxy.

PARASITIC *on many broadleaf trees; causes silver-leaf disease on cherry and plum trees in the form of a white rot in the wood.*

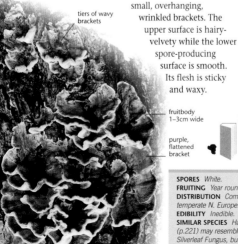

tiers of wavy brackets

smooth, spore-producing surface

fruitbody 1–3cm wide

purple, flattened bracket

SPORES *White.*
FRUITING *Year round.*
DISTRIBUTION *Common, widespread in temperate N. Europe.*
EDIBILITY *Inedible.*
SIMILAR SPECIES *Hairy Curtain Crust (p.221) may resemble faded forms of Silverleaf Fungus, but is thinner and hairier.*

Black Morel

Morchella elata (Morchellaceae)

FOUND *on the ground in parks and open woods, both broadleaf and conifer, also on woodchip mulch.*

Unlike the Morel (p.283), the Black Morel has a tall, conical or tapered cap with pits and ridges arranged in a vertical fashion. When young, the cap is a deep grey-black, grey-brown or even purplish, usually with darker ridges. As it expands with age, the colours lighten and the ridges become thin and sharp-edged. The stem of this fully hollow edible fungus is white and very scurfy.

cap 5–10cm tall

ridged and pitted cap

elongated cap

scurfy, granular stem

white stem

SPORES *Cream.*
FRUITING *Spring to early summer.*
DISTRIBUTION *Locally common, widespread throughout temperate N. Europe.*
EDIBILITY *Edible.*
SIMILAR SPECIES *Has been split into other species; however, they are difficult to separate with certainty and may only be forms.*

Earthfan

Thelephora terrestris (Thelephoraceae)

GROWS *with trees in both broadleaf and conifer woods, especially on acid soils, along tracks and damp gulleys.*

Difficult to spot against the forest floor, this species forms irregular, overlapping, hairy fans. Each fan is dark brown with a paler, fringed or hairy margin. The spore-producing underside of the fan is dark ochre-brown to wood-brown with a warty surface. The fungus fruits at soil level, creeping over soil, stones, and pieces of wood.

fan 4–10cm wide

irregular, hairy fans

spore-producing underside

SPORES *Brown.*
FRUITING *Year round.*
DISTRIBUTION *Common, widespread throughout temperate N. Europe.*
EDIBILITY *Inedible.*
SIMILAR SPECIES *Stinking Earthfan (T. palmata), which is taller with narrow stalks or branches and smells of rotten garlic.*

Glossary

Many of the terms defined here are illustrated in the general introduction (pp.8 –13). For anatomical terms in particular see pp.8 –9. Words in *italic* are defined elsewhere in the glossary.

ADNATE Used to describe *gills* that are joined to the stem by their entire depth.

ADNEXED Used to describe *gills* that are narrower where they are attached to the stem.

BASIC SOIL An alkaline soil with a high pH.

CORTINA Fine, cobweb-like threads usually joining the cap margin to the stem.

CUTICLE A general term referring to the outermost layer or skin of fungal *fruitbodies*.

DECURRENT Used to describe *gills* that join the stem and extend downwards along it.

FAMILY A unit of classification, grouping together related units called *genera*. For example, the *species* Amanita muscaria belongs to the *genus* Amanita, this is placed in the family Amanitaceae.

FREE GILLS Used to describe *gills* that do not attach to the stem.

FRUITBODY A general term for any *spore*-producing fungal structure; more correctly called a sporophore.

GENUS A unit of classification, grouping together closely related *species*, whose relationship is recognized by the same first name in the scientific terminology, e.g. Amanita in Amanita muscaria.

GILLS The thin, flattened, *spore*-bearing structures of cap and stem fungi.

HUMUS The rotted down, soil-like remains of leaves and other organic debris.

HYMENIUM A layer of fertile, *spore*-producing cells spread over *gills*, *tubes*, *spines* etc.

LITTER (leaf, needle) The carpet of fallen leaves or needles and other rotting organic matter in broadleaf or coniferous woods, parks, and gardens.

LOCAL Confined to a small geographic area.

LOCALLY COMMON Refers to fungi which may be uncommon or rare throughout the geographic region overall but are common in certain small geographic areas.

MYCELIUM (adj. **MYCELIAL**) The vegetative body of a fungus (usually below the surface) formed by a mass of fine, thread-like cells called hyphae.

MYCORRHIZAL The symbiotic relationship between a fungus and a plant, in which the fungus penetrates the plant and exchanges nutrients with it, often to their mutual benefit.

NEUROTOXIN Highly dangerous poisons which affect the human central nervous system.

NOTCHED Used to describe gills that turn abruptly up then down as they join the stem.

PARASITE An organism which feeds upon another living organism, usually to the latter's detriment.

PARTIAL VEIL A layer of tissue stretching from the cap margin to the stem; it may form a cobweb-like veil or a membranous ring.

POLYPORE Common name for fungi with woody or tough *fruitbodies* and with a *pored*, tubular *spore*-producing layer.

PORES The openings of the tubular *spore*-producing layer on fungi such as boletes and *polypores*.

RETICULATE Possessing or forming a slightly raised net- or mesh-like feature.

RHIZOMORPHS Thick, cord-like strands of *mycelium*, looking rather like roots.

RING-ZONE A zone at the top of the stem where a *partial veil* was once attached.

SCALES Pieces of surface tissue (often on cap or stem) which break away or peel back.

SPECIES The basic unit of classification for an organism, a discrete group of recognizable organisms that are reproductively compatible.

SPINES Tooth, peg, or spine-like structures over which the *spore*-producing layer is spread.

SPORES The reproductive units of fungi.

STROMA A tough, woody or fleshy structure surrounding the *spore*-producing openings of certain fungi.

SUBSTRATE The material or organism on which a fungus grows.

TOOTH FUNGI Fungi that have their *spore*-producing layer spread over pointed teeth, spines, or pegs.

TROOP A colony or scattered group of fungi, usually individuals, not clumps.

TUBES Fleshy or woody, cylindrical or tubular structures, usually gathered together in a layer and in which the *spore*-producing layer is spread.

UMBO (adj. **UMBONATE**) A bump or hump, usually at the centre of a fungus cap.

UNIVERSAL VEIL A layer of tissue completely surrounding the fungus; the veil may be thin and cobweb-like, thick and skin-like, or even glutinous and sticky.

VEIL A layer of tissue which protects the fungus especially during some early stages of its growth. See also *partial veil* and *universal veil*.

VOLVA Remains of a *universal veil* left at the base of the stem as a sack-like bag or scaly swelling as the fungus expands during growth.

Index

Acknowledgments

DORLING KINDERSLEY would like to thank Bridget Lloyd-Jones for her work as picture editor and administrator.

PICTURE CREDITS
Picture librarians: Richard Dabb, Claire Bowers
Abbreviations key: a = above, b = bottom, c = centre, f = far, l = left, t = top, r = right.

Alan Hills: 31 car; 187cbl; 207 cbr, clb.
Alan Outen: 16 cra, 17 crb, 31 br, cla, 37 br, 43, 69 br, 101 car, 104 bcl, 112 cra, 114 car, 128 cla, 131, 136 cb, 137 car, 151 cal, 154 br, clb, 156 cla, 181 car, 206 car, 239 crb, 246 crb, 253 cra, 254 cal, 276 cal, 279 clb. Barry Hughes: 10 tl, tcl, cla, cra, cbl, cbr, crb, bc, br; 11 tc, cfr, clb, cbl; 12 crb, bl, bcr, bc; 13 tcr, cra, c, cr, crb, crb, bcl, bc, br; 14 bl; 15 br, cal; 16 cb; 17 bl; 20 cb; 19 br, cal; 21 br; 22 ca; 23 cb; 24 car; 25 ca; 26 bl; 27 cb, 28 bcl, car; 29 ca; 30 cb; 32 ca; 33 cb; 34 bc, cal; 35 br; 38 br; 40 cb; 41 cbl, car; 42 cb; 43 bl, car; 44 bl, car; 45 br, car; 46 cal; 47 ca; 48 bl; 49 br, cal; 50 cal; 51 cr; 53 bcr; 54 bcr; 55 cal; 56 br, cal; 57 cla; 58 ca; 60 ca; 61 bl; 62 bcl; 63 car, cb; 64 br, cal; 65 cb; 66 cb; 67 br, ca; 68 cal, car; 69 car; 70 car; 72 ca; 73 br, car; 74 bcr; 76 cra; 77 car; 79 cb; 80 ca; 82 cb; 83 cal, cb; 84 bcl; 85 car; 86 bcl, cra; 87 bc; 89 br, cla; 90 cbr; 91 cla; 92 ca; 93 br, car; 94 cb; 95 br, car; 97 bl, cal; 98 cal; 99 cbr ; 100 bl, ; 102 bcl, car; 104 car; 105 cb; 107 ca; 108 bcr; 109 cal; 111 car, cb; 112 cal, crb; 113 bcr, cal; 114 bl; 115 car; 116 bcl, car; 117 br; 118 cb; 119 car; 120 bcl, car; 121 bcr, car; 122 cl; 123 ar, cbl; 124 bcl; 125 cal, cbr, clb; 127 cal; 128 car; 129 bl, car; 130 ca; 131 bcr; 132 bcr, cal; 134 bcl; 135 cb; 138 br, cal; 14 bcl, br, br; 140 br, cal; 141 cb; 142 bl; 143 bcr, ca; 144 bl, car; 146 cb; 147 cb; 148 br, cal; 149 br, cal; 151 bcr; 152 cb; 153 cb; 154 ca; 156 bcl, cra; 157 car, cb; 158 ca; 159 bl; 160 cb; 161 cal, cb; 162 cb; 163 bcr, cal; 164 br, cal; 165 ca; 166 cal; 168 bl, car; 169 bl, car; 170 bl; 171 cb; 172 bcl, car; 174 bl, car; 175 cb; 176 bl; 177 bl, car; 178 car; 179 bcr, cal, clb; 18 ca; 180 cb; 181 bl, cla; 182 bl; 182 car; 183 car, cb; 184 cb; 185 cb; 186 bl, car; 187 cb; 188 cb; 189 ca; 190 br; 190 cal; 192 cb; 193 cr; 194 ca; 195 cb; 196 br; 197 cbr; 198 bcl, car; 199 br, car; 200 bcl, car; 201 br; 202 bl, car; 203 cb; 204 ca; 205 br, ca; 206 bl; 207 car; 208 bcl, car; 210 bl; 212 cb, cla; 213 bcr, bl; 214 ca; 215 ca; 216 bl, car; 217 cb; 219 car; 220 ca; 221 br, car; 222 cl; 225 bl; 226 br, car; 227 ca; 228 cb; 229 br, cal; 232 cb; 233 car; 234 ca; 236 cb; 237 cb; 238 bcr, br; 239 bl; 241 bl, car; 242 br, cal; 243 car, cb, cla; 244 ca; 245 cb, cla; 247 car, cb; 249 bl, car; 251 cb; 253 car; 254 cb; 255 cr; 257 car; 259 ca; 260 ca; 261 cr; 263 br; 264 cb; 265 br, cal; 268 bl, car; 269 cb; 271 br, cra; 272 car, cbl; 273 br; 274 br; 275 br, cal; 276 cb; 277 bl, cal; 278 bl; 279 br; 280 car, cb; 281 cb; 284 ca; 285 car, cb; 286 car; 287 ca; 288 br, cal. British Mycological Society: 28 cbl. Di Hall: 281 car.

E. Farquharson: 8 crb; 50 cra; 64 cbl; 157 br; 169 cbr, cla; 185 cla; 200 cla; 201 cla; 257 cla; 288 cra. FLPA: B.Bobrell Casals: 70 bcl; W.Meinderts: 57 cb. Geoffrey Kibby: 10 tcr; 13 cfr; 21 clb; 24 bcl; 28 tl; 42 br; 53 cla; 81 cb; 84 bcl; 103 car, cb; 106 cb, ca, cal; 124 ca; 128 car; 131 cal, tr; 132 clb; 134 cla; 138 bcr, bl; 139 cb; 159 cal, cra; 178 crb; 186 crb; 188 cal; 198 car; 200 bcl; 207 cla; 211 cb, ca, car; 228; 234 cb; 243 cb; 209 br; 258 br; 262 c; 266 cb; 270 cal; 274 cal; 281 car. Gordon Dickson: 184 cb. Jens Petersen: 13 car, cl, cb; 62 cal; 62 car; 66 cal; 91 br; 91 clb; 109 bcr; 117 car; 136 car; 145 cb; 145 cfl; 165 cra; 166 bl; 170 car; 173 car; 173 cbl, crb; 182 cal; 188 car; 188 ca; 196 cra, cal; 201 car; 210 br; 210 crb; 215 bl; 219 br; 231 car; 233 cal; 233 cla; 259 cbl; 262 cal; 263 cal; 267 ca; 273 car; 278 cla; 278 cra; 286 cb. Jose Ruiz Fernandez: 209 car, cla. Karl Soop: 15 cra; 16 br; 17 cra; 22 cbl; 23 car, 24 cal, crb; 26 br; 31 bl; 34 cra; 37 clb; 62 crb; 68 cla; 69 cla; 70 br, crb; 72 clb; 75 clb, cra; 76 cal, crb; 77 cla, clb; 83 cra; 86 cla, cal; 88 cl; 89 car; 91 cra; 99 cla; 102 cla, crb; 103 cra; 104 cla, crb; 106 cal; 111 bc, br; 113 car; 114 car; 115 cbr; 116 crb; 119 bcr; 120 cla; 121 cla; 127 clb; 128 crb; 131 clb; 136 cr; 137 clb; 138 cbl; 148 clb; 151 cra; 167 car; 170 br, crb, cla, cal; 172 cal; 174 cla; 179 cra; 184 ca, car; 186 cla, cal; 187 car; 190 clb; 196 clb; 197 clb; 200 crb; 208 crb; 212 car; 219 bl; 226 cla; 242 cra; 247 cla; 248 cal; 272 crb. Malcolm Storey: 9 bc; 53 cal; 139 car, cra; 277 clb. Mark Wright: 139 cb. Mirek Junek: 12 cb; 17 cla; 77 br; 81 cb; 124 cbr, crb; 127 bcr; 128 bcl; 142 car, cla. Natural Image: Bob Gibbons: 21 cal. N.W. Legon: 1 c; 10 cfr; 12 cfr; 13 tcr; 26 cal; 26 cla; 31 cra, car; 35 cal; 38 cal; 43 cla; 48 cal; 49 clb; 53 car; 55 br, clb; 59 cb, cla; 64 cra; 71 cb; 81 cla, ca; 85 cb, br; 92 br; 98 bl; 133 ca; 137 cla; 146 cal, cra; 150 cl; 166 cbr; 233 bl; 235 cr; 238 bl; 252 bl, car; 256 cb; 271 cla; 287 bl. Neil Fletcher: 2–3; 4; 5; 13 cfl, cbl, cbr, bl, bc, bcr; 14 bcr, ca, ca; 15 cfr, tr; 16 cfl, tl; 17 tfr, tr; 21 cfr, tr; 22 tl; 24 tl; 26 cfl; 36 tl; 38 tl; 39 cb; 41 cfr; 44 cfl, tl; 48 tl; 50 br; 61 ca, tr; 62 cfl; 65 tr; 68 tl; 69 cfr; 75 cfr; 85 cfr; 93 tr; 96 cb; 99 tr; 110 ca; 115 cfr; 137 br; 144 cfl; 155 cb; 176 car; 191 ca; 197 cla; 203 bl, 205 tr; car; 213 bcl, br, ca; 218 ca; 223 ca; 224 cr; 225 car; 232 cb; 238 bcl, ca; 240 ca; 250 cbl; 251 ca; 253 br; 257 br; 258 ca; 266 cb; 272 tl; 282 ca; 283 cb. Neil Harris: 245 car. Nick Legon: 28 cla; 46 br; 143 cra. OSF: Harry Fox: 126 c; Overseas Press Agency: 75 cal. Owen L. McConnell: 210 cal, cra. Peter Walker: 16 cal; 126 ca; 173 cla. Pierre-Arthur Moreau: 36 cb, cla. Shelley Evans: 11 (cr); 52 ca, cb; 52 cbl; 72 br; 75 br; 84 car, cla; 115 bl; 140 bcr; 186 cbr, crb; 209 bcr; 231 cla; 200 bcl; 246 bl, car; 248 cb; 274 cra, bcr; 275 cfr; 277 cra, 279 cal. Thomas Jeppesen: 76 bl; 108 car; 119 cb. Thomas Læssøe: 37; 43; 78 cb, cla; 97 br; 101 bcr; 167 cb; 225 crb; 274 clb. Tobias Frøslev: 75 cal; 88 cb, cal; 134 car.

All other images © Dorling Kindersley